INSTRUCTOR'S RESOURCE MANUAL
Lyn Riverstone

Mathematics
for Elementary Teachers

A CONTEMPORARY APPROACH

Ninth Edition

Gary L. Musser
Oregon State University

William F. Burger

Blake E. Peterson
Brigham Young University

John Wiley & Sons, Inc.

ISBN-13 978-0-470-53147-1

10 9 8 7 6 5 4 3 2 1

Printed and bound by Lightning Source, Inc.

TABLE OF CONTENTS

Preface

This manual has been prepared to assist you in using our text. There are several elements in this manual.

Philosophy: In this section, rationale are provided for the selection and organization of the material. You may want to read through this section in its entirety to obtain an overview of the text before reading the rest of this manual.

Chapter Commentaries: Specific suggestions on a section-by-section basis are provided.

Chapter Learning Objectives: A list of expectations, or learning objectives, is provided for each chapter. These have been streamlined in this edition. Also, we have restated many of the objectives, opting for higher-level cognition on Bloom's taxonomy. These lists might be reproduced and distributed to students at the first meeting of the term. In addition to helping the students with their studying and review, the expectations may be useful organizer as you prepare and teach for your classes.

When Will I Teach This Topic?: Often students will ask "Where will I teach this topic." This section provides the approximate grade levels where the material they are studying appears in a school mathematics series.

Exercise Maps: In this edition of the textbook, the Exercise/Problem Sets have been updated. Not only have some new exercises and problems been added, many of the problems from the seventh edition have been deleted or renumbered. The Exercise Map is provided to help you match up both the Part A and Part B Exercise/Problem Sets from the seventh and eighth editions.

Starting Point Solutions: The Starting Points at the beginning of each section are discussion/activity questions that are designed to get the students thinking about and wrestling with the ideas in the section. The solutions to these starting points are provided in this Instructor's Resource Manual.

Answers to Exercise/Problem Sets - Part B: Instead of providing answers to selected problems for all the odd problems, we make it convenient for you and your students by having answers to *all* of the part A portions in the text and *all* of part B in this manual. If you collect assignments, the part B sets can allow for some originality by the students. On the other hand, the part B answers can be removed or copied from this manual and placed in a learning center or library to allow students who want to work additional problems to have access to answers, thus freeing your office hours to work with students on diagnosed difficulties.

Answers for Guide to Problem Solving: The supplement entitled **Guide to Problem Solving** authored by the late Don Miller who taught at St. Cloud State University, artfully walks through all 21 strategies that are introduced in the text and can serve as an excellent source of problems to supplement your discussions of problem solving. Guide to Problem Solving contains answers for the odd-numbered problems whereas this section contains answers for the even-numbered problems. We make copies of these to share with our students.

Many resources and supplements for students and the instructor are available from Wiley on the web and for sale as described in the Preface of our textbook.

We would like this text and its supplements to provide the most effective resources possible for college teachers and their students. Thus, any comments that you can share with us will be appreciated and will permit us to adjust future editions to be as complete and error-free as possible. Please send your suggestions to Gary or Blake at the following addresses:

Gary L. Musser   Blake E. Peterson
1100 Emerald Tint Ct.   Brigham Young University
Las Vegas, NV 89144   Provo, UT 84602-6563
glmusser@cox.net   peterson@mathed.byu.edu
                                                            FAX: 801-422-0511

E-mail or faxes are also welcome.

Philosophy

In writing this text we had two important commitments to balance, one to mathematics and one to elementary/middle school teachers. As experienced mathematicians can appreciate, this is a delicate task. After you see why we took the paths that we did, it may be easier for you to follow our development in its entirety. Also, making our rationale apparent may make it easier for you to adapt the material to fit your particular approach.

Because of research findings and our own experience over many years, we decided to let abstract mathematics naturally evolve from the physical world when introducing new topics. Many students who enter our courses are not operating effectively with abstractions, and these students find our concrete-pictorial-abstract approach particularly valuable. In addition to this dimension, we also like to emphasize the distinction between routine exercises and more challenging problem solving experiences. Thus, we adopted a taxonomy comprised of five cognitive levels. Finally, to help our students better conceptualize what we were trying to accomplish, we organized our content, representational levels, and cognitive taxonomy into a 3-dimensional Mathematics Learning Cube.

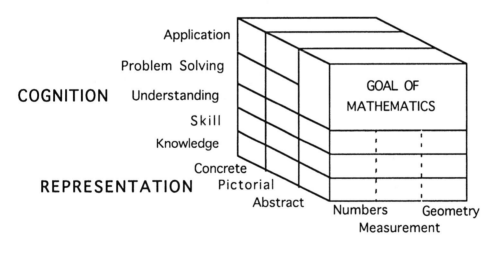

It is our hope that our students will carry this model with them after they study from this text and use this, or a similar model, when they teach. We reinforce the cognitive dimension of our cube in two ways. First, our exercise/problem sets separate practice exercises from problems that require a creative step. Unfortunately, it is impossible to make a perfect dichotomy to fit all students since problems to some students may be exercises to others; conversely, some students may find some exercises to be problems. However, we believe that it is important to try to make such a distinction to keep students attentive to incorporating more problem solving in their own future classrooms. Second, we have included many problems that promote writing and discussing. These problems are found at the end of each section and in the chapter reviews. Third, we have organized the chapter tests into four cognitive levels to help model testing designed to insure coverage of these various levels of sophistication.

We believe that our mathematical development has integrity throughout. Since Gary had taught more formal courses during the "new math" era of the sixties, we were convinced that the pendulum had swung too far to formalism and a "theorem-proof" approach. [Interestingly a member of the Mathematics Association of America's Committee on Undergraduate Preparation (CUPM) of that era confided that panelists were disappointed when they saw the way that textbook authors had interpreted their recommendations - far more formally than the panel had intended.] On the other hand, we believe that it is imperative that our students see the significant logical connections inherent in a sound, mathematical approach. Thus, to balance the demands of intuition and relevance on one hand and the importance of mathematical structure on the other, our approach is to introduce nearly all topics in a concrete, informal fashion (especially early in the text). Then, we gently guide students to abstract mathematical concepts so that they will be able to appreciate how the elementary/ middle school curriculum fits together into a meaningful whole rather than simply being a collection of disparate facts.

In the remainder of this section we discuss our development chapter-by-chapter. In the next section, we have additional chapter commentaries that provide more ideas for the classroom.

Chapter 1 - Introduction to Problem Solving

Problem solving is recognized as one the most important goals of mathematics. We have found Polya's four-step process to be helpful to our students, *especially* when a rich source of strategies (heuristics) is available. A valuable tool for solving a broad range of problems is algebra, so we introduce variables and basic methods of solving algebraic equations in this chapter. After some basic concepts are introduced in this chapter, margin notes are included throughout the text highlighting places where algebraic thinking is used.

We cover this chapter and selected strategies throughout the text when we teach our one-year sequence for elementary teachers. Then, we have a one-quarter course, "Problem Solving for Teachers," where junior/senior level students use the "Problem Solving Study Guide" supplement to have a more in-depth discussion devoted to problem solving. Some instructors may wish to augment this chapter by including an introduction to logic (see Topic 1).

Chapter 2 - Sets, Whole Numbers, and Numeration

Here we introduce the set concepts required to develop all the major ideas in the remainder of the text. An extensive survey of colleagues showed a 50-50 split on the issue of integrating functions throughout the text. In this edition we moved the material on relations and functions from Chapter 2 to Chapter 9 in order to consolidate the study of algebra. We like to cover bases other than ten in this chapter so that we can use them to illustrate algorithms in Chapter 4.

Chapter 3 - Whole Numbers: Operations and Properties

Operations and their properties are covered in this chapter and techniques of computation are covered in Chapter 4. We separate these topics into two chapters rather than integrating them for three reasons. First, the separation allows us to have Chapter 3 focus on the underlying conceptual meanings of the operations before moving on to the derived algorithms. Second, this dichotomy helps to clarify the fact that algorithms are separate from (although based on) the algebraic structure of the whole number system. Third, this separation allows for the broadening of the discussion of algorithms to three modes of computation: mental, electronic (calculators or computers), and written (our common algorithms and alternatives).

In this chapter our emphasis is on the algebraic structure of the whole numbers and the conceptual meaning of the operations with an eye towards how properties are useful in performing calculations. The thinking strategies approach to learning the basic facts is one important use of properties. Research has confirmed that this approach is effective with slow learners and we have had similar success working with individual students of all abilities.

Chapter 4 - Whole Number Computations - Mental, Electronic, and Written

As the chapter title suggests, we believe that students should consider performing computations mentally first (either exactly in simple cases or using estimations in more complex cases), using a calculator second (facility with a computer is also desirable), and using traditional paper-and-pencil algorithms last. Although we develop all the standard algorithms, we do not ask our students to "multiply two seven digit numbers" or "divide a seven digit number by a three digit number." Our reason for including so many nontraditional algorithms in the text and problem sets is that students find them fascinating and, through these algorithms, they can see more vividly that operations and algorithms are not synonymous. Thus, for example, since addition is *not* the addition *algorithm*, it *is* okay to adopt a combination of mental methods together with calculator techniques as an acceptable mode of calculation. Also, showing our students more algorithms helps them to support the various student developed algorithms. Our informal test to measure the effectiveness of an algorithm is to consider efficiency and accuracy when it is applied. In most cases, the mental method/calculator approach wins hands down against written algorithms. One final comment regarding division. Most of our students say that the last time that they used the long division algorithm was when they computed their gas mileage. But with onboard computers in many new cars, even this need is vanishing.

Chapter 5 - Number Theory

The chapter on number theory allows us to accomplish several objectives. First, we develop the content (factoring, GCF, and LCM) sufficient to make the work with fractions go smoothly. Second, the tests for divisibility give us a chance to make some simple proofs so that the tests aren't merely a collection of rules. Third, using some of the examples in our Focus On, we can share the notion of unsolved problems with our students at an understandable, relevant level. Mention is made of the 1995 proof of Fermat's Last Theorem in the Focus On.

Chapter 6 - Fractions

Deciding how to develop the real number system after discussing the whole numbers poses an interesting dilemma. First, one could take the whole numbers - integers - rationals - reals approach. On the surface, this sequence may be appealing due to its efficiency. However, this approach deprives the students of seeing numbers grow out of the physical world, much the way *our* students will be teaching. Thus we took the whole numbers - fractions - integers - rationals - reals approach (the sequence from school mathematics), where first fractions (and hence reciprocals) are motivated via models and next integers (with opposites) are introduced. Then the rationals are generated using fractions and integers. We have found this approach to be the most effective, *relevant* direction to take with elementary teachers and we believe that our coverage is as efficient (in terms of time) as the other approach. Note that, to save time, we defer discussing fraction order relations involving addition and multiplication until rational numbers. However, we do bring them up in the chapter on integers because of the influence of negative numbers.

Chapter 7 - Decimals, Ratio, Proportion, and Percent

We like to view (repeating) decimals and percents as another numeration system for the fractions. Although our work with ratio and proportion is restricted to decimals, we state that this treatment can be used with other number systems (such as the reals which are covered later).

Chapter 8 - Integers

We introduce integers by extending whole number concepts using both a set model (black/red chips) and a measurement model (the integer number line). Our formal definitions of the operations are motivated by the models and patterns. Although there are many ways to define integer addition and multiplication, our approach is to use as definitions the rules that most people use when performing operations on positive and negative numbers mentally.

Chapter 9 - Rational Numbers and Real Numbers, and Algebra

Our treatment of the rational numbers is brisk since the foundation for this material was laid in the chapters on fractions and integers. Real numbers are viewed as the set of all (repeating) decimals *and* as points of a "complete" number line. We like to cover rational exponents so that students can see that whole number and integer exponents can be usefully generalized. Because of their importance in problem solving, we extend the study of solving equations introduced in Chapter 1 to include inequalities and equations with real numbers. Chapter 9 was expanded to include relations and functions to enhance the coverage of algebra. After the real numbers are available, functions and their graphs are studied. Since more and more students are coming to class with graphics calculators, section 9.3, together with the Graphics Calculator webmodule on the website www.wiley.com/college/musser/, can be used to help students see the power of these devices.

Chapter 10 - Statistics

This chapter precedes the chapter on probability because of the topic's high priority in school mathematics and its importance in the everyday world of students and teachers. This also allows for early coverage in shorter courses, as soon as real numbers are developed. In section 10.1 we introduce various ways of organizing and representing data through the use of examples relevant to preservice teachers.

In section 10.2, the most commonly used measures of central tendency and dispersion are discussed, again from a teacher's point of view. We find this particularly useful for students who have not had a course on tests and measurement. The discussion of distributions is geometrical, illustrating the generalization of histograms, rather than delving into probability density functions. Section 10.3 focuses on potential misuses of statistics either in graphs or in sampling bias.

Chapter 11 - Probability

Probability is perhaps the most difficult and misunderstood topic in school mathematics. We suspect that this is due to its abstract nature, particularly the elusiveness of concrete interpretations of probability itself (not just experiments) and its reliance on set theory, ratio concepts, and counting techniques. Because of this, we have developed the major concepts and results about probability assuming no prior background.

Section 11.1 discusses experimental probability and the need for well chosen, albeit arbitrary, theoretical probability. We discuss the case of equally likely outcomes and use simple experiments to motivate the properties of probability. We deliberately avoid any discussion of probability axioms per se; such a treatment is far too abstract for the elementary or middle school classroom. We apply some of the set theory from Chapter 2 as a means of defining the concepts of experiment, sample space, outcome, event, and so on. Examples are chosen to illustrate the central ideas, but not to involve complicated counting techniques.

In section 11.2, we discuss methods for computing probabilities in experiments whose sample spaces may be cumbersome to list. For example, Pascal's triangle is used to enumerate outcomes in binomial experiments. Tree diagrams are introduced as a means of representing the outcomes of experiments involving several stages. Then, probability tree diagrams provide a method for assigning probabilities to the outcomes of such experiments and for computing probabilities of compound events in such experiments.

In section 11.3, we present more sophisticated counting techniques, that is, those using permutations and combinations explicitly. We find the fundamental counting property sufficient for our needs. Again, our main interest is in developing a fundamental understanding of probability and its applications and not in developing skills in counting. Thus, section 11.3 uses these counting techniques to determine the size of a sample space or the number of desired outcomes without having to list the entire set.

Section 11.4 addresses four probability concepts that may be included as time permits. First, the power of simulation is discussed as a simple means of approximating probabilities in highly complex experiments. Expected value is presented to give a glimpse of how probability is applied in establishing payoffs, admission fees, insurance premiums, service contract fees, and so on. Odds are presented as an application of ratios and as an alternate method of representing probability. Finally, conditional probability is introduced to show a generalization of probability, since probabilities in real-life situations are conditional probabilities. For example, insurance rates are set based on carefully researched conditional probabilities. (Some people claim that this is a form of discrimination, which, of course, it is, by definition!)

Chapter 12 - Geometric Shapes

For several reasons, we have chosen to organize the geometry material based on the van Hiele model of development. First, we find it pedagogically advantageous to start with visual experiences and move toward more formal results as we have done with number concepts. Our students have a wide variety of background experiences in geometry (including none), so we need to provide basic conceptual foundations. Second, many students have had unpleasant experiences with geometry in high school, which can be summarized as "too much formalism too soon." As a result, many of our students are apprehensive about studying geometry. By discussing the van Hiele model, we are able to identify the source of many of the difficulties that our students have had. This understanding leads to a sort of healing process and a revived sense of self-esteem. Finally, our students become sensitized to the challenges that elementary and middle school students face when studying geometry and realize that the solution is *not* to delay geometry until high school. Rather, a careful development of geometric concepts throughout the elementary and middle school years is called for - again, much as is done with number concepts.

Chapter 12 was changed in this edition to more closely follow the van Hiele model. In section 12.1, we describe the five van Hiele levels and incorporate an informal introduction to basic two-dimensional shapes at the first two levels of Recognition and Analysis. Sorting and construction-type activities are presented as ways to help students reasoning at Level 0 to develop holistic thinking. In analyzing shapes, we use investigations with paper folding, tracing, and on a square lattice. We are able to establish properties of shapes based on plausible observations, which we verify more formally in later sections. (The plausible observations are, of course, postulates at this point, but we purposely avoid any formal discussion about the role of postulates in geometry. This directly parallels our approach with number systems and their properties.) In section 12.2 we approach two-dimensional geometry at the level of relationships. Through the use of Venn diagram and paper-folding activities, we motivate more abstract definitions of geometric shapes. As a means for exploring relationships among the component parts of these shapes, we introduce the concept of symmetry. In keeping with the van Hiele model, a formal approach to plane geometry is introduced next, in Section 12.3, where we list our basic assumptions, and establish several fundamental results about points, lines, angles, and polygons. In section 12.4 we include a discussion about tessellations as an application of regular polygons and for esthetic reasons. In section 12.5, we describe three dimensional shapes and their properties, delaying measure of volume and surface area until Chapter 13.

Chapter 13 - Measurement

The organization of this chapter was also inspired by the van Hiele model, although we don't refer to it explicitly here. Informal measurement, using natural units, is discussed initially to illustrate holistic thinking in measurement. Once the system of natural units is standardized to the English system, the properties of the system can be discussed, culminating in the properties of an (abstract) ideal system. It is interesting to note that Thomas Jefferson had designed a system of measurement units of weights and measures with all the advantages of an ideal system. Jefferson's system was not adopted and now the metric system flourishes nearly everywhere instead.

In section 13.1, we have provided separate discussions of length, area, volume, weight (English), mass (metric), and temperature in the two systems of units since many of our students do not have a good intuitive understanding of all of these concepts. Yet, they likely will teach them. We include a discussion of dimensional analysis as a problem-solving tool in applied problems and as a procedure for converting among various units.

In sections 13.2, we study measurement as a deductive mathematical process, based on arbitrary units of length and area. (Tessellations of the plane and space are the basis of area and volume measurement.) We derive area formulas for various polygons and circles, based on the area of a rectangle. We give a proof of the Pythagorean theorem based on the areas of squares and right triangles. President Garfield's proof, using the area of a trapezoid, appears in the problem set. (Also, a transformational proof appears in Chapter 16 as a Mathematical Morsel.) In section 13.3 we derive surface area formulas based on previous results. We rely on the connections observed by Archimedes to find the surface area of a sphere. In section 13.4 we derive volume formulas for prisms, cylinders, pyramids, and cones. The formula for the volume of a sphere is done first using the 'Archimedes connection', then more formally using Cavalieri's principle.

Chapter 14 - Geometry Using Triangle Congruence and Similarity

This is the first of three chapters (Chapters 14, 15, and 16), each presenting a specific approach to problem solving in geometry. The three chapters are independent of each other, except that sections 14.1 and 14.2 are prerequisite for sections 16.2 and 16.3. Thus, any or all of the three approaches may be covered. The last section of each of these three chapters may be omitted with no loss of continuity. On the other hand, each provides a nice capstone to its chapter if you can't cover all chapters. If there is time to cover these sections in their entirety, an alternate coverage scheme would be to cover these final sections at the end of your course *after* all three approaches have been introduced to the students.

In section 14.1, the triangle congruence properties are developed and used to justify several classical geometric constructions. In so doing, we are reasoning at van Hiele level two; that is, from the congruence conditions, we can deductively verify the construction procedures. We find this mode of reasoning to be a challenge to many of our students, particularly to those who prefer to reason holistically, that is, on the basis of the construction diagram alone. In order to build our students' skill in using deductive reasoning, we have tried to keep to verifications of only a few major steps at first. In the remainder of section 14.1, we investigate the construction of regular polygons and the consequences of Gauss's theorem.

In section 14.2, we investigate triangle similarity properties and several applications of them. Geometric constructions are covered in sections 14.3 and 14.4. In section 14.5, we apply the triangle congruence and similarity properties in solving geometric problems. In so doing, we verify, at van Hiele level two and three, several results about quadrilaterals that we observed at level one in Chapter 12.

Chapter 15 - Geometry Using Coordinates

We introduce coordinates as a powerful problem solving tool in geometry. In section 15.1 we discuss slope and distance in the coordinate plane, then in section 15.2 we discuss equations of lines and circles, and the geometry of simultaneous linear equations. Finally, in section 15.3, we solve several problems using coordinates. Some students who have experienced difficulties with triangle congruence and similarity prefer a computational approach using coordinates much like some high school students prefer algebra to geometry. Our intention is to show the value of knowing several approaches to solving problems in geometry. Our students, who are expected to have taken three years of college preparatory math, tend to do very well in this chapter.

Chapter 16 - Geometry Using Transformations

In this chapter we present an approach to Euclidean geometry via isometries and similitudes. Our purpose is two-fold: (1) to present an alternative to "synthetic" Euclidean geometry via the triangle congruence and similarity conditions of Chapter 14 and (2) to present an *additional* approach to that of Chapter 14 or 15 that can be applied when advantageous.

In section 16.1, transformations as rigid motions (translation, rotation, reflection, glide-reflection) and similitudes are defined informally. (Note the special notation of directed line segment and directed angle.) Symmetry in the plane is analyzed using transformations, as are Escher-type tessellations. Our goal is to give an overview of transformation geometry, particularly for shorter courses that may not have time for all of the problem solving in section 16.3. Section 16.1 can be done anytime after sections 12.1 and 12.2.

Congruence and similarity of polygons are treated more formally in Section 16.2. We apply several results of sections 14.1 and 14.2 to verify that translations, rotations, reflections, and glide-reflections are isometries. We give a plausible argument that there are no other isometries in the plane. Thus, we can characterize all isometries in the plane and characterize congruence of shapes in general. We also verify properties of size transformations and similitudes, and characterize similarity of shapes in general by means of similitudes. This reasoning borders on level three reasoning since we are investigating the structure of geometry itself; thus, the material must be approached with care and patience. Alternatively, it could be saved for a separate geometry course for preservice teachers.

In section 16.3 we use a transformation approach to problem solving in geometry. For example, we verify the midsegment theorem in a triangle (Example 16.16) by means of size transformations. This result is verified in each of Chapters 14, 15, and 16, using the approach of that particular chapter.

Epilogue - An Eclectic Approach to Geometry

Since we have used this approach so successively in our classes, we decided to formalize it in the book. Talking about using a variety of approaches to geometry is one thing, but providing students with examples and mixed problems is powerful. Students freely express how much they enjoy seeing geometry in this light.

Chapter Commentaries

Chapter 1 - Introduction to Problem Solving

Polya's Four Steps: We find that a careful discussion of Polya's Four Steps is helpful initially. Then we reinforce each step throughout the chapter as we introduce new strategies through problems.

Problem Solving Strategies: Most of our students are initially weak in problem solving, mainly due to lack of practice and knowing where to start. In a survey of research studies, it was concluded that strategies are helpful in problem solving; we find that a toolbox of problem solving strategies gives many students a place to start. Unfortunately, even knowing a list of *strategies* is still not sufficient to produce excellent problem solvers. To take this idea one step further, we have included *clues* to assist students in selecting an appropriate strategy. In the main, these clues were generated by students solving problems from our First Edition. As a further aid for the students, hints and additional hints and written out solutions for all part A problems are provided in the *Hints and Solutions Manual for Part A Problems*. This combination of problems, Polya's four steps, strategies, clues, hints, and solutions is a powerful resource to help students develop their problem solving abilities.

Introduction to Algebra: One of the strategies introduced in this chapter is "Use a Variable". When using this strategy, it is important for students to understand what variables are. Since variables are most often used in some form of an equation, strategies for solving equations containing variables are also discussed. In this chapter, the introduction of algebra is done a basic level and then further developed in chapter 9 after all of the number systems have been introduced.

Chapter 2 - Sets, Whole Numbers, and Numeration

Sets and Operations on Sets: We cover set theory briskly so that we can devote more time to the many other key concepts in the elementary curriculum.

Numbers and Numerals: It is instructive for students to observe the various ways that we use "numbers": "cardinal" numbers to represent how many, "ordinal" numbers to represent an ordering, and "identification" numbers to serve as names.

Numeration Systems: Our emphasis is on the various attributes of numeration systems such as grouping, additivity, multiplicativity, place value, and so on. Also, the Roman and the Mayan systems show how numeration systems evolve; in the case of the Roman system, they extended their additive system to include the subtractive and the multiplicative attributes, and the Mayans changed from a base twenty system to one based on 18×20 due to their calendar. The Babylonian system provides an early example of a place value system as well as an introduction to the notion of a place holder. Our students enjoy a discussion on naming Hindu-Arabic numerals since, although the names are familiar to us, they can be confusing for children. In particular, our students like to rename the numbers 11,12,..., 19 to be "onety-one, onety-two,..., onety-nine" to conform to the way we name 21, 22, 23, and so on.

Ordering Whole Numbers: Although we acknowledge the counting chant and number line as a way children may order numbers (in an ordinal sense), we emphasize the set method for understanding ordering whole numbers (in the cardinal sense). Ordering whole numbers using addition is covered in Chapter 3.

Physical Representations of Whole Numbers: We like our students to be familiar with a variety of representations such as multibase pieces and a chip abacus so that they will carry the philosophy of introducing mathematics at the concrete level to their students. Low-cost representations can easily be made or can be found in the materials cards in our Student Activity Manual.

Nondecimal Numeration Systems: We cover this topic so that we may introduce various algorithms in Chapter 4 in an unfamiliar setting for our students, namely using a nondecimal base. This approach gives our students much more insight into how one might better teach algorithms in base ten. Although this section and the coverage of other bases is optional, we recommend its coverage keeping in mind that its usefulness is in providing students with a different point of view when studying various other number concepts in the text.

Chapter 3 - Whole Numbers: Operations and Properties

Addition: Addition is introduced using physical models and then properties are drawn out of the models. Algorithms are studied in the next chapter to make clear the separation between operations and properties, and algorithms. On the other hand, we want to emphasize as much mental mathematics as possible. Thus, we include the thinking strategies approach for learning the basic facts in this chapter. The thinking strategies lead nicely into mental math techniques that are introduced in Chapter 4.

Subtraction: We believe that students should see subtraction in various forms: take-away and missing addend, and both of these with comparison. Also, it is critical to show students how to use addition to get subtraction facts by combining the addition facts with the missing addend approach.

Multiplication: As with addition and subtraction, we introduce multiplication through models. Properties evolve from viewing appropriate models.

Division: With division, as well as with all four operations, it is important that the focus be on the underlying meaning of the operation, which is why the ideas of sharing and measurement division are introduced. The development of multiplication and division closely parallels that of addition and subtraction with division being defined using the missing factor approach in place of the missing addend approach. Students appreciate the diagram in Figure 3.33, which shows the interrelationships among the four operations.

Ordering Whole Numbers Using Addition: With addition now available, we can define the most mathematically useful form of order, namely, $a < b$ if and only if $a + n = b$ for some nonzero n. Then one can discuss theorems such as "If $a < b$, then $a + c < b + c$" time permitting.

Exponents: Exponents and resulting "rules" are introduced as shortcuts for multiplication. Note that the definition of exponent must be restated in the case $a^1 = a$ if one does not permit a "factor" to appear alone. After exponents are introduced, the order of operations is discussed along with the pneumonic device "**P**lease **E**xcuse **M**e **D**ear **A**unt **S**ally". (Order of operations is also mentioned in the calculator section in the next chapter.)

Chapter 4 - Whole Number Computation—Mental, Electronic, and Written

Mental Math: Because of the need to move away from excessive work with written algorithms toward more emphasis on mental math and calculators for calculations, we begin this chapter on computation with a thorough treatment of mental math. Techniques developed in this subsection arise from properties of whole numbers and were the techniques that were observed in children who were effective mental calculators.

Computational Estimation: The techniques introduced in this subsection, which are commonly used in K-8 mathematics text series, were observed by researchers in children who were good estimators. The notion of rounding to compatible numbers is an especially powerful estimation technique.

Using a Calculator: We have found that although many students use calculators, they are not aware of many of the functions available on a scientific calculator. This subsection contains an introduction to several calculator keys. Uses of other specialized keys, such as fractions, change-of-sign, and so on, are introduced when their corresponding mathematical concepts are developed. We encourage students to get *fraction* scientific calculators (if not graphics calculators).

Written Algorithms for Whole Number Addition: We have several objectives in this chapter. First and foremost, we want students to realize that algorithms are step-by-step procedures to obtain answers. Second, since our customary algorithms will likely continue to be taught (but probably used less) for many years to come, they can be presented more effectively to students by using concrete models before moving to symbolic place value representations. Third, there are (have been) many algorithms for the four basic operations and that we are using one of each *among many*. Fourth, it is appropriate for students to use any correct algorithm. Our students like the "left-to-right" mental addition method since it allows them to focus on *understanding* the process rather that having to always follow the *rule* "always add starting on the right." Left-to-right mental methods lead quite naturally into left-to-right written algorithms.

Written Algorithms for Whole Number Subtraction: One of our favorite subtraction algorithms is the "subtract-from-the-base" method, which is easily motivated using multibase pieces. It is much like the standard "borrowing" method except that the exchanges are not made; thus, one only needs to know how to subtract from the base rather than know all the usual subtraction facts. For example, to find 35 - 17, we view this problem as (25 + 10) - (10 + 7), or (20 - 10) + (10 - 7 + 5) instead of the usual (20 + 15) - (10 + 7) = (20 - 10) + (15 - 7). Students see the value of this alternative algorithm when we actually have a race in class *in different bases* by having volunteers use this method against the rest of the class using the standard algorithm. Invariably, students find this algorithm easier since they only need to know how to subtract from the base and add.

Written Algorithms for Whole Number Multiplication: Students find the transition from the intermediate algorithms to the standard algorithms very helpful. Although the expanded multiplication technique involving more digits than available on a typical calculator display may not be used often, it does illustrate how to use mental math, a calculator, and understanding of mathematics to extend even what a calculator can do.

Written Algorithms for Whole Number Division: Here, again, a succession of intermediate algorithms, in addition to a concrete example with base-ten blocks, helps students better understand the long division algorithm and to appreciate just how difficult teaching this algorithm will be.

Algorithms in Base Five: This section affords students an opportunity to test various algorithms in unfamiliar situations. Students find many nontraditional algorithms more to their liking when doing computations in other bases. This gives us another chance to discuss the role and evaluation of algorithms. Notice that students will find that trying a long division problem in another base can be a humbling experience since they cannot perform the necessary prerequisite mental computations nor estimate in other bases.

Chapter 5 - Number Theory

Primes and Composites: The definitions of prime and composite numbers using numbers of factors provide a nice partition of the counting numbers, namely, 1 (one factor), primes (exactly two factors), and composites (more than two factors).

Tests for Divisibility: The proofs of the tests for divisibility are accessible to students; moreover, the students appreciate understanding why the various tests work in the ways that they do. Also, these proofs provide a convenient place to discuss logical terms such as biconditional and converse (at least informally).

Counting Factors: This is a nice technique that is usually overlooked. One of its applications is to serve as a check to see if one has found *all* the factors of a number. The table provides a nice visual proof of why this technique works.

Greatest Common Factor: In most instances, the prime factorization method is preferred by students. Our focus is on the GCF as a concept to be used in simplifying fractions. Also, we have included the Euclidean algorithm which, when combined with a calculator, can be used to find the GCFs of larger numbers more easily.

Least Common Multiple: Here, again, students prefer the prime factorization approach because of its efficiency. Also, finding the LCM by first finding the GCF and using the relationship $GCF(a,b)LCM(a,b) = ab$ is nice. Students will likely have a difficult time with the infinitude of primes proof the first time through. But, after applying it to several other primes, such as 3, 5, 7, and so on, and to one composite, say 4, they catch on and appreciate the proof.

Chapter 6 - Fractions

The Concept of Fraction: This was one of the toughest parts of the text to compose since there are two distinct notions that we need to get across (numeral and number), yet we didn't want to carry around the excess baggage of two names (fraction and fractional number) or equivalence classes of ordered pairs of whole numbers. We hope that your students will understand the many facets of the concept of a fraction as a numeral/number after working through this section. We decided to try to hit this issue head on instead of glossing over it as is done so often. Our definition of fraction equality is the usual cross multiplication definition, which naturally flows from models.

Ordering Fractions: Fractions are ordered using common denominators first since students find this approach to be a natural extension of whole number ordering. Then, the usual cross multiplication test for inequality is then derived. Density is introduced via the interesting theorem "if $\frac{a}{b} < \frac{c}{d}$, then $\frac{a}{b} < \frac{a+c}{b+d} < \frac{c}{d}$." This result surprises students and provides an opportunity to reinforce the fact that $\frac{a}{b} + \frac{c}{d} \neq \frac{a+c}{b+d}$ in general.

Addition and its Properties: Here, again, the definitions of addition and subtraction flow from work with models. Then we try to emphasize how properties of fraction addition are consequences of similar whole number properties.

Subtraction: Subtraction is motivated from models similar to addition.

Multiplication and its Properties: The definition of fraction multiplication evolves first as an extension of whole number multiplication; finally, a model is used to motivate the general definition.

Division: Our introduction of fraction division is novel, though not from a long-term historical perspective as can be seen in the Focus On. We try to enlighten students who have no *feeling* for fraction division, only a *rule* to invert and multiply. (How can such students possibly motivate this concept to children - in fact, most teachers don't; they just teach it as a rule much as stories are passed on from generation to generation.) Once, just after we had completed this unit, an excellent, mature, returning student confided that he was relieved to know that the operation of fraction division *existed*; he had always thought that there were only *three* fraction operations (no one ever used division since it was always changed to multiplication). Although many of our students may leave us with the "invert and multiply" rule still their predominant way of viewing fraction division, they do know that division is a legitimate operation and that it is multifaceted.

Mental Math and Estimation: Techniques introduced in Chapter 4 are extended to fractions. This approach reinforces the earlier work with whole numbers.

Chapter 7 - Decimals, Ratio, Proportion, and Percent

Decimals: Decimals are introduced as a natural extension of whole numbers using the number line and a hundreds square. Also, the fractions with terminating decimals are characterized.

Mental Math and Estimation: The techniques developed in Chapter 4 are extended to decimals. In addition, a new technique, using fraction equivalents, is introduced. Research found that skilled mental estimators would often convert decimals to convenient fractions and compatible numbers to estimate products.

Algorithms for Operations with Decimals: The key idea in this section is that computations involving decimals can be done by temporarily suppressing the decimal points *mentally*, performing the corresponding whole number algorithm, and then correctly inserting a decimal point in the answer. Multiplying decimals is a good place to apply rounding techniques and to do approximate calculations.

Classifying Repeating Decimals: This subsection allows us to completely describe the fractions in terms of their decimal representations.

Ratio: The work in ratios parallels the work with fractions *except* that numerators and denominators aren't restricted to whole numbers. Notice that ratios may have zero "denominators" (e.g. the ratio of men to women on an NFL football team). However, we restrict our study to ratios that have nonzero 'denominators'.

Proportion: Paying close attention to respective units is a key to success in solving proportions. The mental technique of scaling up/down is included to encourage mental math when solving proportions.

Converting Percents: Developing skill in converting among fractions, decimals, and percents is a prerequisite to solving percent problems mentally.

Mental Math and Estimation: The powerful mental technique of using fraction equivalents is introduced. This allows students to estimate answers as they do more formal percent calculations, perhaps using calculators.

Solving Percent Problems: Applied problems involving percent are solved using both the proportion and the equation methods. Work with calculators is especially relevant here, although one needs to watch for the different ways that various calculators handle percent.

Chapter 8 - Integers

Integers and the Integer Number Line: The set of integers and their opposites are introduced using both a black/red chip model and the integer number line. Note that the term opposite will be synonymous with additive inverse once that concept has been introduced.

Addition and its Properties: We have observed that students find the black/red chip model to be very helpful when learning integer operations. Addition is viewed as a natural extension of whole number addition when using colored chips.

Subtraction: Subtraction is demystified when using the chip model since the take-away approach naturally leads to the adding the opposite approach. Again, in the spirit of extending number systems, subtraction is shown to have an equivalent missing addend version. The two methods of whole number subtraction are extended to integer subtraction. In addition, the add-the-opposite approach is developed using models. Students profit from seeing that these three approaches to subtraction are equivalent. The mathematical morsel at the end of this section can be generalized to any finite collection of integers.

Multiplication and Its Properties: We motivate the definition of multiplication using patterns. However, one could use the chip model for this purpose as illustrated in exercises 4 and 5 of Exercise/Problem Set 8.2 - Part A. The results that $(-a)b = -ab$ and $(-a)(-b) = ab$ deserve special attention since most students view them simply as statements about the product of a negative and a positive, and the product of two negatives respectively. However, these are more general statements involving *additive inverses*.

Division: Just as with whole number division, integer division is viewed using the missing factor approach. We omit division with remainder due to its lack of application.

Negative Integers and Scientific Notation: Since decimals and the set of integers with its operations have been introduced, this is a natural place to study integer exponents and scientific notation.

Ordering Integers: Ordering integers is introduced as an extension of whole number ordering. Care must be taken to distinguish integer ordering, though, when multiplying both sides of an inequality by a negative (integer).

Chapter 9 - Rational Numbers and Real Numbers, with Algebra

Rational Numbers - An Extension of Fractions and Integers: Here we take a more formal approach than in earlier chapters. For example, our definition of equality is the familiar cross-multiplication definition (which extends a similar property in the fractions chapter). Also, our definition of addition is the general case involving unlike denominators. Since the rational numbers extend both the fractions and integers, this section can be covered at a brisk pace. The major "new" result is $-\dfrac{a}{b} = \dfrac{-a}{b} = \dfrac{a}{-b}$.

Ordering Rational Numbers: The material in this subsection ties together similar ideas in the fractions and integers.

Real Numbers- An Extension of Rational Numbers: There are several proofs to show that there is no rational number whose square is two - the one we selected can be easily generalized thus displaying the power of abstraction in mathematical reasoning. Figure 9.7, which shows the subset relationships among the number systems through the reals, is useful in helping students see the big picture.

Rational Exponents: Our students appreciate seeing how the definitions of fraction and rational exponents unfold. Although we did not include an extensive discussion of properties of radicals, they are developed in the problem set.

Algebra: In chapter 1, we had students solve equations using intuitive or "natural" methods such as guess and test, cover-up, and work backward. In this chapter, we use balance scale models to illustrate how to solve equations using the various properties of equality. Rules for solving inequalities are then developed abstractly by reasoning from the corresponding order properties. The equations and inequalities use rational numbers further extending what was introduced in chapter 1.

Relations and Functions: We use arrow diagrams to introduce relations and to illustrate relations that are reflexive, symmetric, and transitive. The notion of equivalence relation is covered since this concept appears in the studies of congruence and similarity among other areas. Understanding the concept of function is often difficult for students, so we carefully develop the definition and then have students explore a variety of function representations, concrete to abstract, including: arrow diagrams, tables, function machines, sets of ordered pairs, graphs, and geometric transformations.

Functions and their Graphs: A variety of functions such as linear, quadratic, cubic, and step functions and their graphs are studied. This is a great place to bring a graphics calculator to class to show how useful these powerful calculators are (*and* at an affordable price).

Chapter 10 - Statistics

Organizing Information: We find that our students are especially interested in educational examples. Charts and graphs from *USA_Today* or similar news publications provide a variety of examples. *The Statistical Abstract of the United States* and various almanacs are excellent sources˙ of data for graphs and tables.

Measuring Central Tendency: Notice how box and whisker plots incorporate central tendency *and* dispersion.

Measuring Dispersion: Interpreting the variance and standard deviation of a collection of data can be a challenge. For large, roughly normally distributed collections, the standard deviation is about one-fourth of the range. Also, if $\bar{x}$ is the mean and s is the standard deviation, then for such collections, the intervals $\bar{x} \pm s$ and $\bar{x} \pm 2s$ capture about 68% and 95% of the data, respectively.

The fact that the mean and the standard deviation are the two parameters determining the shape of a normal distribution helps our students appreciate their prominence in statistics. The use of z-scores and percentiles allows for direct comparison of performances on several exams or other measurements. That is, z-scores and percentiles indicate relative positions within distributions (in standard deviation units.)

Deceptive Statistics: Since statistical information continues to be an influential factor in society, we used the last section to focus on the potential misuses of statistics. An understanding of these misuses should help your students and their future students become better consumers and citizens.

Chapter 11 - Probability

Simple Experiments: We find that a careful discussion of events using set theory is very useful before any assignment of probabilities.

Computing Probabilities in Simple Experiments: We have found that an informal treatment of the meaning of probability, say using relative frequency, is essential at the start. Examples from games, sports, medicine, and science are very useful.

Tree Diagrams and Counting Techniques: The relationship between outcomes in binomial experiments and Pascal's triangle can be explained using diagrams such as in Figures 11.20, 11.21, and 11.22. We have found that representing multistep experiments with probability tree diagrams is a very effective way of computing probabilities.

Probability Tree Diagrams: The additive property of probability tree diagrams is a direct application of the probability of a union of disjoint events. The multiplicative property of probability tree diagrams follows from multiplication of fractions. These two properties can be applied to equally likely and unequally likely outcomes, and to multistage experiments.

Extended Counting Techniques and Computing Probabilities: Since listing a large sample space can be unreasonable, advanced counting techniques are introduced to be used to determine the number of elements in a sample space or event. These numbers are then used to compute a probability.

Simulation: With the widespread availability of computers (and scientific calculators with random number generators), simulation of experiments provides a powerful approach to approximating probabilities. Simulations using numbered chips, dice, or random digit tables are alternatives to computer simulations.

Expected Value: In experiments with numerical sample spaces, expected value can be used to describe the most likely value, or the "weighted average." This couples nicely with simulation of complex experiments.

Odds: Odds are most naturally explained in the case of equally likely outcomes, but can easily be generalized.

Conditional Probability: An initial discussion of sample spaces "reduced" to reflect a given condition (with corresponding adjustments in probabilities) can be generalized to conditional probability as a ratio.

Chapter 12 Geometric Shapes

The van Hiele Theory: We find that our students are intrigued by the hierarchy of reasoning processes described by the van Hieles. We include a discussion of children's misconceptions about geometric shapes in part to help clear up some of our students' misconceptions. We are careful to point out that our approach to geometry will be at the lowest four levels, and not at the level of axiomatics. However, we do employ both informal and formal deduction.

Recognizing Geometric Shapes: We find that our students are generally weak in visualization skills and are challenged by the exercises and problems requiring them. Tables 12.1 and 12.2 provides descriptions of basic geometric shapes as well as examples of the corresponding shapes found in the world around us.

Analyzing Geometric Shapes: We gradually build up a vocabulary for describing components of shapes and, consequently, various types of shapes.

Relationships Among Geometric Shapes: Relationships among classes of triangles are shown in Figure 12.27 and quadrilaterals are shown in Figure 12.34.

Symmetry: The tests for parallel and perpendicular line segments can be interpreted in Chapter 16 using reflections. We discuss only reflection and rotation symmetry here, leaving a discussion of more general transformations for Chapter 16.

Points and Lines in a Plane: We find that our students better understand the abstract nature of points, lines, and planes if we use an analogy to numbers; that is, we can represent the concepts with pictures (as with numbers and numerals), but the objects themselves exist only in our imaginations. The "protractor" device here is actually a fan of rays used to measure angles.

Angles: Several consequences of the parallel postulate (property 3 of points and lines) are developed and illustrated reasoning deductively.

Regular Polygons: From the angle sum in a triangle property, we are able to derive the measures of angles in regular *n*-gons.

Tessellations: Tessellations with triangles and quadrilaterals illustrate several major results (see the exercise/problem sets).

Tessellations with Regular Polygons: We are able to classify all of the regular tessellations based on our previous results about angle measures. (In the problem set, the semiregular tessellations are characterized.)

Circles: Circles are compared to regular polygons, an approach that we exploit in computing the area of a circle and the volumes and surface areas of cones and cylinders in Chapter 13.

Planes, Skew lines, and Dihedral Angles: We purposely avoid defining dihedral angles formed by half planes since the applications of interest to us involve polyhedra. The relationships between lines and planes are important when discussing polyhedra, also.

Polyhedra: Analogies between regular polyhedra and regular tessellations (semiregular polyhedra/tessellations) are useful.

Curved Shapes in Three Dimensions: We include a general definition of cylinder and cone, and determine their volumes in Chapter 13. Three-dimensional symmetry is investigated in the problems.

Chapter 13 - Measurement

Nonstandard Units: Many students (and teachers) seem to confuse measurement and geometry, or think of measurement as linear measurement only. Thus, we discuss the *process* of measurement and bring in systems of units in a historical way.

Standard Units - The English and Metric Systems: We emphasize common metric prefixes (e.g., kilo-, centi-, milli-) and show the usefulness of "metric converters" such as in Figure 13.11. We find that the three "metric cubes" in Figure 13.22 are useful in illustrating the interrelatedness of metric units of length, volume, and mass. We like to distinguish between volume and capacity. A flat circular disk of clay has volume, but no capacity (it doesn't hold any water poured on it). However, if the clay is formed into a dish, its volume is the same and it now has capacity. Notice that there are different (though connected) units for volume and capacity in the English system (e.g., cubic units and quarts).

Dimensional Analysis: Our students need practice in estimation and approximation. Dimensional analysis gives us the opportunity to estimate first, then convert/compute. It also simplifies conversions within the English system, and, when necessary, between English and metric units.

Length: We include a brief discussion of distance on a line in part to show the relationship between order properties of the real numbers and betweenness.

Area: Our discussion of area occurs at van Hiele level two since we deduce area formulas from the area of a rectangle. It is important to point out that the area of a triangle is the product of the length of a base and its *corresponding* height, since there are *three* such pairs from which to choose.

The Pythagorean Theorem: Results about construction of irrational lengths follow immediately from the Pythagorean theorem. We can also illustrate algebraic results, such as $\sqrt{ab} = \sqrt{a} \cdot \sqrt{b}$, say on a square lattice, if one of a or b is a perfect square. The triangle inequality is useful in deciding whether three arbitrary lengths determine a triangle.

Surface Area and Volume: Our students benefit greatly from concrete experiences such as those in the Student Activity Manual. Students need practice in visualizing 'unfolded' shapes as well as the relationship between the area of the base of a right prism/cylinder and its volume. This has been one of the most difficult geometry units for our students, in part, we think, due to a lack of concrete background experiences. We urge a careful intuitive approach at first. Table 13.11 shows analogies in the volumes and surface areas of prisms/cylinders and pyramids/cones.

Chapter 14 - Geometry Using Triangle Congruence and Similarity

Congruence: We have found that many students prefer to think of triangle congruence informally ("same size and shape") rather than as a relationship (literally an equivalence relation) between triangles whose vertices are made to correspond in a suitable way. Thus, we encourage our students to extend their reasoning beyond holistic thinking. We motivate the triangle congruence properties through analytical reasoning in specific cases. (For more concrete approaches, see the Student Activity Manual.) Then we apply the congruence conditions to short verifications of properties of polygons.

Similarity: We find that students need some review of ratio and proportion in order to understand the proportionality of the sides in similar triangles.

Geometric Constructions: We have deliberately separated the construction procedures from their justifications in order to emphasize the deductive verifications using triangle congruence. We find that students benefit from practice in simply learning the procedures. You may wish to discuss only a few of the justifications, as time permits.

Constructing Regular n-gons: Our students are intrigued by the interplay between Gauss's classification of constructible regular n-gons and the unsolved problem of the existence of more Fermat primes. In our courses, we discuss some consequences about the constructibility of certain angles, e.g. as central angles or vertex angles in regular *n*-gons.

Geometric Problem Solving Using Triangle Congruence and Similarity: Several classical results, illustrated in Chapter 12, are verified here. Example 14.15, the converse of the Pythagorean theorem, actually uses the Pythagorean theorem! Many of the results of this section can be investigated inductively using exploration software before searching for deductive verifications.

Chapter 15 - Geometry Using Coordinates

Coordinates: If coordinates were not studied in section 9.3, the first few pages of that section could be covered here.

Distance: The midpoint formula can also be verified using triangle congruence (or similarity) if you prefer.

Slope: An analogy to the grade of a road or the pitch of a roof is helpful in understanding slope as a ratio. We have purposely kept the derivations of slope properties independent of Chapter 14. If you've discussed Chapter 14, you may wish to use triangle congruence or similarity properties in verifying the slopes of parallel lines property. We establish only the slope-intercept form of the equation of a nonvertical line to keep our treatment as lean as possible (others are found in the problem set, though). As enrichment, you may wish to discuss the geometry of other forms of a line.

Simultaneous Equations: We will apply results of this section in section 15.3 when establishing the concurrence of the medians and of the altitudes in a triangle.

Equations of Circles: We develop equations of circles to show that curves other than lines have analytical characterizations. You may wish to discuss other curves, such as the remaining conic sections. (See the problems in 15.2B.) We also apply the equation of a circle in finding the circumscribed circle of a triangle.

Geometric Problem Solving Using Coordinates: Example 15.8 is much more difficult using only triangle congruence or similarity. Results about the medians and altitudes of triangles can be motivated by constructions or exploration software.

Chapter 16 - Geometry Using Transformations

Transformations: Construction or drawing activities in addition to the use of a dynamic geometry software package are helpful for many of our students in developing an intuitive feeling for transformations. See the Student Activity Manual.

Symmetry: Tessellations, wallpaper, flooring, and clothing are sources of symmetric patterns. Miras are very useful for investigating reflection symmetry.

Making Escher-Type Patterns: There are several books available from Dale Seymour Publications and Creative Publications on tessellations and Escher-type patterns that our students enjoy.

Congruence: We present a special case of the verification that reflections preserve distance to avoid overwhelming the students with too much detail. The classification of isometries can be convincingly demonstrated with construction activities, as a more concrete approach.

Similarity: The development parallels that of congruence via size transformations.

Geometric Problem Solving Using Transformations: Example 16.12 is an alternative to an approach using congruence. (The latter technically involves betweenness considerations.) Several interesting applications of half-turns appear. An argument based on area of parallelograms also suffices.

Epilogue - An Eclectic Approach to Geometry

Enjoy this section - your students will too! Proving the midsegment theorem using three approaches—synthetic, coordinate, and transformation—opens students' eyes to the value of multiple approaches to geometry. Give students a chance to vote on their favorite approach and discuss the pros and cons of each method. This is a great capstone to the study of geometry.

Chapter Learning Objectives

Chapter 1 - Introduction to Problem Solving

Students are expected to be able to:

1-1   Distinguish between solving a problem and solving an exercise in mathematics.

1-2   Solve problems using Polya's 4-step problem-solving process:
        understand the problem   carry out the plan
        devise a plan   look back

1-3   Apply the process illustrated in the following diagram for formulating and solving mathematical problems.

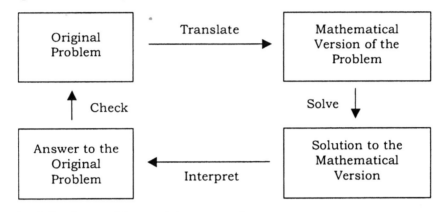

1-4   Use the following problem-solving strategies:
        guess and test   look for a pattern
        draw a picture   make a list
        use a variable   solve a simpler problem

1-5   Identify "clues" in the statements of problems that are helpful for selecting an appropriate problem-solving strategy.

1-6   Apply these terms when using algebra:
        equation
        solution
        solve

Chapter 2 - Sets, Whole Numbers, and Numeration

Students are expected to be able to:

2-1   Demonstrate understanding of the concepts of:
        set   equal sets
        element of a set   empty set

2-2   Use set-builder notation to denote sets.

2-3   Formalize the meaning of whole number using the concept of equivalent sets (one-to-one correspondence.)

2-4   Determine whether a given set is finite or infinite.

2-5   Construct a new set from two or more sets using the operations of:
        union   set difference
        intersection   Cartesian product
        complement

2-6   Use Venn diagrams to illustrate:
        subset   the union of two sets
        proper subset   the intersection of two sets
        universal set   the complement of a set
        disjoint sets   the difference of two sets

2-7   Explain the difference between a number and a numeral.

2-8   Distinguish between the three uses of whole numbers:
        cardinal number
        ordinal number
        identification number

2-9   Explain what is meant by the number of elements in a finite set.

2-10   Use sets and a whole-number line to describe the relations of less than and greater than for whole numbers.

2-11   Express whole numbers using these numeration systems:
        Egyptian   Mayan
        Roman   Hindu-Arabic
        Babylonian

2-12   Compare the attributes (additive, subtractive, multiplicative, positional, place value) of the following numeration systems:
        tally   Babylonian
        Egyptian   Mayan
        Roman   Hindu-Arabic

2-13   Explain what is meant by the base of the Hindu-Arabic numeration system.

2-14   Express a Hindu-Arabic numeral in any base in expanded notation and convert from expanded form to the numeral represented.

2-15 Describe the naming procedure for Hindu-Arabic numerals.

2-16 Convert a numeral from any base to base 10 and vice versa.

Chapter 3 - Whole Numbers: Operations and Properties

Students are expected to be able to:

3-1   Use a set model and a measurement model to represent addition and subtraction of whole numbers.

3-2   Demonstrate knowledge of the properties of whole number addition:
        closure   associativity
        commutativity   identity

        and verify that subtraction has none of these properties.

3-3   Apply the following thinking strategies to learn basic addition facts in other bases and to simplify computations:
        commutativity   counting on by 1 and 2
        doubles   associativity
        adding zero   combinations to 10
        adding 10   doubles +/- 1 and +/- 2

3-4   Use the take-away and missing-addend approaches to define subtraction of whole numbers and apply comparison to each of the above approaches.

3-5   Use the missing-addend approach and four-fact families to relate addition and subtraction.

3-6   Use the repeated-addition, rectangular-array, and Cartesian-product approaches, in combination with a set model and a measurement model, to represent multiplication of whole numbers.

3-7   Demonstrate knowledge of the properties for multiplication of whole numbers and the distributive property of multiplication over addition (and subtraction) and verify that division of whole numbers has none of these properties.

3-8   Apply the following thinking strategies for learning basic multiplication facts and simplifying computations:
        commutativity   multiplication by 5
        multiplication by zero   multiplication by 9
        multiplication by 1   associativity
        multiplication by 2   distributivity

3-9   Differentiate between sharing and measurement division.

3-10   Use the missing-factor and the repeated-subtraction approaches to define division of whole numbers, including division problems involving zero.

3-11   Use the missing-factor approach and four-fact families to relate multiplication and division and illustrate the division algorithm using a number line model.

3-12   Use the operation of addition to define less than and greater than with whole numbers.

3-13 Demonstrate knowledge of the following properties of less than:
    transitivity
    property of less than and addition
    property of less than and multiplication.

3-14 Define whole number exponents using repeated multiplication.

3-15 Provide a proof for each of the following theorems about whole-number exponents, where a and b are whole numbers, and m and n are non-zero whole numbers:
    (a) $a^m \cdot a^n = a^{m+n}$
    (b) $a^m \cdot b^m = (ab)^m$
    (c) $(a^m)^n = a^{mn}$; $a^m \div a^n = a^{m-n}$, if $m \geq n$; $a^0 = 1$ for all nonzero whole numbers a
    (d) 0^0 is undefined

3-16 Apply the order of operations to evaluate arithmetic expressions.

Chapter 4 - Whole Number Computations—Mental, Electronic, and Written

Students are expected to be able to:

4-1   Apply the problem-solving strategy "use indirect reasoning."

4-2   Identify and apply the following mental math techniques:
use properties
compatible numbers
compensation (additive, equal additions, and multiplicative)
left-to-right methods
multiply by powers of 10
multiply by special factors

4-3   Identify and apply the following computational estimation techniques: front-end estimation (range, one- and two-column), and rounding (up, down, truncate, round a 5 up, to the nearest even, to compatible numbers).

4-4   Distinguish between arithmetic and algebraic logic on calculators by listing the mathematical convention for order of operations.

4-5   Use the following keys on a calculator (in addition to the usual number keys):
parentheses keys   exponent keys
constant function keys   memory keys

4-6   Interpret scientific notation as it appears on scientific calculators.

4-7   Model the standard written algorithms for addition, subtraction, multiplication and division using concrete models (multibase pieces and chip abacus).

4-8   Justify the standard written algorithms for addition, subtraction, multiplication and division using place value and properties.

4-9   Compute sums and products with (a) intermediate algorithms for addition and multiplication that lead to the standard algorithms and (b) the lattice methods for addition and multiplication.

4-10   Use nontraditional algorithms for subtraction.

4-11   Explain long-division algorithms (including the scaffold method) that lead to the standard algorithm.

4-12   Use a calculator to perform division with remainders.

4-13   Compute sums and products in bases 2 through 12 with (a) intermediate algorithms for addition and multiplication and (b) the lattice methods for addition and multiplication.

4-14   Compute differences in bases 2 through 12 with (a) the standard subtraction algorithm and (b) subtract from the base.

4-15   Compute quotients in bases 2 through 12 with (a) the scaffold method and (b) the standard long-division algorithm.

Chapter 5 - Number Theory

Students are expected to be able to:

5-1   Apply the problem-solving strategy "use properties of numbers."

5-2   Use the sieve of Eratosthenes to find prime numbers.

5-3   Use a factor tree to write the prime factorization of a given composite number.

5-4   Apply the fundamental theorem of arithmetic.

5-5   Apply each of the following terms:
      divides   factor
      divisor   is divisible by
      multiple

5-6   Use tests for divisibility (by 2, 3, 4, 5, 6, 8, 9, 10, 11, and 12), together with the Prime Factor Test, to determine whether a given number is prime or composite.

5-7   Use the exponents in the prime factorization of a number to count its factors.

5-8   Use (a) the set intersection method, (b) the prime factorization method, and (c) the Euclidean algorithm to find the greatest common factor of a given pair of numbers.

5-9   Use (a) the set intersection method, (b) the prime factorization method, and (c) the build-up method find the least common multiple of a given pair of numbers.

5-10 Relate the GCF and LCM of any two numbers to the product of the numbers.

Chapter 6 - Fractions

Students are expected to be able to:

6-1   Apply the problem-solving strategy "solve an equivalent problem."

6-2   Illustrate fractions that represent parts of a whole (numerals) which are written as pairs of whole numbers and a relative amount (numbers).

6-3   Apply the following terms
      numerator   mixed number
      denominator   complex fraction
      improper fraction

6-4   Use cross multiplication to determine which of two given fractions is greater or whether the two fractions are equal.

6-5   Express a fraction in simplest form (lowest terms).

6-6   Use concrete models show how to motivate the definitions of addition and subtraction of fractions.

6-7   Compute sums and differences of given pairs of fractions.

6-8   Apply the following properties of addition of fractions and determine which hold for subtraction of fractions:
      closure   associativity
      commutativity   identity

6-9   Use the following mental math/estimation techniques for adding and subtracting fractions:
      properties
      additive compensation
      equal-additions method of subtraction
      range estimation
      rounding to compatible numbers
      front-end with adjustment
      rounding to the nearest 1/2 or whole

6-10   Use concrete models show how to motivate the definitions of multiplication and division of fractions.

6-11   Compute products of given pairs of fractions.

6-12   Use the three equivalent approaches to find the quotient of two given fractions:
      common-denominator approach
      divided-the-numerators-and-denominators approach
      invert-the-divisor-and-multiply approach

6-13   Apply the following properties of multiplication of fractions and determine which hold for division of fractions:

closure   identity
commutativity   inverse
associativity

and apply the distributive property of fraction multiplication over addition (and subtraction).

6-14   Use the following mental math/estimation techniques for multiplying and dividing fractions:

properties
compatible numbers
range estimation
rounding to the nearest 1/2 or whole

Chapter 7 - Decimals, Ratio, Proportion, and Percent

Students are expected to be able to:

7-1   Apply the problem-solving strategy "work backward."

7-2   Use a hundreds square and number line to represent decimals.

7-3   Write a given decimal numeral in expanded form.

7-4   Translate decimal numerals into their word names and vice versa.

7-5   Characterize the fractions with terminating decimal representations.

7-6   Order decimals in four ways:
          using a hundreds square
          using a number line
          comparing the numbers in fraction form
          comparing place values in decimal form

7-7   Use the following mental math/estimation techniques for adding and
          multiplying decimals:
          properties   range estimation
          compatible (decimal) numbers   rounding
          compensation   front-end with adjustment
          fraction equivalents

7-8   Justify the "moving the decimal point" when multiplying or dividing by a power
          of 10.

7-9   Compute sums, differences, products, and quotients of numbers in decimal
          form (a) using the standard algorithms and (b) using a calculator.

7-10   Use scientific notation to represent decimal numbers.

7-11   Convert any given fraction to its decimal form and any given repeating decimal
          to its fraction form.

7-12   Classify repeating decimals and characterize the fractions that have repeating,
          nonterminating decimal representations.

7-13   Use ratios to make (a) part-to-part and (b) part-to-whole comparisons of the
          relative sizes of two quantities.

7-14   Interpret the units of a ratio as a rate.

7-15   Solve proportions using (a) cross multiplication and (b) scaling up (or down).

7-16   Use 10-by-10 grids to represent n% (n percent).

7-17   Convert between the fraction, decimal and percent form of a given number.

7-18   Use the following mental math/estimation techniques for finding/estimating the percent of a number:

fraction equivalents   compensation

compatible numbers   rounding

7-19   Solve percent problems using the following approaches: (a) grid approach, (b) proportion approach, and (c) equation approach.

7-20   Use a calculator to solve percent problems.

Chapter 8 - Integers

Students are expected to be able to:

8-1   Apply the problem-solving strategy "use cases."

8-2   Use (a) colored chips (a set model) and (b) the integer number line (a measurement model) to represent integers and to model addition and subtraction of integers.

8-3   Apply the following properties of integer addition and determine which hold for subtraction:
        closure   additive identity
        commutativity   additive inverse
        associativity

8-4   Apply the additive cancellation for integers and the opposite of the opposite for integers theorems.

8-5   Subtract given pairs of integers using each of these approaches:
        take-away
        adding the opposite
        missing addend

8-6   Motivate the definition for integer multiplication using: (a) repeated addition and (b) patterns.

8-7   Apply the following properties of integer multiplication and determine which hold for division of integers:
        closure   associativity
        commutativity   multiplicative identity

and apply the distributive property of integer multiplication over addition (and subtraction).

8-8   Use the following results to calculate products of integers:
        (a) $a(-1) = -a$
        (b) $-a(b) = -(ab) = a(-b)$
        (c) $-a(-b) = ab$.

8-9   Use the missing-factor approach to explain division of integers.

8-10   Use negative exponents and scientific notation.

8-11   Use (a) the number-line approach and (b) the addition approach to order a given set of integers.

8-12   Apply the following properties of less than (and greater than):
        transitivity
        less than and addition
        multiplication by a positive and by a negative

Chapter 9 - Rational Numbers and Real Numbers, with an Introduction to Algebra

Students are expected to be able to:

9-1   Apply the problem-solving strategy "solve an equation."

9-2   Apply the following properties of addition of rational numbers:
  closure   additive identity
  commutativity   additive inverse
  associativity

9-3   Apply the additive-cancellation-for-rational-numbers and the opposite-of-the-opposite-for-rational-numbers theorems.

9-4   Subtract given pairs of rational numbers using the adding-the-opposite and the missing-addend approaches.

9-5   Apply the following properties of multiplication of rational numbers:
  closure   identity
  commutativity   multiplicative inverse
  associativity

and apply the distributive property of multiplication over addition (and subtraction).

9-6   Use the three equivalent approaches to find the quotient of two given rational numbers:
  common-denominator approach
  divide-the-numerators-and-denominators approach
  invert-the-divisor-and-multiply approach

9-7   Order rational numbers using the following approaches:
  the number line   addition
  common positive denominators   cross multiplication

9-8   Determine whether a given real number is rational or irrational.

9-9   Use the Pythagorean theorem to find the length of a line segment given on a square lattice and to construct irrational lengths.

9-10   Apply the definitions of the following terms:
  nth root
  unit fraction exponent
  rational exponent

and apply properties of rational exponents.

9-11   Solve equations of the forms:
        (a) $x + a = b$
        (b) $ax + b = c$
        (c) $ax + b = cx + d$

and represent the solution process both concretely (using a balance scale model) and abstractly (using algebraic symbols.)

9-12   Solve inequalities using the following properties of order:
        (a) if $a < b$ and $b < c$, then $a < c$
        (b) if $a < b$, then $a + c < b + c$
        (c) if $a < b$ and $c > 0$, then $ac < bc$
        (d) if $a < b$ and $c < 0$, then $ac > bc$.

9-13   Use arrow diagrams to represent relations and determine whether a given arrow diagram represents a relation that is reflexive, symmetric, or transitive, and whether the relation is an equivalence relation.

9-14   Determine whether a given sequence is arithmetic, geometric, or otherwise; if arithmetic (geometric), find the common difference (ratio) and the nth term.

9-15   Use function notation to express a given relationship between two sets (the domain and codomain.)

9-16   Represent functions as:
        arrow diagrams   graphs
        tables   formulas
        function machines   geometric transformations
        ordered pairs

9-17   Plot points with given coordinates in the Cartesian coordinate system.

9-18   Construct and interpret graphs of the following kinds of functions:
        linear   cubic
        quadratic   step
        exponential

9-19   Apply the vertical line test to determine if a graph is the graph of a function.

Chapter 10 - Statistics

Students are expected to be able to:

10-1 Apply the problem-solving strategy "look for a formula."

10-2 Interpret the following types of graphs:

line plots	line graphs
stem and leaf plots	circle graphs
bar graphs	pictographs
histograms	scatterplots

10-3 Construct appropriate types of graphs for a given collection of data.

10-4 Identify clusters and gaps (if they exist) on stem and leaf plots.

10-5 Use the regression line for a scatterplot to identify outliers and make predictions.

10-6 Describe any of the following misleading attributes of a given graph:
scaling
axis manipulation
reversing the category order
cropping
three-dimensional effects
exploding, deceptive pictorial embellishments
using an inappropriate type of graph

10-7 Identify the population and the sample for a given data-gathering situation.

10-8 Describe sources of bias in sampling.

10-9 Determine the following measures of central tendency for given data:
mode
median
mean

10-10 Calculate the lower quartile, upper quartile, and the interquartile range (IQR), and identify any outliers for a box and whisker plot.

10-11 Explain the meaning of the percentile rank of a value in a given set of data.

10-12 Determine the following measures of dispersion for a given data set, using written and calculator methods:

range	standard deviation
variance	the z-score of a particular data value

10-13 Give a geometric interpretation of the mode, median, and mean of a distribution and, for a normal distribution, the mean, standard deviation, and z-scores.

Chapter 11 - Probability

Students are expected to be able to:

11-1   Apply the problem-solving strategy "do a simulation."

11-2   Apply each of the following terms: experiment, outcome, event, and sample space.

11-3   Determine experimental and theoretical probabilities for events with equally likely outcomes.

11-4   Apply the following properties of probability:
     (a) For any event A, $0 \leq P(A) \leq 1$.
     (b) $P(\varnothing) = 0$.
     (c) $P(S) = 1$ where S is the sample space.
     (d) For all events A and B , then $P(A \cup B) = P(A) + P(B) - P(A \cap B)P(A \cup B)$.
     (e) If $\overline{A}$ denotes the complement of event A , then $P(\overline{A}) = 1 - P(A)$.

11-5   Construct tree diagrams to represent the outcomes in a sample space.

11-6   Use the fundamental counting property to determine the number of outcomes in a sample space and in an event.

11-7   Distinguish between experiments that consist of drawing with replacement and those that consist of drawing without replacement and determine probabilities in such experiments.

11-8   Construct probability tree diagrams and apply the multiplicative and additive properties of probability to compute probabilities in complex experiments.

11-9   Apply Pascal's triangle to count outcomes in experiments that consist of a sequence of smaller identical experiments, each having two equally likely possibilities.

11-10 Compute the number of permutations or combinations of r objects chosen from n objects.

11-11 Relate the row entries of Pascal's triangle to the values of the corresponding combinations.

11-12 Use permutations and combinations to compute probabilities.

11-13 Use simulations to model complex experiments and compute experimental probabilities.

11-14 Compute expected values for experiments whose outcomes are real numbers.

11-15 Convert between the probability of an event and the odds in favor or against the event.

11-16 Compute conditional probabilities.

Chapter 12 - Geometric Shapes

Students are expected to be able to:

12-1 Apply the problem-solving strategy "use a model."

12-2 Identify the van Hiele level, Level 0 (Recognition) or Level 1 (Analysis), at which a student is operating.

12-3 Characterize geometric figures in terms of their component parts and attributes:
- line segments
- angles
- various types of triangles
- quadrilaterals
- other polygons

12-4 Use paper folding, dot paper, or tracings to identify characteristics of triangles and quadrilaterals, including equal side lengths, parallel sides, or perpendicular sides.

12-5 Classify various types of triangles and quadrilaterals according to common properties and relationships among general types.

12-6 Use Venn diagrams to represent relationships among various types of triangles and quadrilaterals.

12-7 Illustrate properties of triangles and quadrilaterals, including reflection and rotation symmetries, using paper folding or tracings.

12-8 Use models to represent the abstract concepts of plane, point, and line, and demonstrate the properties of lines in the plane and the distance between points.

12-9 Use a protractor to determine the measure of a given angle.

12-10 Apply formal definitions of the following geometric figures:
- line segment
- parallel lines
- perpendicular lines
- angle
- acute angle
- right angle
- obtuse angle
- straight angle
- reflex angle
- adjacent angles
- vertical angles
- supplementary angles
- complementary angles
- right triangle
- acute triangle
- obtuse triangle

12-11 Apply the corresponding angles property, the alternate interior angles property, and the angle sum in a triangle property.

12-12 Determine the measures of the following types of angles in a regular polygon:
- central angle
- vertex angle
- exterior angle

12-13 Use tessellations to illustrate properties of arbitrary triangles and quadrilaterals.

12-14   Analyze tessellations composed of polygons, particularly those involving regular polygons.

12-15   Apply the definitions of the following terms:
        circle   radius
        center   diameter

12-16   Use paper folding to investigate properties of circles, including symmetry.

12-17   Describe pairs of lines and planes in three dimensional space according to the following relationships:
        parallel   perpendicular
        intersecting   skew

12-18   Determine the measure of a dihedral angle.

12-19   Apply the definitions of the following families of polyhedra:
        prisms (right and oblique)   regular polyhedra
        pyramids (right and oblique)   semiregular polyhedra

12-20   Illustrate Euler's formula for polyhedra.

12-21   Apply the definitions of the following curved shapes in three dimensions:
        cylinders (right and oblique)
        cones (right and oblique)
        spheres

Chapter 13 - Measurement

Students are expected to be able to:

13-1   Apply the problem-solving strategy "use dimensional analysis."

13-2   Use both non-standard and standard units and the three steps of the
measurement process to measure:

length	capacity
area	weight
volume	temperature

13-3   Convert between units of measure within the English system, within the
metric system, and from the English system to the metric system (and vice
versa).

13-4   Work with the following metric prefixes:

milli-	deka-
centi-	hecto-
deci-	kilo-

13-5   Find the perimeter of geometric figures, including polygons and circles.

13-6   Apply formulas to find areas of the following geometric figures:

rectangle	parallelogram
square	trapezoid
triangle	circle

13-7   Verify the Pythagorean theorem, both informally (using a visual "proof") and
formally (using algebra.)

13-8   Apply the Pythagorean theorem to determine lengths.

13-9   Use the triangle inequality to determine whether a given set of lengths could
be used to form a triangle.

13-10   Justify formulas to find the surface area of the following three-dimensional
figures:

prism	cone
cylinder	sphere
pyramid	

13-11   Apply formulas to find the surface area of the following three-dimensional
figures:

prism	cone
cylinder	sphere
pyramid	

13-12   Justify formulas to find the volume of the following three-dimensional figures:

prism	cone
cylinder	sphere
pyramid	

13-13 Apply formulas to find the volume of the following three-dimensional figures:

prism   cone
cylinder   sphere
pyramid

Chapter 14 - Geometry Using Triangle Congruence and Similarity

Students are expected to be able to:

14-1 Apply the problem-solving strategy "identify subgoals."

14-2 Establish a correspondence between two triangles to determine if they are congruent.

14-3 Apply the Side-Angle-Side (SAS), Angle-Side-Angle (ASA), and Side-Side-Side (SSS) congruence properties.

14-4 Establish a correspondence between two triangles to determine if they are similar.

14-5 Apply the Side-Angle-Side (SAS), Angle-Angle (AA), and Side-Side-Side (SSS) similarity properties.

14-6 Use similar triangles to solve application problems involving indirect measurement.

14-7 Perform the following basic compass and straightedge constructions:
      (a) copy a line segment
      (b) copy an angle
      (c) construct the perpendicular bisector of a line segment
      (d) bisect an angle
      (e) construct the line perpendicular to a given line through a specified point on the line
      (f) construct the line perpendicular to a given line through a specified point not on the line
      (g) construct the line parallel to a given line through a specified point not on the line.

14-8 Use triangle congruence properties and other results to justify each of the basic constructions (a)-(g) above.

14-9 Locate the circumcenter, centroid, incenter, and orthocenter for any given triangle using a compass and straightedge.

14-10 Use compass and straightedge to construct:
      (a) the circumscribed circle of a triangle
      (b) the inscribed circle of a triangle
      (c) an equilateral triangle with a given side

14-11 Use Gauss's theorem to determine which regular n-gons can be constructed using a compass and straightedge.

Chapter 15 - Geometry Using Coordinates

Students are expected to be able to:

15-1   Apply the problem-solving strategy "use coordinates."

15-2   Use the coordinate distance formula to:
        (a) find the distance between any two points and
        (b) determine whether three given points are collinear.

15-3   Use the midpoint formula to find the midpoint of a given line segment.

15-4   Use the slope formula:
        (a) to determine the slope (if it exists) of a line with two given points
        (b) and apply the concept of slope to determine whether three given
            points are collinear.

15-5   Apply the slopes of parallel lines theorem and the slopes of perpendicular lines theorem.

15-6   Determine the slope-intercept form of the equation of the line:
        (a) containing a given pair of points
        (b) containing a given point and having a given slope

15-7   Solve pairs of simultaneous equations and interpret the solution(s) geometrically.

15-8   Determine the equation of a circle given its center and radius and vice versa.

15-9   Use coordinate geometry to verify properties of triangles and quadrilaterals.

15-10 Use equations of lines and circles to illustrate geometric constructions in the coordinate plane.

Chapter 16 - Geometry Using Transformations

Students are expected to be able to:

16-1   Apply the problem-solving strategy "use symmetry."

16-2   Use dot paper, paper folding, tracings, and compass/straightedge to locate the
        image of a given point, line segment, angle, triangle, and quadrilateral under
        any of the following transformations:
            isometries (translation, reflection, rotation, or glide reflection)
            size transformation
            similitude

16-3   Describe an isometry that will map a given point to another given point, and a
        line segment, angle, triangle, or quadrilateral to a another given congruent
        figure.

16-4   Describe a similitude that will move a given triangle to a given similar triangle.

16-5   Determine whether a given tessellation of the plane has any the following types
        of symmetry:
            translation
            rotation
            reflection
            glide reflection

16-6   Verify the properties of isometries theorem.

16-7   Apply the triangle congruence and isometries theorem and the congruent
        polygons theorem to determine whether two given triangles or polygons are
        congruent.

When Will I Teach This?

The shaded regions in the following scope and sequence chart indicate when topics in *Mathematics for Elementary Teachers - A Contemporary Approach* may be covered in the typical K-8 curriculum. Topics are introduced at the conceptual level in earlier grades. Then students develop skills and facility with problem solving and application in later grades.

Grade Level

Chapter	Topic	K	1	2	3	4	5	6	7	8
1	Problem Solving	■	■	■	■	■	■	■	■	■
2	Whole Number Concepts	■	■	■	■	■	■	■	■	■
	Numeration	■	■	■	■	■	■	■	■	■
3	Whole Number Operations	■	■	■	■	■	■	■	■	■
4	Whole Number Computation		■	■	■	■	■	■	■	■
5	Number Theory			■	■	■	■	■	■	■
6	Fractions			■	■	■	■	■	■	■
7	Decimals				■	■	■	■	■	■
	Ratio and Proportion					■	■	■	■	■
	Percent						■	■	■	■
8	Integers							■	■	■
9	Rational Numbers								■	■
	Real Numbers									■
	Solving Equations	■	■	■	■	■	■	■	■	■
10	Statistics	■		■	■	■	■	■	■	■
11	Probability			■	■	■	■	■	■	■
12	Geometric Shapes	■	■	■	■	■	■	■	■	■
13	Measurement	■	■	■	■	■	■	■	■	■
14	Geometry - Synthetic				■	■	■	■	■	■
15	Geometry - Coordinates					■	■	■	■	■
16	Geometry - Transformations				■	■	■	■	■	■

Exercise/Problem Sets Map for the Ninth Edition

The following Exercise/Problem Sets Map describes changes from the eighth edition. Except where noted, problems in Part A remained Part A problems, and Part B remained Part B.

CHAPTER 1		14	14	1	1	13	13	12	12
Section 1.1A		15	15	2	2	14	14	13	13
9th ed.	8th ed.	16	3	3	3	15	15	14	14
1	1	17	4	4	4	16	16	15	15
2	2	18	5	5	5	17	17	16	16
3	3	19	6	6	6	18	18	17	17
4	4	20	7	7	7	19	19	18	18
5	5	21	8	8	8	20	20	19	19
6	6	22	9	9	9	21	21	20	20
7	7	23	10	10	10	22	22	21	21
8	8	24	11	11	11	23	23	22	22
9	9	25	12	12	12	24	24	23	23
10	10	26	13	13	13	25	25	24	24
11	11	27	14	14	14	26	26	25	25
12	12	28	15	15	15	27	27	26	26
13	13	29	16	16	16	28	28	27	27
14	14	30	17	17	17	29	29	28	28
15	15	31	18	18	18	30	30	29	29
16	16	32	19	19	19	31	31	30	30
17	17	Section 1.2A		20	20	32	32	31	31
18	18	1	21	21	21	33	33	32	32
19	19	2	22	22	22	34	34	33	33
20	20	3	23	23	23	35	35	34	34
21	21	4	4	24	New	36	36	35	35
22	22	5	5	25	New	37	37	36	36
23	23	6	6	26	New	38	38	37	37
24	24	7	7	27	New	39	39	38	38
25	25	8	8	28	New	40	40	39	39
26	26	9	9	29	New	41	41	40	40
27	27	10	10	CHAPTER 2		42	42	41	41
Section 1.1B		11	11	Section 2.1A		43	43	42	43
1	1	12	12	9th ed.	8th ed.	44	44	43	42
2	2	13	13	1	1	Section 2.1B		44	New
3	3	14	14	2	2	1	1	45	New
4	4	15	15	3	3	2	2	46	New
5	5	16	16	4	4	3	3	47	New
6	6	17	17	5	5	4	4	48	New
7	7	18	18	6	6	5	5	49	New
8	8	19	19	7	7	6	6	Section 2.2A	
9	9	20	20	8	8	7	7	1	1
10	10	21	21	9	9	8	8	2	2
11	11	22	22	10	10	9	9	3	3
12	12	23	23	11	11	10	10	4	4
13	13	Section 1.2B		12	12	11	11	5	5

6	6	7	7	26	26	15	15	3	3
7	7	8	8	27	27	16	16	4	4
8	8	9	9	28	28	17	17	5	5
9	9	10	10	29	29	18	18	6	6
10	10	11	11	30	30	19	19	7	7
11	11	12	12	31	31	20	20	8	8
12	12	13	13	32	32	21	21	9	9
13	13	14	14	33	New	22	22	10	10
14	14	15	15	34	New	23	New	11	11
15	15	16	16	35	New	24	22A	12	12
16	16	17	17	36	New	25	New	13	13
17	17	18	18	37	New	26	New	14	14
18	18	19	19	38	New	27	New	15	15
19	19	20	20	**CHAPTER 3**		28	New	16	16
20	20	21	21	**Section 3.1A**		29	New	17	17
21	21	22	22	**9th ed.**	**8th ed.**	30	New	18	18
22	22	23	23	1	1	**Section 3.2A**		19	19
Section 2.2B		24	24	2	2	1	1	20	20
1	1	25	25	3	3	2	2	21	21
2	2	26	26	4	4	3	3	22	22
3	3	27	27	5	5	4	4	23	23
4	4	28	28	6	6	5	5	24	24
5	5	29	29	7	7	6	6	25	25
6	6	30	30	8	8	7	7	26	26
7	7	31	31	9	9	8	8	27	27
8	8	32	32	10	10	9	9	28	28
9	9	**Section 2.3B**		11	11	10	10	29	29
10	10	1	1	12	12	11	11	30	30
11	11	2	2	13	13	12	12	31	31
12	12	3	3	14	14	13	13	32	32
13	13	4	4	15	15	14	14	33	New
14	14	5	5	16	16	15	15	34	New
15	15	6	6	17	17	16	16	35	New
16	16	7	7	18	18	17	17	36	New
17	17	8	8	19	19	18	18	37	New
18	18	9	9	20	20	19	19	38	New
19	19	10	10	21	21	20	20	39	New
20	20	11	11	**Section 3.1B**		21	21	40	33A
21	New	12	12	1	1	22	22	41	New
23	New	13	13	2	2	23	23	**Section 3.3A**	
23	New	14	14	3	3	24	24	1	1
24	New	15	15	4	4	25	25	2	2
25	New	16	16	5	5	26	26	3	3
26	New	17	17	6	6	27	27	4	4
27	New	18	18	7	7	28	28	5	5
Section 2.3A		19	19	8	8	29	29	6	6
1	1	20	20	9	9	30	30	7	7
2	2	21	21	10	10	31	31	8	8
3	3	22	22	11	11	32	32	9	10
4	4	23	23	12	12	**Section 3.2B**		10	11
5	5	24	24	13	13	1	1	11	12
6	6	25	25	14	14	2	2	12	13

13	14	7	7	15	15	17	17	21	21
14	15	8	8	16	16	18	18	22	22
15	16	9	9	17	17	19	19	23	23
16	17	10	10	18	18	20	20	24	24
17	18	11	11	19	19	21	21	25	25
18	19	12	12	20	20	22	22	26	26
19	20	13	13	21	21	23	23	27	27
20	21	14	14	22	22	24	24	28	28
21	22	15	15	23	23	25	25	29	29
22	23	16	16	24	24	26	26	30	30
23	24	17	17	25	25	27	27	31	31
Section 3.3B		18	18	26	26	28	28	32	32
1	1	19	19	27	27	29	29	33	33
2	2	20	20	28	28	30	30	34	34
3	3	21	21	29	29	31	31	35	35
4	4	22	22	30	30	32	32	36	36
5	5	23	23	31	31	33	33	37	37
6	6	24	24	32	32	34	34	38	38
7	7	25	25	33	33	35	35	39	39
8	8	26	26	34	34	36	36	40	40
9	10	27	27	35	35	37	37	41	41
10	11	28	28	36	36	38	38	42	42
11	12	29	29	37	37	39	39	43	43
12	13	30	30	38	38	40	40	44	44
13	14	31	31	39	39	41	41	45	45
14	15	32	32	40	40	42	42	47	New
15	16	33	33	41	41	43	43	48	New
16	18	34	34	42	New	44	44	49	New
17	19	35	35	43	New	45	45	50	New
18	20	36	36	44	42	46	46	51	47
19	21	37	37	45	New	47	47	52	New
20	22	38	38	46	New	**Section 4.2B**		53	New
21	23	39	39	47	New	1	1	54	New
22	24	40	40	48	New	2	2	**Section 4.3A**	
23	New	41	41	49	New	3	3	1	New
24	New	42	42	**Section 4.2A**		4	4	2	2
25	9A	43	43	1	1	5	5	3	3
26	New	**Section 4.1B**		2	2	6	6	4	4
27	9	1	1	3	3	7	7	5	5
28	17	2	2	4	4	8	8	6	6
29	New	3	3	5	5	9	9	7	New
30	New	4	4	6	6	10	10	8	7
31	New	5	5	7	7	11	11	9	8
CHAPTER 4		6	6	8	8	12	12	10	9
Section 4.1A		7	7	9	9	13	13	11	10
9th ed.	**8th ed.**	8	8	10	10	14	14	12	New
1	1	9	9	11	11	15	15	13	11
2	2	10	10	12	12	16	16	14	14
3	3	11	11	13	13	17	17	15	New
4	4	12	12	14	14	18	18	16	13
5	5	13	13	15	15	19	19	17	14
6	6	14	14	16	16	20	20	18	15

9th	8th	9th	8th	9th	8th	9th	8th	9th	8th
19	16	15	15	19	19	14	9	30	25
20	17	16	16	20	20	15	New	31	26
21	18	17	17	21	21	16	11	32	27
22	19	18	18	22	22	17	12	33	28
23	20	19	19	23	23	18	13	34	29
24	21	20	20	24	24	19	14	35	30
Section 4.3B		21	21	25	25	20	15	36	31
1	New	22	22	26	26	21	16	37	New
2	2	23	23	27	27	22	17	38	New
3	3	24	24	28	28	23	18	39	32
4	4	25	25	29	29	24	19	40	New
5	5	26	26	30	30	25	20	41	New
6	6	27	27	31	31	26	21	42	New
7	New	28	28	32	32	27	22	43	New
8	7	29	29	33	33	28	23	**CHAPTER 6**	
9	8	30	30	34	34	29	24	**Section 6.1A**	
10	9	31	31	35	35	30	25	9th ed.	8th ed.
11	10	32	32	36	36	31	26	1	1
12	New	33	33	37	37	32	27	2	2
13	11	34	34	38	38	33	28	3	3
14	12	35	35	39	39	34	29	4	4
15	New	36	36	40	40	35	30	5	5
16	13	37	37	41	41	**Section 5.2B**		6	6
17	14	38	38	42	42	1	1	7	7
18	15	39	39	43	43	2	2	8	8
19	16	40	40	44	44	3	New	9	9
20	17	41	41	45	45	4	3	10	10
21	18	42	42	46	46	5	4	11	11
22	19	43	43	47	47	6	5	12	12
23	New	44	44	48	48	7	6	13	New
24	New	45	45	49	New	8	7	14	13
25	New	46	46	50	New	9	New	15	14
26	New	47	47	51	New	10	8	16	15
27	New	**Section 5.1B**		52	New	11	10	17	16
28	New	1	1	53	New	12	New	18	17
CHAPTER 5		2	2	54	New	13	New	19	18
Section 5.1A		3	3	55	New	14	9	20	19
9th ed.	8th ed.	4	4	56	New	15	New	21	20
1	1	5	5	**Section 5.2A**		16	11	22	21
2	2	6	6	1	1	17	12	23	22
3	3	7	7	2	2	18	13	24	23
4	4	8	8	3	New	19	14	25	24
5	5	9	9	4	3	20	15	26	25
6	11	10	10	5	4	21	16	27	26
7	6	11	11	6	5	22	17	28	27
8	7	12	12	7	New	23	18	29	28
9	8	13	13	8	7	24	19	30	29
10	9	14	14	9	New	25	20	31	30
11	10	15	15	10	8	26	21	**Section 6.1B**	
12	12	16	16	11	10	27	22	1	1
13	13	17	17	12	New	28	23	2	2
14	14	18	18	13	New	29	24	3	3

4	4	16	11	34	New	2	2	2	2
5	5	17	12	35	New	3	3	3	3
6	6	18	13	35	New	4	4	4	4
7	7	19	14	36	New	5	5	5	5
8	8	20	17	37	New	6	6	6	6
9	9	21	18	38	31	7	13	7	7
10	10	22	19	39	New	8	14	8	8
11	11	23	20	40	New	9	15	9	9
12	New	24	21	**Section 6.3A**		10	21	10	10
13	12	25	22	1	1	11	7	11	11
14	13	26	23	2	2	12	8	12	12
15	14	27	24	3	3	13	9	13	13
16	15	28	25	4	4	14	10	14	14
17	16	29	26	5	5	15	11	15	15
18	17	30	27	6	6	16	12	16	16
19	18	31	28	7	13	17	New	17	17
20	19	32	29	8	14	18	14	18	18
21	20	33	30	9	15	19	15	19	19
22	21	**Section 6.2B**		10	21	20	16	20	21
23	22	1	1	11	7	21	17	**Section 7.1B**	
24	23	2	2	12	8	22	18	1	1
25	24	3	3	13	9	23	19	2	2
26	25	4	4	14	10	24	20	3	3
27	26	5	7	15	11	25	22	4	4
28	27	6	8	16	12	26	23	5	5
29	28	7	9	17	New	27	24	6	6
30	29	8	15	18	New	28	25	7	7
31	30	9	5	19	New	29	26	8	8
32	32	10	6	20	16	30	27	9	9
33	New	11	New	21	17	31	28	10	10
34	New	12	New	22	18	32	29	11	11
35	31	13	New	23	19	33	30	12	12
36	New	14	16	24	20	34	31	13	13
37	New	15	10	25	22	35	32	14	14
38	31A	16	11	26	23	36	33	15	15
39	New	17	12	27	24	37	34	16	16
Section 6.2A		18	13	28	25	38	35	17	17
1	1	19	14	29	26	39	36	18	18
2	2	20	17	30	27	40	37	19	19
3	3	21	18	31	28	41	38	20	New
4	4	22	19	32	29	42	39	21	20
5	7	23	20	33	30	43	New	22	New
6	8	24	21	34	31	44	New	23	New
7	9	25	22	35	32	45	39A	24	New
8	15	26	23	36	33	46	40A	25	New
9	8	27	24	37	34	47	40	26	New
10	6	28	25	38	35	48	New	27	New
11	New	29	26	39	36	49	New	**Section 7.2A**	
12	New	30	27	40	37	**CHAPTER 7**		1	1
13	New	31	28	41	38	**Section 7.1A**		2	2
14	16	32	29	**Section 6.3B**		9th ed.	8th ed.	3	3
15	10	33	30	1	1	1	1	4	New

5	6	22	23	32	32	9	8	16	15
6	7	23	24	33	34	10	9	17	16
7	8	24	25	**Section 7.3B**		11	10	18	17
8	9	25	26	1	1	12	11	19	18
9	10	26	27	2	2	13	12	20	19
10	11	27	28	3	3	14	13	21	20
11	12	28	29	4	4	15	14	22	21
12	13	29	30	5	5	16	15	23	22
13	14	30	31	6	6	17	16	24	23
14	15	31	32	7	7	18	17	25	24
15	16	32	33	8	8	19	18	26	25
16	17	33	34	9	9	20	19	27	26
17	18	34	New	10	10	21	20	28	27
18	19	35	New	11	11	22	21	29	28
19	20	36	36A	12	12	23	22	30	29
20	21	37	New	13	13	24	23	31	30
21	22	38	35	14	14	25	24	32	31
22	23	39	New	15	15	26	25	33	32
23	24	40	New	16	16	27	26	34	33
24	25	41	New	17	17	28	27	35	34
25	26	**Section 7.3A**		18	18	29	28	36	35
26	27	1	1	19	19	30	29	37	36
27	28	2	2	20	20	31	30	38	37
28	29	3	3	21	21	32	31	39	38
29	30	4	4	22	22	33	32	40	39
30	31	5	5	23	23	34	33	41	40
31	32	6	6	24	24	35	34	42	41
32	33	7	7	25	25	36	35	43	42
33	34	8	8	26	26	37	36	44	43
34	35	9	9	27	27	38	37	45	44A
Section 7.2B		10	10	28	28	39	38	46	New
1	1	11	11	29	29	40	39	47	New
2	2	12	12	30	30	41	40	48	New
3	3	13	13	31	31	42	41	49	New
4	New	14	14	32	32	43	42	50	45A
5	6	15	15	33	33	44	43	51	44
6	7	16	16	34	New	**Section 7.4B**		**CHAPTER 8**	
7	8	17	17	35	33A	1	New	**Section 8.1A**	
8	9	18	18	36	New	2	1	**9th ed.**	**8th ed.**
9	10	19	19	37	New	3	2	1	1
10	11	20	20	38	New	4	3	2	2
11	12	21	21	39	New	5	4	3	3
12	13	22	22	40	34	6	5	4	4
13	14	23	23	**Section 7.4A**		7	6	5	5
14	15	24	24	1	New	8	7	6	6
15	16	25	25	2	1	9	8	7	7
16	17	26	26	3	2	10	9	8	17
17	18	27	27	4	3	11	10	9	14
18	19	28	28	5	4	12	11	10	8
19	20	29	29	6	5	13	12	11	9
20	21	30	30	7	6	14	13	12	13
21	22	31	31	8	7	15	14	13	10

14	11	2	2	15	14	20	New	33	25
15	12	3	3	16	15	21	11	34	26
16	15	4	4	17	16	22	New	35	27
17	16	5	5	18	17	23	New	36	28
18	18	6	6	19	18	24	14	37	29
19	19	7	9	20	19	25	15	38	30
20	20	8	7	21	20	26	New	39	31
21	21	9	8	22	21	27	18	40	32
22	22	10	New	23	22	28	19	41	New
23	23	11	10	24	23	29	20	42	31A
24	24	12	11	25	24	30	22	43	New
25	25	13	12	26	25	31	23	44	New
26	26	14	13	27	26	32	24	45	New
27	27	15	14	28	27	33	25	46	New
28	28	16	15	29	28	34	26	47	New
Section 8.1B		17	16	30	29	35	27	**Section 9.2A**	
1	1	18	17	31	30	36	28	1	1
2	2	19	18	32	31	37	29	2	2
3	3	20	19	33	32	38	30	3	3
4	4	21	20	34	33	**Section 9.1B**		4	4
5	5	22	21	35	34	1	1	5	5
6	6	23	22	36	35	2	New	6	6
7	7	24	23	37	36	3	3	7	7
8	17	25	24	38	37A	4	4	8	8
9	New	26	25	39	37	5	5	9	9
10	8	27	26	40	New	6	2	10	10
11	9	28	27	41	New	7	6	11	11
12	New	29	28	42	New	8	7	12	12
13	10	30	29	43	New	9	New	13	13
14	11	31	30	44	New	10	New	14	14
15	12	32	31	**CHAPTER 9**		11	New	15	15
16	15	33	32	**Section 9.1A**		12	8	16	16
17	16	34	33	**9th ed.**	**8th ed.**	13	New	17	17
18	18	35	34	1	1	14	New	18	18
19	19	36	35	2	New	15	9	19	19
20	20	37	36	3	3	16	10	20	20
21	21	38	38	4	4	17	New	21	New
22	22	**Section 8.2B**		5	5	18	New	22	22
23	23	1	1	6	2	19	New	23	23
24	24	2	2	7	6	20	New	24	24
25	25	3	3	8	7	21	11	25	25
26	26	4	4	9	New	22	New	26	26
27	28	5	5	10	New	23	New	27	27
28	New	6	6	11	New	24	14	28	28
29	New	7	9	12	8	25	15	29	29
30	27	8	7	13	New	26	New	30	30
31	New	9	8	14	New	27	18	31	31
32	New	10	New	15	9	28	19	32	32
33	New	11	10	16	10	29	20	33	33
34	New	12	11	17	New	30	22	34	34
Section 8.2A		13	12	18	New	31	23	35	35
1	1	14	13	19	New	32	24	36	36

37	37	**Section 9.3A**		20	20	8	11	**Section 10.1B**	
38	38		2.4A	21	21	9	12	1	1
39	39	1	1	22	22	10	13	2	2
40	40	2	2	23	23	11	7	3	3
Section 9.2B		3	3	24	24	12	New	4	4
1	1	4	4	25	25	13	15	5	5
2	2	5	5	26	26	14	16	6	6
3	3	6	6	27	27	15	17	7	7
4	4	7	7	28	28	16	18	8	8
5	5	8	8	29	30A	17	4	9	9
6	6	9	9	30	29	18	5	10	10
7	7	10	10	31	New	19	19	11	11
8	8	11	11	32	New	20	20	12	12
9	9	12	12	33	New	21	21	13	13
10	10	13	13	34	New	22	22	14	14
11	11	14	14	35	New	23	23	15	15
12	12	15	15	**Section 9.4A**		24	24	16	16
13	13	16	16		9.3A	25	25A	17	17
14	14	17	17	1	1	26	25	18	18
15	15	18	18	2	2	27	26	19	New
16	16	19	19	3	3	28	New	20	20
17	17	20	20	4	6	29	New	21	New
18	18	21	21	5	8	30	New	22	22
19	19	22	22	6	9	31	New	23	New
20	20	23	23	7	10	**CHAPTER 10**		24	New
21	21	24	24	8	11	**Section 10.1A**		25	25
22	22	25	25	9	12	**9th ed.**	**8th ed.**	26	New
23	23	26	26	10	13	1	1	27	27
24	24	27	27	11	7	2	2	28	28
25	25	28	28	12	14	3	3	29	New
26	26	29	29	13	15	4	4	30	New
27	27	**Section 9.3A**		14	16	5	5	31	New
28	28		2.4A	15	17	6	6	32	New
29	29	1	1	16	18	7	New	33	28A
30	30	2	2	17	4	8	8	34	29
31	31	3	3	18	5	9	9	35	27A
32	32	4	4	19	14	10	10	36	New
33	33	5	5	20	19	12	12	**Section 10.2A**	
34	34	6	6	21	20	13	13	1	1
35	35	7	7	22	21	14	14	2	New
36	36	8	8	23	22	15	15	3	3
37	37	9	9	24	23	16	16	4	New
38	38	10	10	25	24	17	17	5	New
39	39	11	11	**Section 9.4B**		18	18	6	New
40	40	12	12		9.3B	19	19	7	7
41	New	13	13	1	1	20	New	8	8
42	New	14	14	2	2	21	New	9	9
43	New	15	15	3	3	22	New	10	10
44	New	16	16	4	6	23	New	11	11
45	New	17	17	5	8	24	24	12	12
46	New	18	18	6	9	25	25	13	13
47	42	19	19	7	10	26	New	14	14

15	15	11	New	24	24	18	18	8	8
16	New	12	10	**Section 11.1B**		19	19	9	9
17	17	13	11	1	1	20	20	10	10
18	18	14	12	2	2	21	21	11	11
19	New	15	13	3	3	22	22	12	12
20	20	16	16	4	4	23	23	13	13
21	21	17	17	5	5	24	24	14	14
22	22	18	18	6	6	25	25	15	15
23	23	19	19	7	7	26	26	16	16
24	New	20	20	8	8	**Section 11.2B**		17	17
25	22A	21	New	9	9	1	1	18	18
26	New	22	22	10	10	2	2	19	19
27	New	23	23	11	11	3	3	20	20
Section 10.3A		24	24	12	12	4	4	21	21
1	1	25	25	13	13	5	5	22	22
2	2	26	26	14	14	6	6	23	23
3	3	27	27	15	15	7	7	24	24
4	4	28	28	16	16	8	8	25	25
5	5	29	29	17	17	9	9	26	26
6	6	30	30	18	18	10	10	27	27
7	7	31	29A	19	19	11	11	28	28
8	8	32	New	20	20	12	12	**Section 11.3B**	
9	9	33	New	21	21	13	13	1	1
10	14	34	New	22	22	14	14	2	2
11	New	35	New	23	23	15	15	3	3
12	10	36	New	24	24	16	16	4	4
13	11	**CH APTER 11**		25	25	17	17	5	5
14	New	**Section 11.1A**		26	27	18	18	6	6
15	13	**9th ed.**	**8th ed.**	27	New	19	19	7	7
16	16	1	1	28	New	20	20	8	8
17	17	2	2	29	New	21	21	9	9
18	New	3	3	30	New	22	22	10	10
19	19	4	4	31	26A	23	23	11	11
20	New	5	5	32	New	24	24	12	12
21	21	6	6	**Section 11.2A**		25	25	13	13
22	22	7	7	1	1	26	26	14	14
23	23	8	8	2	2	27	27	15	15
24	24	9	9	3	3	28	28	16	16
25	25	10	10	4	4	29	New	17	17
26	26	11	11	5	5	30	New	18	18
27	27	12	12	6	6	31	New	19	19
28	28	13	13	7	7	32	New	20	20
Section 10.3B		14	14	8	8	33	New	21	21
1	1	15	15	9	9	34	27A	22	22
2	2	16	16	10	10	**Section 11.3A**		23	23
3	3	17	17	11	11	1	1	24	24
4	4	18	18	12	12	2	2	25	25
5	5	19	19	13	13	3	3	26	26
6	6	20	20	14	14	4	4	27	27
7	7	21	21	15	15	5	5	28	28
9	9	22	22	16	16	6	6	29	29A
10	New	23	23	17	17	7	7	30	30

31	New	16	16	4	4	9	4	15	12
32	New	17	17	5	5	10	New	16	13
33	New	18	18	6	6	11	15	17	14
34	29	19	19	7	11	12	13	18	15
35	New	20	20	8	12	13	17	19	New
Section 11.4A		21	21	9	6	14	9	20	17
1	1	22	22	10	5	15	10	21	18
2	2	23	23	11	New	16	New	22	19
3	3	24	24	12	13	17	New	23	22
4	4	25	25	13	14	18	New	24	New
5	5	26	26	14	15	19	22-12.1B	25	New
6	6	27	27	15	16	20	21-12.1A	26	New
7	7	28	28	16	17	21	18	27	20
8	8	29	29	17	20	22	18A	28	20A
9	9	30	30	18	12	**Section 12.3A**		29	21A
10	10	31	31A	19	14	1	1	30	New
11	11	32	New	20	7	2	2	**Section 12.4A**	
12	12	33	New	21	8	3	3	1	7-12.2A
13	13	34	31	22	9	4	4	2	1
14	14	35	New	23	10	5	New	3	New
15	15	36	New	24	21	6	New	4	2-12.2A
16	16	**CHAPTER 12**		25	New	7	6	5	2
17	17	**Section 12.1A**		26	New	8	7	6	3
18	18	**9th ed.**	**8th ed.**	27	New	9	8	7	4
19	19	1	New	28	New	10	New	8	5
20	20	2	2	29	New	11	9	9	6
21	21	3	New	30	New	12	New	10	7
22	22	4	4	**Section 12.2A**		13	10	11	8
23	23	5	5	1	New	14	11	12	9
24	24	6	6	2	New	15	12	13	10
25	25	7	11	3	New	16	13	14	11
26	26	8	12	4	11	17	14	15	14
27	27	9	6	5	New	18	15	16	12
28	28	10	5	6	New	19	17	17	13
29	29	11	New	7	1	20	18	18	15
30	30	12	13	8	3	21	19	19	16
Section 11.4B		13	7	9	4	22	New	20	8-12.2A
1	1	14	8	10	New	**Section 12.3B**		21	New
2	2	15	9	11	9	1	1	22	16
3	3	16	10	12	10	2	2	23	17
4	4	17	14	13	13	3	3	24	18
5	5	18	15	14	14	4	4	25	19
6	6	19	16	15	New	5	New	26	20
7	7	20	17	**Section 12.2B**		6	New	27	21
8	8	21	18	1	New	7	6	28	22
9	9	22	19	2	New	8	7	29	23
10	10	23	12	3	New	9	8	30	24
11	11	24	13	4	11	10	New	31	20-12.1A
12	12	**Section 12.1B**		5	New	11	9	**Section 12.4B**	
13	13	1	New	6	New	12	New	1	7-12.2B
14	14	2	2	7	1	13	10	2	1
15	15	3	3	8	3	14	11	3	New

9th ed.	8th ed.	9th ed.	8th ed.	9th ed.	8th ed.	9th ed.	8th ed.	9th ed.	8th ed.
4	2-12.2B	16	New	1	1	18	16	28	24
5	2	17	16	2	2	19	17	29	25
6	3	18	17	3	3	20	18	30	26
7	4	19	18	4	New	21	19	31	27
8	5	20	19	5	New	22	20	32	28
9	6	21	20	6	4	23	21	33	29
10	7	22	21	7	5	24	22	34	30
11	8	23	22	8	6	25	23	35	31
12	9	24	23	9	7	26	24	36	32
13	10	25	24	10	8	27	25	37	33
14	11	26	25	11	9	28	26	38	34
15	14	27	26	12	10	29	27	39	35
16	12	28	27	13	11	30	28	40	36
17	13	**Section 12.5B**		14	12	31	29	41	37
18	15	1	1	15	13	32	30	42	38
19	16	2	2	16	14	33	31	43	39
20	8-12.2B	3	3	17	15	34	32	44	40
21	New	4	4	18	16	35	New	45	41
22	16	5	5	19	17	36	33A	46	42
23	19	6	6	20	18	37	34A	47	43
24	17	7	7	21	19	38	34	**Section 13.2B**	
25	18	8	8	22	20	39	New	1	1
26	19	9	9	23	21	40	New	2	2
27	20	10	10	24	22	41	New	3	3
28	21	11	11	25	23	**Section 13.2A**		4	4
29	22	12	12	26	24	1	1	5	5
30	25	13	14	27	25	2	2	6	6
31	16-12.3B	14	13	28	26	3	3	7	11
32	25A	15	New	29	27	4	4	8	13
33	24	16	New	30	28	5	5	9	19
34	25	17	15	31	29	6	6	10	New
35	17-12.2A	18	16	32	30	7	11	11	7
36	New	19	17	33	31	8	13	12	8
37	New	20	18	34	32	9	19	13	9
38	New	21	19	**Section 13.1B**		10	New	14	10
39	New	22	20	1	1	11	7	15	New
Section 12.5A		23	21	2	2	12	8	16	New
1	1	24	22	3	3	13	9	17	14
2	2	25	23	4	New	14	10	18	15
3	3	26	24	5	New	15	New	19	18
4	4	27	25	6	4	16	New	20	New
5	5	28	26	7	5	17	14	21	16
6	6	29	27A	8	6	18	15	22	20
7	7	30	28A	9	7	19	18	23	21
8	8	31	28	10	8	20	New	24	22
9	9	32	New	11	9	21	16	25	12
10	10	33	New	12	10	22	20	26	17
11	11	34	New	13	11	23	21	27	23
12	12	35	New	14	12	24	22	28	24
13	14	**CHAPTER 13**		15	13	25	12	29	25
14	13	**Section 13.1A**		16	14	26	17	30	26
15	15	**9th ed.**	**8th ed.**	17	15	27	23	31	27

32	28	6	6	30	29	8	8	14	13
33	29	7	7	31	30	9	9	15	14
34	30	8	8	32	31	10	10	16	15
35	31	9	9	**Section 13.4B**		11	11	17	16
36	32	10	10	1	1	12	12	18	17
37	33	11	11	2	2	13	13	19	18
38	34	12	12	3	3	14	14	20	19
39	35	13	13	4	4	15	15	21	20
40	36	14	14	5	5	16	16	22	21
41	37	15	15	6	6	17	17	23	22
42	38	16	16	7	7	18	18	24	23
43	39	17	17	8	8	19	19	**Section 14.2B**	
44	40	18	18	9	9	**Section 14.1B**		1	1
45	41	19	19	10	10	1	1	2	2
46	42	20	20	11	New	2	2	3	3
47	43	21	New	12	11	3	3	4	4
48	New	22	New	13	12	4	4	5	5
49	New	23	New	14	13	5	5	6	6
50	New	24	New	15	14	6	6	7	7
51	New	25	New	16	15	7	7	8	8
52	New	26	21A	17	16	8	8	9	New
53	45A	27	21	18	17	9	9	10	9
54	New	**Section 13.4A**		19	18	10	10	11	10
55	New	1	1	20	19	11	11	12	11
56	New	2	2	21	20	12	12	13	12
Section 13.3A		3	3	22	21	13	13	14	13
1	1	4	4	23	22	14	14	15	14
2	2	5	5	24	23	15	15	16	15
3	3	6	6	25	24	16	16	17	16
4	4	7	7	26	25	17	17	18	17
5	5	8	8	27	26	18	18	19	18
6	6	9	9	28	27	19	New	20	19
7	7	10	10	29	28	20	New	21	20
8	8	11	New	30	29	21	New	22	21
9	9	12	11	31	30	22	19	23	22
10	10	13	12	32	New	23	20	24	23
11	11	14	13	33	32A	24	New	25	24
12	12	15	14	34	New	25	New	26	New
13	13	16	15	35	New	**Section 14.2A**		27	New
14	14	17	16	36	31	1	1	28	New
15	15	18	17	37	New	2	2	29	New
16	16	19	18	38	New	3	3	30	25
17	17	20	19	**CHAPTER 14**		4	4	31	24A
18	18	21	20	**Section 14.1A**		5	5	**Section 14.3A**	
19	19	22	21	**9th ed.**	**8th ed.**	6	6	1	1
20	20	23	22	1	1	7	7	2	2
Section 13.3B		24	23	2	2	8	8	3	3
1	1	25	24	3	3	9	New	4	4
2	2	26	25	4	4	10	9	5	5
3	3	27	26	5	5	11	10	6	6
4	4	28	27	6	6	12	11	7	7
5	5	29	28	7	7	13	12	8	8

9	10	9	10	12	12	22	22	18	18
10	9	10	11	13	13	23	23	19	19
11	11	11	12	14	14	**Section 15.1B**		20	20
12	12	12	8	15	15	1	1	21	21
13	13	13	13	16	16	2	2	22	22
14	14	14	14	**Section 14.5B**		3	3	23	23
15	15	15	15	1	1	4	16	24	24
16	16	16	16	2	2	5	17	25	25
17	17	17	17	3	3	6	4	26	26
18	18	18	18	4	4	7	5	27	27
19	19	19	19	5	5	8	6	28	28
20	20	20	20	6	6	9	7	29	29
21	21	**Section 14.4B**		7	7	10	8	30	30
Section 14.3B		1	1	8	8	11	9	31	31
1	1	2	2	9	9	12	10	**Section 15.2B**	
2	2	3	3	10	10	13	11	1	1
3	3	4	4	11	11	14	12	2	2
4	4	5	5	12	12	15	13	3	3
5	5	6	6	13	13	16	14	4	4
6	6	7	7	14	14	17	15	5	5
7	7	8	9	15	15	18	18	6	6
8	8	9	10	16	17A	19	19	7	7
9	10	10	11	17	17	20	20	8	8
10	9	11	12	18	New	21	21	9	9
11	11	12	8	19	New	22	22	10	10
12	12	13	13	20	New	23	23	11	11
13	13	14	14	21	16	24	24	12	12
14	14	15	15	22	New	25	New	13	13
15	15	16	16	**CHAPTER 15**		26	25	14	14
16	16	17	17	**Section 15.1A**		27	New	15	15
17	17	18	18	**9th ed.**	**8th ed.**	28	New	16	16
18	18	19	19	1	1	29	New	17	17
19	19	20	20	2	2	30	24A	18	18
20	20	21	21A	3	3	31	25A	19	19
21	21	22	New	4	16	**Section 15.2A**		20	20
22	22	23	21	5	17	1	1	21	21
23	23	24	New	6	4	2	2	22	22
24	22A	25	New	7	5	3	3	23	23
25	New	26	New	8	6	4	4	24	24
26	New	27	22	9	7	5	5	25	25
27	New	**Section 14.5A**		10	8	6	6	26	26
28	New	1	1	11	9	7	7	27	27
29	23A	2	2	12	10	8	8	28	28
Section 14.4A		3	3	13	11	9	9	29	29
1	1	4	4	14	12	10	10	30	30
2	2	5	5	15	13	11	11	31	31
3	3	6	6	16	14	12	12	32	New
4	4	7	7	17	15	13	13	33	New
5	5	8	8	18	18	14	14	34	32A
6	6	9	9	19	19	15	15	35	33
7	7	10	10	20	20	16	16	36	32
8	9	11	11	21	21	17	17	37	New

38	6-Ch. Test	**CHAPTER 16**		16	16	**Section 16.2B**		3	3
Section 15.3A		**Section 16.1A**		17	17	1	1	4	4
1	1	**9th ed.**	**8th ed.**	18	18	2	2	5	5
2	2	1	1	19	19	3	3	6	6
3	3	2	2	20	20	4	4	7	7
4	4	3	3	21	21	5	5	8	8
5	5	4	4	22	22	6	6	9	9
6	6	5	5	23	23	7	7	10	10
7	7	6	6	24	New	8	8	11	11
8	8	7	7	25	24	9	9	12	12
9	9	8	8	26	New	10	10	13	13
10	10	9	9	27	25	11	11	14	14
11	11	10	10	28	26	12	12	15	15
12	12	11	11	29	27	13	13	16	16
13	13	12	12	30	28	14	14	17	New
14	14	13	13	31	29	15	15	18	New
15	15	14	14	32	30	16	16	19	New
16	16	15	15	33	31	17	17	20	17
17	17	16	16	34	32	18	18	21	16A
18	18	17	17	35	33	19	19		
19	19	18	18	36	New	20	20		
20	20	19	19	37	New	21	21		
21	21	20	20	38	New	22	22		
Section 15.3B		21	21	39	New	23	23		
1	1	22	22	40	New	24	24		
2	2	23	23	41	New	25	25		
3	3	24	New	**Section 16.2A**		26	New		
4	4	25	24	1	1	27	26A		
5	5	26	New	2	2	28	26		
6	6	27	25	3	3	29	27		
7	7	28	26	4	4	30	New		
8	8	29	27	5	5	31	New		
9	9	30	28	6	6	32	New		
10	10	31	29	7	7	**Section 16.3A**			
11	11	32	30	8	8	1	1		
12	12	33	31	9	9	2	2		
13	13	**Section 16.1B**		10	10	3	3		
14	14	1	1	11	11	4	4		
15	15	2	2	12	12	5	5		
16	16	3	3	13	13	6	6		
17	17	4	4	14	14	7	7		
18	18	5	5	15	15	8	8		
19	19	6	6	16	16	9	9		
20	20	7	7	17	17	10	10		
21	21	8	8	18	18	11	11		
22	New	9	9	19	19	12	12		
23	New	10	10	20	20	13	13		
24	New	11	11	21	21	14	14		
25	New	12	12	22	22	15	15		
26	22A	13	13	23	23	**Section 16.3B**			
27	23A	14	14	24	24	1	1		
28	23	15	15	25	25	2	2		

Starting Point Solutions

Section 1.1: Starting Point
There are several possible approaches. Algebra may be the preferred approach. However, some students may use guess and test and/or make a table. The correct answer is 13 yards by 6 yards.

Section 1.2: Starting Point
One way of keeping track of the rectangles is to use one of the vertices of the set of rectangles. For example, the left upper vertex is the upper left hand corner of 12 different rectangles. Moving to the right, the various vertices have 10, 8, 6, 4, 2 rectangles. Moving down to the middle line and repeating, there are 6, 5, 4, 3, 2, 1 rectangles. In all, there are $12 + 10 + 8 + 6 + 4 + 2 + 6 + 5 + 4 + 3 + 2 + 1 = 63$ rectangles.

Section 2.1: Starting Point
The students in the shaded region will be those with curly hair that don't have brown eyes and don't have brown hair. A person whose name is not in any of the circles has none of the attributes: brown eyes, brown hair, curly hair.

Section 2.2: Starting Point
Answers will vary. Students may use various groupings like in the Egyptian and Roman systems. For example, one symbol could be a one, one a six, and the third a twelve. Then, these symbols be would written repeatedly and the absence of any symbols would represent zero.

Section 2.3: Starting Point
$68 = 2Q + 3N + 3P$, 8 coins; $39 = 1Q + 2N + 4P$, 7 coins;
$83 = 3Q + 1N + 3P$, 7 coins; $97 = 3Q + 4N + 2P$, 9 coins.
The minimum number of nickels would be four since if there were 5, the student would exchange them for a quarter and then have fewer coins. The process of exchanging for a minimum number of coins is similar to the carrying process used in base 5 numbers. Any amount of money less than $1.25 can be represented with a maximum of 4 of each type of coin.

Section 2.4: Starting Point
Various relationships are possible. One relationship would associate the numbers 2, 3, 4, and 5 with any of their multiples. Another is to associate the numbers 2, 3, 4, and 5 with the numbers 12, 3, 24, and 15 because they have the same one's digits.

Section 3.1: Starting Point
To find $7 + 2$, one possibility is that the student would say 7 and then count 8-9. To find $2 + 7$, the student may say 2 and then count 3-4-5-6-

7-8-9. To the student, there is clearly a difference in these two problems. However, by using objects, the student will be able to see the similarity and, in this way, discover commutativity.

Section 3.2: Starting Point
In Joshua's case, he may think as follows: $12 - 3 = 9$, $9 - 3 = 6$, $6 - 3 = 3$, $3 - 3 = 0$. Thus, there are four 3s in 12. On the other hand, Emily may think about distributing the loaves to the neighbors one at a time until the twelve loaves were gone. She would find that each neighbor would end up with four loaves.

Section 3.3: Starting Point
Although counting number exponents are usually viewed as a shortcut for multiplication, 4^0 does not mean 4×0 just like 4^2 does not mean 4×2. To decide what 4^0 should be, consider the pattern $4^3 = 64$, $4^2 = 16$, $4^1 = 4$. Notice that if we divide the answer 64 by 4, we get the answer 16. Also, 16 divided by 4 is 4. So, continuing the pattern, 4 divided by 4, or 1, would suggest that $4^0 = 1$.

Section 4.1: Starting Point
Answers may vary. $32 \cdot 26 - 23 \cdot 32 = 32(26 - 23) = 32 \cdot 3 = 96$. Commutativity for multiplication and distributivity.
$(16 \times 9) \times 25 = (16 \times 25) \times 9 = 400 \times 9 = 3600$, Commutativity and associativity for multiplication.
$25 + (39 + 105) = (39 + 105) + 25 = 39 + (105 + 25) = 39 + 130 = 169$. Commutativity for addition and associativity for addition.
$49 + 27 = 50 + 26 = 76$. Associativity for addition.
$152 - 87 = 155 - 90 = 65$. Equal additions.
$46 \times 99 = 46(100 - 1) = 4600 - 46 = 4554$. Distributivity.
$252 \div 12 = (240 \div 12) + (12 \div 12) = 20 + 1 = 21$. Right distributivity of division over addition.

Section 4.2: Starting Point
Nick shows the best understanding of place value. He adds the tens, then the ones. Trevor shows the least understanding, but he is good at applying the common addition algorithm. Courtney also has a very good understanding of place value. Which one is best? All three methods are good methods. Trevor's is likely the most efficient in the long run, but the other two are likely the most meaningful for students.

Section 4.3: Starting Point
To find $34_{seven} + 65_{seven}$, think in terms of base seven blocks. Three longs plus six longs equals one flat plus two longs. Four units plus five units equals one long plus two units. Thus, we have one flat, three longs, and two units, or 132_{seven}.

Section 5.1: Starting Point

12 Squares 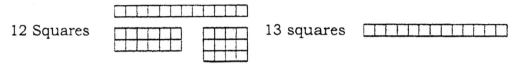 13 squares

More rectangles can be made with 12 squares than with 13 because 12 has more factors than 13. The dimensions of the rectangles are the various factors of the two numbers.

12: 12 × 1, 6 × 2, 4 × 3, shows that 12 has six factors.

13: 13 × 1, shows that 13 has two factors.

Section 5.2: Starting Point

The only lockers that will be open after all 1000 students entered the school are the those with perfect square numbers on them: 1, 4, 9, 16, 25, 36, ..., 961. This is because, to be open at the end, a locker must have been "changed" by an odd number of students. Thus, lockers with numbers with an odd number of factors will be open – these are the perfect squares. To see why, consider listing the factors of numbers in pairs. Since the "middle pair" of factors for a perfect square is the same number listed twice, there are odd number of factors for perfect squares. For example, 16 has factor pairs of (1, 16), (2, 8), (4, 4). When the factors of 16 are listed - 1, 2, 4, 8, 16 - it can be seen that there are an odd number of factors because 4 is only listed once.

Section 6.1: Starting Point

1. The amount shaded in the circle on the left is larger than the amount shaded in the circle on the right. Thus, the student may think that $\frac{2}{3} > \frac{3}{4}$. To compare fractions, the whole must be the same size.

2. A student may not think that the shaded regions are 'equal' since they are different shapes.

3. A student may think that the shaded region in the triangle on the right represents $\frac{1}{3}$ of the triangle since it is one of three parts. A student may misunderstand the need for having "equal" parts.

Section 6.2: Starting Point

If the two shaded regions are added, they will exceed one whole rectangle. However, $\frac{4}{6}$ is less than one rectangle. Thus, $\frac{3}{4} + \frac{1}{2}$ cannot be equal to $\frac{4}{6}$.

Section 6.3: Starting Point
a) If I have three whole pizzas and I think each person who comes for dinner will eat half of a pizza, how many people can I feed?

b) If one-third of Ricardo's birthday cake is divided evenly among four people, how much of the whole cake did each person get?

c) Chiara has $\frac{5}{8}$ of a gallon of paint and it takes one-fourth of a gallon to paint a door. How many doors can Chiara paint?

Section 7.1: Starting Point
Let the block represent one. Then, a flat is .1 of the block since 10 flats make a block. The symbol .10 represents 10 longs, which is equal to one flat. The symbol .100 represents 100 units, which is one flat. Thus, .1 = .10 = .100.

Section 7.2: Starting Point
Consider the problem 0.2 × 0.1. The result is 0.02, which is smaller than either factor. Similarly, 0.2 ÷ 0.1 = 2 and 2 is larger than either 0.2 or 0.1. The reason for the misconceptions is that the rules 'multiplication makes bigger' and 'division makes smaller' are true for all counting numbers greater than 1. It is when 1, 0, and fractions/decimals between 0 and 1 are considered that the rules are no longer valid.

Section 7.3: Starting Point
Piece A is $\frac{1}{3}$ as big as piece B: i) If A is $\frac{1}{3}$ of B and one thinks of B has having three pieces equal to A, then there are 4 equal pieces that make up the entire board so A is $\frac{1}{4}$ of the board. ii) B is three times as big as A. iii) The ratio of A to B is 1 to 3.

Piece A is $\frac{3}{4}$ as big as piece B: i) If piece A is $\frac{3}{4}$ as big as B and one thinks of B as having four pieces, then three of those pieces would be equal to A. Then the whole board would have 7 equal pieces and A would be $\frac{3}{7}$ of the board. ii) B is $\frac{4}{3}$ times as big as A. iii) The ratio of A to B is 3 to 4.

Piece A is $\frac{2}{5}$ as big as piece B: i) If piece A is $\frac{2}{5}$ as big as B and one thinks of B as having five pieces, then two of those pieces would be equal to A. Then the whole board would have 7 equal pieces and A would be $\frac{2}{7}$ of the board. ii) B is $\frac{5}{2}$ times as big as A. iii) The ratio of A to B is 2 to 5.

Section 7.4: Starting Point
Suppose the wholesale price of the jacket is $100. Then, when it is marked up 40%, the retail price is $140. When it is reduced 40% from the retail price, the sale price is $84. The reason that the sale price is less is that the 40% reduction was applied to the retail price.

Section 8.1: Starting Point
-30 + 14: I wrote a check for $30 and deposited $14. Thus, my checking account was -$16 from where I started.

-30 − 14: I wrote a check for $30 and deleted $14 that I had mistakenly written in as a deposit. Thus, my checking account was -$44 from where I started.

-30 + (-14): I wrote one check for $30 and a second check for $14. Thus, my checking account was -$44 from where it started.

Section 8.2: Starting Point
Consider $7^3 \div 7^5 = \dfrac{7^3}{7^5} = \dfrac{1}{7^2}$ but according to the previous properties of exponents, $7^3 \div 7^5 = 7^{3-5} = 7^{-2}$ so it should be the case that $7^{-2} = \dfrac{1}{7^2}$. Similarly, consider $7^2 \times 7^{-2}$. Their product should be $7^{2+(-2)} = 7^0 = 1$. Thus, $7^{-2} = \dfrac{1}{7^2}$.

Section 9.1: Starting Point
Answers may vary. Using the number line, -(2/3) can be thought of as the point two-thirds of the way from 0 to −1. The number (-2)/3 can be thought of one-third of the way from 0 to −2 on the number line which is the same point in both cases.

Section 9.2: Starting Point
Two examples are 0.101101110111101111l....
and 0.1234567891011121314151617181920212223.....

Section 9.3: Starting Point
Tanika starts going downhill and is coasting, but not quite on level ground. Marcelle began going down a steep hill, which became a more gradual downhill until she finally was going on the level.

Section 10.1: Starting Point

By simply arranging the lists in increasing order, one can see that it is likely that University B has more students that live nearer to their parents and that, perhaps, University A has more out-of-state students.

Section 10.2: Starting Point

The graph on the left is a bar graph and the one on the right is a line graph. The line graph seems to show a dramatic decrease in the number of crimes. However, this is because the vertical scale starts at 23. Mayor Marcus would use the line graph to show how crime has fallen dramatically during his reign. On the other hand, Councilwoman Claudia would display the bar graph to show that the crime rate is down very modestly since the bars are only slightly different in length.

Section 10.3: Starting Point

Once, again, arrange the two lists in increasing order. Team 1 has the tallest two players, while team 2 has the two shortest players. Both teams have the same average (mean). These factors would indicate that team 1 is taller. However, both teams have players of height 65, 66 and 67 inches and team 2 has 5 players taller than these three and team 1 has only 3 players taller than these three. This contributes to team 2 having both a taller median and mode.

Section 11.1: Starting Point

The way to determine this is to list all possible draws and to compare the number of ones that have a red with the total number of draws. All possible draws are:

RR   RW   RB
WR   WW   WB
BR   BW   BB

Of these, five have a red. Thus, the probability of having a red is $\dfrac{5}{9}$.

Section 11.2: Starting Point

This one may seem to be the same as the Starting Point for section 11.1 but the existence of two identical red cubes makes it quite different. Although the red cubes are indistinguishable, they do represent distinct outcomes. Thus all possible outcomes are:

RR   RR   RW   RB
RR   RR   RW   RB
WR   WR   WW   WB
BR   BR   BW   BB

To better see these distinct outcomes, we can label one red cube R1 and the other one R2. Then the possible outcomes would look like the following:

R1R1	R1R2	R1W	R1B
R2R1	R2R2	R2W	R2B
WR1	WR2	WW	WB
BR1	BR2	BW	BB

Since there are 16 total outcomes with 4 that consist of a Red and a Blue, the probability of a Red and a Blue is $\frac{4}{16} = \frac{1}{4}$.

Section 11.3: Starting Point

This problem can be solved by considering all different combinations of the letters R and B, or equivalently, how many different possibilities of H and T (for R and B) are there when tossing four coins. You can first break the problem into the combinations of 4 Reds, 3 Reds and 1 Blue, 2 Reds and 2 Blues, 1 Red and 3 Blues, and 4 Blues. We can the rearrange each of these combinations to form different towers for a total of 16 different towers. Pascal's Triangle can also be used to solve this problem. we can see that there are 2^4, or 16, ways.

Section 11.4: Starting Point

This problem can be solve by doing a simulation or using the ideas of expected values. One sample simulation produced an average payment of $9.30. In that case, Sterling should have accepted the $10. If a probability tree diagram is constructed, it can be determined that

$$P(\$2) = \frac{6}{21}, \quad P(\$6) = \frac{4}{21}, \quad P(\$11) = \frac{8}{21}, \quad P(\$15) = \frac{2}{21}, \quad \text{and} \quad P(\$20) = \frac{1}{21}$$

. Thus if Sterling drew from the bag 21 times, would expect to get $2 six times, $6 four times, $11 eight times, $15 two times, and $20 once for a total of $174 over 21 weeks. This would average out to be $8.29 per week. Even though he would make more than $10 over half of the time, it is still a better deal to take the $10.

Section 12.1: Starting Point

There will be a variety of methods used but it should quickly become apparent how important and useful commonly understood vocabulary can be.

Section 12.2: Starting Point

The descriptions and vocabulary will vary but the general idea is that Category 1 figures are convex. The figures in Category 1 an also be described as having the following property: For any two points in the interior of the figure, the line segment having those two points as endpoints lies in the interior of the figure. The figures in Category 2 all contain at least two points which are the endpoints of a segment that does not lie entirely inside of the figure.

Section 12.3: Starting Point

1. Three parallel lines.   2. All three lines intersect in a single point. 3. One line crosses the other two that are parallel.   4. The three lines intersect forming a triangle.   5. Impossible. The most points of intersection for three lines is three points.   6. The lines can be in space, namely, skew lines.

Section 12.4: Starting Point

One way (Option 1) to find the desired sum is to draw two diagonals from any vertex as shown. This creates three triangles whose angles combine to make up the sum of interest. Thus $a + b + c + d + e = 3 \cdot 180 = 540$.

A second approach (Option 2) would be to draw a point anywhere in the interior of the pentagon as shown below. This creates 5 triangles whose combined angles yield the desired sum plus an extra 360 around the interior point. Thus $a + b + c + d + e = 5 \cdot 180 - 360 = 540$.

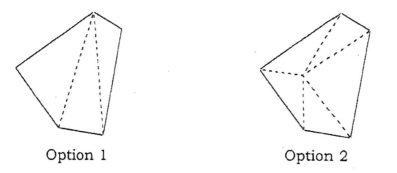

Option 1   Option 2

Section 12.5: Starting Point

There are 6 different possible block stacks that could have the three view shown. The top views of each of those six stacks is shown below with the number representing the number of blocks in each stack.

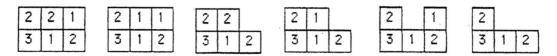

The back view and right side view for all of these stacks are shown below. All 4 views for all 6 stacks would be the same.

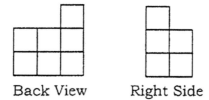

Back View   Right Side

Section 13.1: Starting Point

When ordering carpeting, one orders in *square* yards, but when ordering concrete, one orders *cubic* yards.

Section 13.2: Starting Point

1. Area is the amount of a plane that is enclosed in a geometric figure.
2. The reason that squares are used is that they easily fit together along their edges (i.e. they tessellate). 3. Other possible units would be triangles or regular hexagons because they also tessellate.

Section 13.3: Starting Point

First, consider all possible boxes that could hold 24 cubic blocks and then calculate the surface area of each box.

Shape of Box	Surface Area
1 by 1 by 24	98 sq. units
1 by 2 by 12	76 sq. units
1 by 3 by 8	70 sq. units
1 by 4 by 6	68 sq. units
2 by 2 by 6	56 sq. units
2 by 3 by 4	36 sq. units

Thus, the minimum surface area is when the box is 2 by 3 by 4.

Section 13.4: Starting Point

The volume of the new box would be eight times as large as the original box. If the player doubled in height and, perhaps, in all three dimensions, one could expect him to weigh 640 pounds.

Section 14.1: Starting Point

Corey is correct since A and B have the same size and shape. Whitney is incorrect. For the triangles to be equal, they must be the same set of points. However, because they are two distinct triangles they cannot be equal.

Section 14.2: Starting Point

Objects are similar in geometry if they have the same shape but the term similar is used in the English language in a much more general sense.
  a) A volleyball and a basketball are 'similar' in that they are both spherical. However, because of the different makeup of their skins, they are technically not geometrically similar.
  b) A father and his son are not similar in a geometric sense but we may say that they look similar based on our understanding of the English language.
  c) Two squares are similar because they all have the same shape.

d) The two soda cups are not necessarily the same shape, hence are not similar.

e) The two pieces of paper would be similar if they were the same shape. The fact that there is writing on one of them should not affect the shape.

Section 14.3: Starting Point

Properties of the diagonals of a kite:
1. One diagonal divides the kite into two congruent triangles
2. One diagonal bisects the other.
3. They are perpendicular to each other.
4. One diagonal bisects the vertex angles of the kite.

Properties of the diagonals of a rhombus:
1. They divide the rhombus into two congruent triangles.
2. They bisect each other.
3. They are perpendicular to each other.
4. They bisect the vertex angles of the rhombus.

The diagonals of a rhombus bisect the vertex angles, bisect each other, and create two congruent triangles whereas only one diagonal does this in a kite. These properties play a significant role in the various basic compass and straightedge constructions.

Section 14.4: Starting Point

Points on a perpendicular bisector of a line segment are equidistant from the endpoints of the segment. Thus, if the perpendicular bisectors are constructed to each line segment connecting pairs of cities, the intersection of the three will be equidistant from all three cities.

Section 14.5: Starting Point

Without the crosspiece A, pieces B and C form a parallelogram with two pickets of the gate. As shown with the parallelograms in the box, the gate may be unstable. However, with the crosspiece A in place, the pieces A, B and the right picket form a unique triangle because of the SSS property. Thus the triangle can have only one shape making the gate stable.

Section 15.1: Starting Point

There are three points each of which will form a parallelogram with points A, B, and C. They are (-3,4), (3,-4), (7,2)

Section 15.2: Starting Point

There are infinitely many correct answers. Namely, starting at the point (-1,4) move left 3 units and up 2 units to find the point (-4, 6). Repeat to find (-7,8) and so on. More points can also be found by moving right 3 units and down 2 units to find (2, 2) and (5, 0) and so forth.

Section 15.3: Starting Point
In addition to being perpendicular, the diagonals also bisect each other. To prove this, the midpoint of each of the diagonals can be found and checked to see if it is the same for both diagonals. The midpoint of *XZ* is (2,1) and the midpoint of *WY* is (2, 1). Thus the diagonals bisect each other.

Section 16.1: Starting Point
ΔABC can be moved to ΔA'B'C' using a turn or a combination of a slide and a turn. ΔDEF can be moved to ΔD'E'F' using a combination of a flip.

Section 16.2: Starting Point
A rotation around the intersection of lines *m* and *l* where the angle of rotation is twice as big and the angle between *l* and *m*.

Section 16.3: Starting Point
Imagine a colored ball being reflected over one of the sides. If the cue ball is aimed at the reflected image, the path of the cue ball should line up exactly with the actual colored ball as shown below.

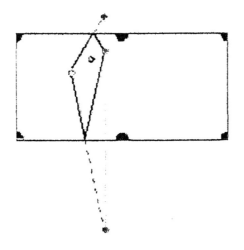

ANSWERS TO EXERCISE/PROBLEM SETS, PART B

Chapter 1

Section 1.1

1. 41,312,432

2. Same number. Let x be your number. The $[([(5x + 8) \times 4 + 9] \times 5) - 105] \div 100 - 1 = [(20x + 32 + 9) \times 5 - 105] \div 100 - 1 = [(100x + 205) - 105] \div 100 - 1 = x$.

3. 15 items

4. Here 12 toothpicks form 5 squares. Remove some to solve the rest of the problem.

5. 78 and 79

6. For example, place 10 in the center. Then place numbers across from each other whose sum is 20.

7. $(6 + 6) \times 6 - 6 = 66$

8. 2520 feet

9. Product must be even since one page must have an even number on it.

10. 2 spares

11. 11 pieces

12. 3 moves

13. Pat: $68.54, Chris: $32.46

14. $2178 \times 4 = 8712$

15. $n + (n + 1) + (n + 2) + (n + 3) = 4n + 6$, thus the sum of four consecutive counting numbers is even since $4n + 6 = 2(2n + 3)$.

16. Bill

17. Top row: 4 10 6
    Bottom row: 11 16 5

18. Baseball - 0.35 pounds
    Football - 0.9 pounds
    Soccer ball - 1 pound

19. The answer will always be 5.
    Proof: $[(n + n + 1 + 9) \div 2] - n = [(2n + 10) \div 2] - n = n + 5 - n = 5$.

20. In the fifth row, the 3 should be 33.

21. 12 triangles

22. 18 and 22 are impossible. There are multiple possibilities for 19, 20, and 21.

23.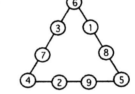

24.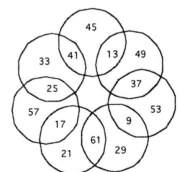

25. Solve the equation $3n - 3 = 87$ to obtain $n = 30$ or 30 dots on each side.

26. Since y is divided by 5 and then 12 is added to that quotient to obtain 23, working backward, we should subtract 12 from 23 and then multiply that difference by 5.

Analyzing Student Thinking

27. Ask Wesley to test a few guesses to see what he can learn about possible solutions. Guess and test is a good way to get started, but since the solution is not a whole number, it will probably be more time consuming than solving the equation using algebra.

28. Rosemary, the Guess and Test strategy is useful because it can help you gain a better understanding of the problem and give you a good idea of what the answer is.

29. Ceclia, drawing a picture can help you gain a better understanding of problems involving physical situations. Use it when you are not sure what the problem is asking or when no solution method is obvious to you.

30. Damian, these equations are the same: one uses a box to represent a number and the other uses a letter (variable) to represent a number. We don't usually introduce students to variables until they are older.

31. Byron, let's represent the sum of three consecutive odd numbers using a variable:
$n + (n + 2) + (n + 4) = 3n + 6 = 96$
Solving this equation for n, the first of the three consecutive odd numbers, we get $n = 30$, an even number. This shows us that our equation has no solution.

32. Vance and Joule, both of your methods are valid and each one has its advantages. Drawing a picture and guessing and testing are powerful strategies that can help you gain a better understanding of a problem, and often can help you to develop an equation. In many cases, using an equation is more efficient than guess and test, and it is a good

way to look back at your solution after using guess and test.

Problems Related to the NCTM Standards and Curriculum Focal Points

1. An appropriate strategy for problem 11 of Set B is "drawing a picture" of cuts on a pizza because that is what the problem is about. Answers may vary.

2. To solve problem 24 of Set A, one might start with a hexagon with 3 dots on a side and then 4 dots on a side in order to generalize the pattern to the case where there are n dots on a side. Answers may vary.

3. Problem 13 of set A uses a box to represent a variable. This is one of the initial conceptions of a variable.

Section 1.2

1. (a) 26   (b) $\frac{5}{4}$

   (c) 486   (d) 2347

2. (a)   (b)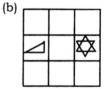

3. (a)

Rectangular Number	Number of Dots in Shape
1	$2 = 1 \cdot 2$
2	$6 = 2 \cdot 3$
3	$12 = 3 \cdot 4$
4	$20 = 4 \cdot 5$
5	$30 = 5 \cdot 6$
6	$42 = 6 \cdot 7$

(b)

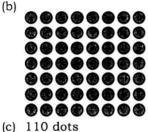

(c) 110 dots
(d) 19th number
(e) $n(n + 1)$
(f) The nth rectangular number is twice the nth triangular number.

4. (a)

Pentagonal Number	Number of Dots in Shape
1	1
2	5
3	12
4	22
5	35

(b)

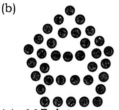

(c) 117 dots
(d) No, the 11th has 176 dots and the 12th has 210 dots.
(e) $1 + 4 + 7 + \ldots + [n + n + (n - 2)]$
$$= \frac{n(3n - 1)}{2}$$

5. (a) $12 \rightarrow 5 \rightarrow 25 \rightarrow 29 \rightarrow 85 \rightarrow$
$89 \rightarrow 145 \rightarrow 42 \rightarrow 20$
$\rightarrow 4 \rightarrow 16 \rightarrow 37 \rightarrow 58 \rightarrow$
$89 \rightarrow$ (a loop begins here)

$13 \rightarrow 10 \rightarrow 1$ etc.

$19 \rightarrow 82 \rightarrow 68 \rightarrow 100 \rightarrow 1 \rightarrow$
$1 \rightarrow$ etc.

$21 \rightarrow 5 \rightarrow 25 \rightarrow$ (see 12 above)

$127 \rightarrow 54 \rightarrow 41 \rightarrow 17 \rightarrow 50$
$\rightarrow 25 \rightarrow$ (see 12 above)

(b) The cycle eventually ends when you reach the number 1 or the numbers cycle and 4 is the smallest number obtained. For 13 and 19, the process ends with a 1.

(c) $111 \rightarrow 3 \rightarrow 9 \rightarrow 81 \rightarrow 65 \rightarrow 61$
$\rightarrow 37 \rightarrow 58 \rightarrow 89 \rightarrow 145 \rightarrow 42$
$\rightarrow 20 \rightarrow 4 \rightarrow 16 \rightarrow 37 \rightarrow 58$
$\rightarrow 89 \rightarrow$ (a loop begins here)

6. 35

7. $1 + 49 = 50$ and $25 + 25 = 50$

8. 220

9. (a) $16 \times 10 = 160$
(b) $10,000 \times 199 = 1,990,000$

10. $1 + 1 + 2 + 3 + \ldots + 144 = 377 - 1$
$= 376$

11. (a) Every third term is even, or a term is even if the number of the term is a multiple of 3.
(b) Fibonacci numbers that are even: F_{51}, F_{150}, F_{300}
Odd: F_{38}, F_{200}
(c) Every fourth term is divisible by 3, or a term is divisible by 3 if the number of the term is a multiple of 4.
(d) Fibonacci numbers that are multiples of 3: $F_{48}, F_{196}, F_{1000}$
Not multiples of 3: F_{75}, F_{379}

12. 609

13. (a) 3, 7, 15
(b) Example: To move 4 disks from the left post to the center post, the top 3 disks must first be moved to the right post. To move those three disks to the right posts, the top two disks must first be moved to the center post. To move the top two disks to the center post, the top disk must first be moved to the right post. This general reasoning allows one

to move the disks in the fewest number of moves.

(c) 63 moves

14. (a) 25 = 10 + 15
         26 = 10 + 15 + 1
         27 = 21 + 6
         28 = 28
         29 = 28 + 1
         30 = 21 + 3 + 6
         31 = 21 + 10
         32 = 21 + 10 + 1
         33 = 15 + 15 + 3
         34 = 28 + 6
         35 = 28 + 6 + 1
     (b) 74 = 36 + 28 + 10
         81 = 66 + 15
         90 = 66 + 21 + 3

15. (a) Products are both equal to 30.
     (b) Products of alternate numbers are always the same.

16. 18, 20, 22, 24, 26, 28, 30

17. (a)

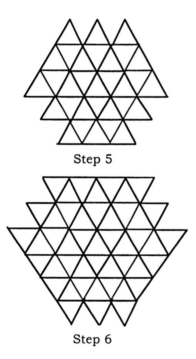

Step 5

Step 6

(b)

Step	Number of Unit Triangles
1	1
2	4
3	10
4	19
5	31
6	46

(c) 64
(d) 136, 571, 3676

18. 13

19. (a) 27   (b) 13   (c) 3^{n-1}
     (d) For $n \geq 2$, $3^{n-2} + 3^{n-3} + \ldots + 1$

20. (a) 900   (b) 148   (c) 859

21. (a) 18, 29, 47
     (b) 60, 111, 189

22. A seven can be formed in six different ways, so seven is likeliest to appear.

23. The key idea here is that once the frog jumps out, it won't slip back down the two feet. It will make it out of a five-foot well in three days and out of a twenty-foot well in 18 days. This is an example of the Solve a Simpler Problem strategy.

Analyzing Student Thinking

24. Both students extended the pattern in a way that makes sense—there is more than one correct answer.

To find each term after the initial 2 in the pattern, Marietta multiplied the previous term by 2: $4 = 2 \times 2$, $8 = 4 \times 2$, $16 = 8 \times 2$, $32 = 16 \times 2$, … .

while Pascuel added successive even numbers to the previous term, starting with the initial 2:

$4 = 2 + \underline{2}$, $8 = 4 + \underline{4}$, $14 = 8 + \underline{6}$, $22 = 14 + \underline{8}$, ...

25. Eula, to apply the solve a simpler problem strategy, reduce the sum to something that is more manageable, such as $1 + 3$, then look at $1 + 3 + 5$, then $1 + 3 + 5 + 7$, etc. Look for a pattern in each of these sums that you can generalize to the original problem.

26. Mickey, try listing these systematically by keeping one of the numbers fixed and listing all the possibilities for the second die. For example, list all the possibilities where you roll a 1 on the first die: (1, 1), (1, 2), (1, 3), (1, 4), and then list all the possibilities where you roll a 2 on the first die, etc.

27. Bridgette, notice that the differences between numbers increase by 2 each time.

    3, 5, 9, 15, 23
     ∨ ∨ ∨ ∨
     2 4 6 8

    Following this pattern, the next two numbers would be 33 and 45.

28. Jeremy, the rectangle given in the original problem is divided into 5 sections by 3 sections. Both of these numbers are odd, so it makes sense for the simpler problem to involve a rectangle divided similarly, such as this one that is divided into 3 sections by 1 section:

29. Janell, yes, the strategies you used are frequently used together.

Problems Related to the NCTM Standards and Curriculum Focal Points

1. The additional problem where the strategy "Solve a Simpler Problem" is used is an example of a more sophisticated strategy. In order to solve the original problem, one must first look at simpler cases. Once the simpler cases have been solved, a pattern must be identified and used to solve the original problem. Answers may vary.

2. Answer will vary depending on the individual experiences.

3. If a table and graph are constructed, one can more readily see how the pattern grows.

Day	Pay	Day	Pay
1	1	11	1024
2	2	12	2048
3	4	13	4096
4	8	.	
5	16	.	
6	32	.	
7	64	N	2^{N-1}
8	128	.	
9	256	.	
10	512	31	2^{31}

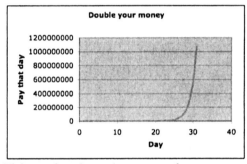

This makes it easier to see the symbolic rule.

Chapter 2

Section 2.1

1. (a) {9, 10, 11,...}
   (b) {1, 3, 5, 7, ..., 99}
   (c) { } or Ø

2. (a) $\{x \mid x$ is one of the 50 United States$\}$
   (b) $\{x \mid x$ is a whole number that ends in 1 or 6$\}$
   (c) $\{x \mid x$ is a letter of the alphabet$\}$
   (d) $\{x \mid x$ is an odd number less than 10$\}$

3. (a) F (b) F (c) T (d) T (e) T

4. $1 \to x$ $1 \to y$ $1 \to z$
   $2 \to y$ $2 \to z$ $2 \to w$
   $3 \to z$ $3 \to w$ $3 \to x$
   $4 \to w$ $4 \to x$ $4 \to y$
   There are many other correct correspondences.

5. For example: {1, 2, 3, 4, 5, 6}

6. (a) No (b) No (c) No (d) No
   (e) No (f) No (g) No (h) Yes

7. { }, {O}, {△}, {□}, {O,△}, {△,□}, {O,□}, {O,△,□}
   All but the last one.

8. 31

9. (a) $\in$ (b) $\subseteq$ or $\subset$
   (c) $\not\subset$, ~   (d) $\in$
   (e) $\subseteq$, ~, =   (f) $\subseteq$ or $\subset$

10. (a) {1, 2, 3, ..., 19}
    (b) {1, 2, 3, ..., 14}

11. (a) Match to {4, 6, 8, ..., $n + 2$, ...}
    (b) Match to {51, 52, 53, 54, ..., $n + 1$, ...}

12. (a) F (b) T (c) F (d) T (e) T
    (f) T

13. (a) T (b) T (c) F

14. (a) True (b) False
    (c) True (d) False

15. (a)
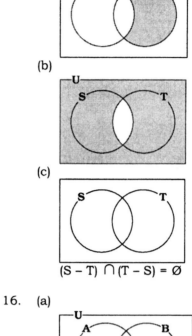

    (b)

    (c)

$(S - T) \cap (T - S) = \varnothing$

16. (a)
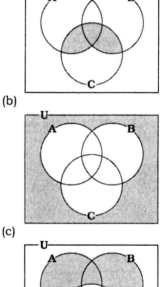

    (b)

    (c)

17. (a) $[A - (B \cup C)] \cup [(B \cup C) - A]$
    (b) $(B - C) \cup (A - C) \cup (B \cap C)$
    (c) $(A \cup C) - (B \cap C)$

18. (a)
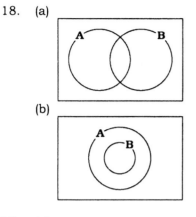

(b)
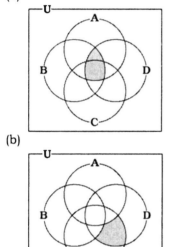

19. (a)
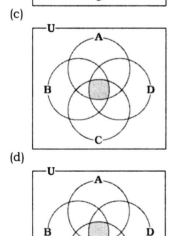

(b)

(c)

(d)

(e)
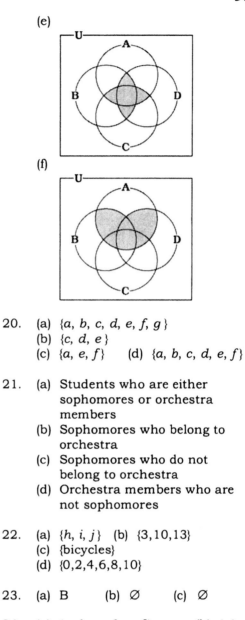

(f)

20. (a) $\{a, b, c, d, e, f, g\}$
    (b) $\{c, d, e\}$
    (c) $\{a, e, f\}$ (d) $\{a, b, c, d, e, f\}$

21. (a) Students who are either sophomores or orchestra members
    (b) Sophomores who belong to orchestra
    (c) Sophomores who do not belong to orchestra
    (d) Orchestra members who are not sophomores

22. (a) $\{h, i, j\}$ (b) $\{3, 10, 13\}$
    (c) $\{bicycles\}$
    (d) $\{0, 2, 4, 6, 8, 10\}$

23. (a) B   (b) $\varnothing$ (c) $\varnothing$

24. (a) $\{a, b, c, d, e, f\}$ (b) $\{c\}$
    (c) $\{a, b, c, x, y, z\}$ (d) $\varnothing$
    (e) $\{c, d, e, f, x, y, z\}$ (f) $\varnothing$
    (g) $\{x, y, z\}$

25. (a) $\{50, 55, 60, 65, 70, 75, 80\}$
    (b) $\{60, 70, 80\}$ (c) $\{60, 70, 80\}$
    (d) $\{60, 70, 80\}$ (e) $\{50\}$ (f) $\{50\}$

26. (a) Yes, because $X \cap Y \subseteq X \cup Y$
    (b) No, because x may be an element of $X - Y$ or $Y - X$.

27. (a) $\overline{A \cap B} = \overline{A} \cup \overline{B} =$
           {2, 6, 10, 12, 14}
           Yes, the sets are the same.

     (b) $\overline{A \cap B}$ and $\overline{A} \cup \overline{B}$ are both
          represented by:

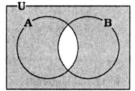

          Yes, the diagrams are the
          same.

28. (a) {(*a*, 1), (*b*, 1), (*c*, 1)}
     (b) {(1, *p*), (1, *q*), (1, *r*), (2, *p*), (2, *q*),
          (2, *r*)}
     (c) {(*p*, 1), (*p*, 2), (*q*, 1), (*q*, 2), (*r*, 1),
          (*r*, 2)}
     (d) {(*a*, 1)}

29. (a) 4   (b) 8   (c) 21

30. (a) {*a*} × {*b*}   (b) {1} × {1, 2}
     (c) {*d*} × {*e*, *f*, *g*}   (d) {3, 4} × {5, 6}
     (e) {*g*} × {*v*, *w*, *x*, *y*, *z*}
     (f) {1, 2} × {3, 4, 5}
     (g) {512} × {10, 11, 122, 205, 197,
          20, 21}
     (h) { } × { }

31. (a) X = {*b*, *c*} , Y = {*c*}
     (b) X = {2, 5} , Y = {1, 2, 3}

32. (a) F   (b) F   (c) F   (d) T

33. (a) 2   (b) 24   (c) 720
     (d) $m(m-1)(m-2) \cdots (2)(1)$

34. (a) *A, B* not disjoint
     (b) not possible
     (c) *E, F* disjoint
     (d) *G* and *K* are empty sets.

35. 105

36. Rays whose endpoints are the
     center of the circle produce a 1-1
     correspondence between the circle
     and the triangle.

37. Rays whose endpoints are some
     point P in the interior of the

triangle produce a 1-1
correspondence between the circle
and the triangle.

38. $13 \times 12 \times 11 \times \cdots \times 1$

39. (a) 16   (b) 25   (c) 2

40. (a) 7 cars (b) 23 cars (c) 16 cars

41. Since A is a proper subset of B, all
     its elements are elements of B.
     Since it is a *proper* subset, there
     must be at least one element of B
     which is not in A. Therefore, B
     must have at least 24 elements.

Analyzing Student Thinking

42. Jake is correct. If two sets are
     equal, they have the *same*
     elements. Therefore, they have
     the same *number* of elements, and
     are equivalent. Kaylee is
     incorrect, however. If two sets are
     equivalent, it means they have the
     same *number* of elements, not the
     same elements. Therefore, they
     could be, but are not necessarily,
     equal.

43. Yes, Tonia is correct. Any 3-
     element set has 8 subsets; 7 of
     these are proper subsets (do not
     include the whole 3-element set)
     and 7 are non-empty subsets (do
     not include the empty set).

44. Amanda is partially correct. While
     it is true that the first set (the
     counting numbers) *does* contain
     an infinite number of numbers
     that the second set (the even
     counting numbers) does not, she
     is incorrect in saying that the sets
     cannot be matched. The two sets
     can be matched like this: $n \leftrightarrow$
     $2n$.

45. LaNae is incorrect. $A \cup B$ has the
     same number of elements as both
     A and B in the case
     that $A \cup B = A = B$.

46. Marshall is incorrect. $A \cap B$ has the same number of elements as both A and B in the case that $A \cap B$ $A = B$,

47. Michael is incorrect; for example, let $A = \{1, 3, 5, ...\}$ and $B = \{2, 4, 6, ...\}$. Then, $A \cap B = \emptyset$, a finite set.

48. DeDee, to find the set $A - B$, we remove from A any elements that are also in B. We can do this whether B is a subset of A or not.

Problems Related to the NCTM Standards and Curriculum Focal Points

1. Young students must learn the 1-1 correspondence between the spoken words – one, two, three, four, ... - and the objects at which they are pointing. If the 1-1 correspondence isn't maintained, they aren't counting objects, they are just reciting words.

2. Two sets are equivalent if there is a 1-1 correspondence between them. Another way to think about finite sets being equivalent is if they have the same number of objects. Thus, if one knows "how many" are in each of the two sets, they then know if the sets are equivalent.

3. Venn diagrams are used to show the relationships between the elements of sets. Thus if a problem requires knowing what is common between two sets, the region on the Venn diagram representing the intersection can be used to solve the problem.

Section 2.2

1. Answers will vary but here are three examples.
   (a) A total of 45 students attended a meeting.
   (b) Bob was the 45th customer to enter the store.
   (c) Katy wore number 45 on her softball jersey.

2. (a) Numeral (b) Number
   (c) Numeral (d) Number

3. (a) Cannot be used because the sets do not match.
   (b) Cannot be used; the sets are equivalent but we don't begin counting elements with 0.
   (c) Should be used; it is an equivalent set using consecutive counting numbers beginning with 1.

4. Number. A numeral is a symbo; a number is an idea.

5. 9 is greater than 4.
   (i) use the counting chat: 9 comes after 4.
   (ii) use the number line: 9 is to the right of 4.
   (iii) use sets: A set with 4 elements can be matched with a proper subset of a set with 9 elements.

6. The number 5 can be represented as $n(\{a, b, c, d, e\})$. Any whole number less than 5 must be represented by a set that matches a proper subset of $\{a, b, c, d, e\}$. Such sets must have 0, 1, 2, 3, or 4 elements.

7. (a)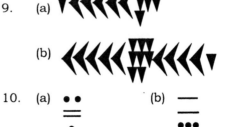
   (b)

8. (a) LXXIX (b) MMMLIV

9. (a)
   (b)

10. (a) ••   (b) ——
       ══   ——
       •   •••
       ——   ——

11. (a) 14,405   (b) 432
     (c) 1247   (d) 72,022

12. (a) ▼▼⧖ ,⑨∩∩ , CXX

     (b) ▼▼◀◀▼▼ ,

         ⑨∩∩∩∩IIII , ∴∴

     (c) ◀◀▼▼◀◀ ◀◀◀ ,

         C̄IIXXX , (Mayan dots/bars)

     (d)

         ⑨⑨⑨⑨ ⑨⑨⑨∩∩IIIII

         DCCXXVI, (Mayan symbol)

13. Yes, Roman numerals form such a
     system because the position of the
     symbols matters but the value of
     the symbol is not multiplied by a
     place value.

14. 1989

15. (a) All 9's
     (b) 9876543210 or 98765432
          (depending on size of
          calculator display)

16. (a) 80: 八十   19: 十九   52: 五十二

         400: 四百   603: 六百三

         6031: 六千三十

     (b) Yes. Yes. Yes.

17. (1) If A and B are in the same
          row, then B is taller than the
          rest of the row and A.
     (2) If A and B are in the same
          column, then A is shorter
          than the rest of the column
          and B.
     (3) If they are in different rows
          and columns, let C be in the
          same column as A and same

row as B. Since A is shortest
in its column, A < C. Since B
is tallest in its row, C < B.
Thus, A < C < B.

18. (a) 124,797
     (b) 8,724,640,224

19. Eiffel Tower: 984 feet
     Great Pyramid of Giza: 480 feet
     Big Ben: 316 feet
     Statue of Liberty: 305 feet
     Leaning Tower of Pisa: 179 feet

20. Impossible. There are 32 white
     squares and 30 dark squares. But
     each domino covers a white and a
     dark square.

Analyzing Student Thinking

21. No, Tammie is not correct. Let $A =$
     $\{a\}$ and $B = \{b, c\}$. Then
     $n(A) = 1 \leq 2 = n(B)$, but A is not a
     subset of B.

22. A child first learns to say the
     counting chant before they have
     an understanding of the concept
     of number.

23. Anthony, the tally system is easy
     for small numbers, but for larger
     numbers it is cumbersome—for
     example, which is easier, writing
     the numeral 100, or writing our
     100 tally marks?

24. Misti is correct—it would require 9
     of the numerals for a hundred, 9
     of the numerals for ten, and 9 of
     the numerals for one, or 27
     numerals.

25. Shalonda, to say that a
     numeration system is additive,
     subtractive or multiplicative, we
     are describing properties of the
     system, not which operations can
     be done in that system. To say
     that the Roman Numeration
     System is additive means that the
     total value of a numeral is found
     by adding the values of the
     individual numerals, like XI = 10 +

1 = 11. When we say that this system is subtractive, we mean that the value of some numerals is found by subtracting a smaller numeral to the left of a larger one, as in 10 − 1 = 9. The Roman Numeration System is also multiplicative since we can indicate 1000 times a number by writing a bar above the numeral, as in $\overline{X} = 1000 \times 10 = 10,000$. You can do division in the Roman system. However, division is not used to represent numerals in the Roman system.

26. Natalie, this symbol serves as a placeholder in the Babylonian System, much like a zero in our own system, but the Babylonians did not recognize the value of this symbol as zero.

27. Bianca, the Mayan System does have a symbol to represent zero, it's ⬯.

Problems Related to the NCTM Standards and Curriculum Focal Points

1. Since cardinality is the number of elements of a set, a young child could look at several different sets of objects with three elements in it and notice the common cardinality. That common cardinality is the concept of number.

2. Young students would need to understand that the numerals are just symbols that represent the idea of a number and the idea of a number is "how many" objects are in a set.

3. Since the Mayan and Babylonian systems are both place value systems, numerals in each of these systems can be decomposed similar to the Hindu-Arabic system. A numeral in either system could be decomposed by multiplying the value of the symbols by the corresponding place values.

Section 2.3

1. (a) $4 \times 100 + 0 \times 10 + 9 \times 1$
    (b) $7 \times 1000 + 0 \times 100 + 9 \times 10 + 4 \times 1$
    (c) $7 \times 100 + 4 \times 10 + 6 \times 1$
    (d) $8 \times 100,000 + 4 \times 10,000 + 1 \times 1$

2. (a) 3075   (b) 70,600
    (c) 603,009   (d) 60,900,000

3. (a) Thousand
    (b) Ten
    (c) One

4. Seven, Eight, Nine, Ten

5. (a) Thirty-two million ninety thousand forty seven
    (b) Four hundred one billion two million, five hundred sixty thousand three hundred.
    (c) Ninety eight quadrillion

6. (a) 27,069,014
    (b) 12,000,070,003,005

7. It is multiplicative because each digit is multiplied by its place value. It is additive because the various products are added together to the find the value of the number.

8. 2121_{three}

9. (a)
    (b)
    (c)

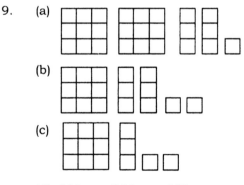

    (d) 112_{four}, 221_{four}, 122_{four}
    (e) The first digit is multiplied by the place value and in different

bases the place value is different. Thus a 2 could be $2 \cdot 9$ or $2 \cdot 16$, depending on the base.

10. 1, 2, 1, 3

11. With bundles of sticks:
    (a) 3 bundles of ten, 8 units
    (b) 5 bundles of six, 2 units
    (c) 1 bundle of one hundred twenty five, 3 bundles of five, 2 units

    With a chip abacus:
    (a)

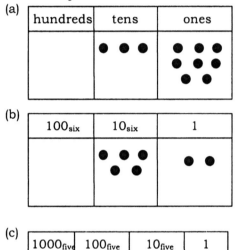

    (c)

12. (a) 120_{eight} (b) 140_{six}
    (c) 1010_{three}

13. Base 26; 675

14. When using multibase blocks in a base-six numeration system, 6 units are exchanged for a long so only the symbols 0, 1, 2, 3, 4, and 5 are needed to describe the number of ones. Similarly, 6 longs are exchanged for a flat so 6 symbols are sufficient to describe the number of tens and so forth.

15. (a) True   (b) False
    (c) True

16. (a) 1 2 3 10 11 12 13 20 21
        22 23 30 31 32 33 100
        101 102 103 110
    (b) 127

    (c) 1 2 3 4 5 10 11 12 13 14
        15 20 21 22 23 24 25 30
        31 32 33 34 35 40 41 42
        43 44 45 50 51 52 53 54
        55 100
    (d) 1000_{nine}

17. (a) $22_{three} = 2(3) + 2(1)$
    (b) $212_{three} = 2(3^2) + 1(3) + 2(1)$
    (c) $12110_{three} = 1(3^4) + 2(3^3) +$
        $1(3^2) + 1(3) + 0(1)$

18. (a) 111111_{two}
    (b) 1000000_{two}
        1000001_{two}
        1000010_{two}

19. $99 = 10200_{three}$
    $100 = 10201_{three}$

20. (a) ET_{twelve} (b) 1001000_{two}
    (c) 347_{eight}

21. (a) 97   (b) 1572   (c) 45

22. (a) 164   (b) 16,910

23. (a) 11_{eight} (b) 66_{eight}
    (c) 252_{eight} (d) 57_{eight}

    A shortcut is to mark off the base-two numeral in groups of three digits and then to express each group as a base eight digit.

24. (a) 7_{nine} (b) 60_{nine}
    (c) 750_{nine}

25. (a) Eight   (b) Eleven   (c) Six

26. None. Since the base number is always greater than any of the digits, if a is less than b (so that a_b makes sense), then b is greater than a (and b_a is incorrect notation).

27. One possibility is onety-one, onety-two, onety-three, onety-nine.

28. 1234

29. 36

30. (a) The numbers are placed on the cards according to their base 2 representations. Since 6 = 110_2 , it appears on the "4" card and "2" card.

    (b) The numbers 1-15 can be expressed in base 2 using 4 digits, so 4 cards each containing 8 numbers will suffice. The "1" card will contain the numbers 1,3,5,7,9,11,13,15, the "2" card will contain 2,3,6,7,10,11,14,15, etc.

31. (a) In base 2, any number from 1 to 31 can be represented in terms of 1's, 2's, 4's, 8's, and 16's. For example, 13 = 1101_2, or 13 = 8 + 4 + 0 + 1

    (b) 1, 3, 9, 27 will do it.

32. Base 2 is used in computers because the 0 and 1 can be simply represented by "off" and "on"; all numbers we type into the computer are converted to base 2, operated on in that base, then translated back into base 10 for output. Base 16 is also used in computers.

Analyzing Student Thinking

33. Jason, by studying other systems and bases, it helps us to better understand our own base-10 system.

34. Brandi, the chip abacus is a model that helps us to visualize the place-value aspects of our numeration system.

35. Jamie is not correct; the numeral 512 ought to be read "five hundred twelve," without the word "and." We say, "and" to indicate a decimal point.

36. Juan, your idea is very clever. Since 'onety' could mean '1 ten' just like 'forty' means '4 tens', 'onety-three' makes a lot of sense as a name for 13.

37. Gladys, numerals in base two require lots of zeros and ones. Another possibility is that base ten was commonly used because we had ten digits on our two hands.

38. Riann is incorrect; "one million" is a base 10 numeral name. We'd read this numeral in base 2 as "one zero zero zero zero zero zero, base 2."

Problems Related to the NCTM Standards and Curriculum Focal Points

1. Using base-ten pieces, bundling sticks or a chip abacus all require a physical regrouping of some sort which would emphasize grouping of tens and ones.

2. Idea 1: When you add 1 + 0 you get 1 but when you write 10 it represents the number of fingers on two hands.
   Idea 2: In some cases a 4 represents four and other cases it represents forty depending on its placement.
   Both cases show how the same digits can have very different meanings.

3. Some physical models are base ten pieces, bundling sticks and a chip abacus. All of these provide different representations of numbers.

Chapter 3

Section 3.1

1. Set model:

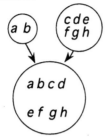

   Number line model:

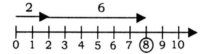

2. (b) and (c). Part (a) is false since g is common to both.

3. (a) Yes. All are multiples of 3 and the sum of two multiples of 3 is a multiple of 3.
   (b) No. $1 + 1 = 2$ and $2 \notin \{1\}$.
   (c) No. $1 + 5 = 6$ and $6 \notin \{1, 5, 9, ...\}$
   (d) Yes. All are multiples of 4 greater than 4.
   (e) No. $1 + 16 = 17$ and 17 is not greater than 17.

4. (a) 0, identity
   (b) 5, commutative
   (c) 3, associative
   (d) 6, commutative
   (e) 4, commutative
   (f) Whole, closure

5. (a)

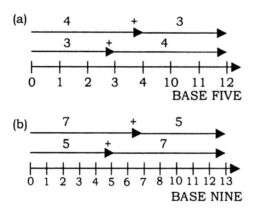

6. By commutativity and associativity, they're equal.

7. (a) $(94 + 6) + (27 + 13) = 100 + 40 = 140$
   Associative and commutative
   (b) $(5 + 25) + (13 + 47) + 31 = 30 + 60 + 31 = 121$
   Associative and commutative

8. (a)

+	0	1	2	3	4	5
0	0	1	2	3	4	5
1	1	2	3	4	5	10
2	2	3	4	5	10	11
3	3	5	10	11	12	13
4	4	5	10	11	12	13
5	5	10	11	12	13	14

   (b) (i) $5_{six} + ? = 13_{six}; 4_{six}$
   (ii) $4_{six} + ? = 5_{six}; 1_{six}$
   (iii) $4_{six} + ? = 12_{six}; 4_{six}$
   (iv) $2_{six} + ? = 10_{six}; 4_{six}$

9. (a) $3_{six} + 2_{six} = 5_{six},$
   $5_{six} - 3_{six} = 2_{six},$
   $5_{six} - 2_{six} = 3_{six}.$
   (b) $5_{six} + 2_{six} = 11_{six},$
   $2_{six} + 5_{six} = 11_{six},$
   $11_{six} - 2_{six} = 5_{six}.$

10. (a) $x = 279 + 156$
    (b) $279 = x + 156$
    (c) $279 = x + 156$

11. (a) $7 - 3$, set model, comparison approach.
    (b) $8 - 3$, set model, missing-addend approach.
    (c) $6 - 2$, measurement model, take-away approach

12. (a) $x = 0$ (b) $x = y$
    (c) $z = 0, x \geq y$
    None are true for all.

13. (a) Set, missing addend, comparison, $200 + x = 362$

(b) Measurement, missing addend, no comparison, $114 + x = 250$

(c) Set, missing addend, no comparison, $105 + x = 1095$

14. (a) Mike needs to dig a 9-foot long trench. He's already dug 5 feet of the trench. How much more does he have left to dig?

(b) Marta and Julio are making Valentine's cards. Marta has made 9 cards and Julio has made 5 cards. How many more cards has Marta made?

(c)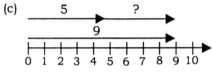

(d) Marta's Cards   Julio's Cards

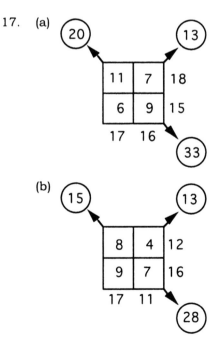

15. (a) For example, 6, 19, 12, 15, 18, 21

(b) Since 24 is the sum of eight 3's.

16. 5, 10, 15, ...

17. (a)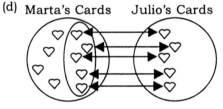

(b)

(c) Let a, b, c and d represent the entries in the four squares. Then all four sums described are equal to $a + b + c + d$.

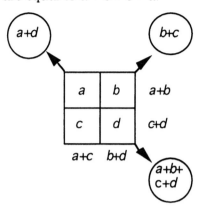

18. One possibility is shown.

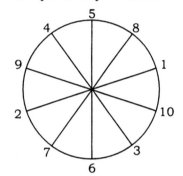

19.

16	2	3	13
5	11	10	8
9	7	6	12
4	14	15	1

20.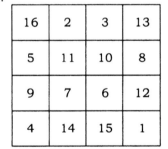

21. The sums along all lines are equal to 90. The sums of opposite triangles are equal.

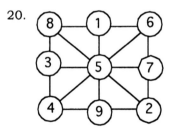

22. Yes. Consider a pan balance where *a* + *c* chips on one pan balance *b* + *c* chips on the other pan. Remove *c* chips from each pan and observe that they still balance.

Analyzing Student Thinking

23. Show Kaitlyn two sets *A* and *B* that are *not* disjoint, and ask her to find the sum *n*(*A*) + *n*(*B*).

24. No, because Enrique is not considering the case that a number can be "linked" to itself. Consider the set {0, 1}. This set is not closed since 1 + 1 = 2 and 2 is not an element of {0, 1}.

25. By using thinking strategies, Monique will be able to figure out any addition facts she might forget. Also, with thinking strategies, she won't have as many facts to remember. Thinking strategies can be extended to multidigit numbers.

26. Yes, Theresa can use a number line model to illustrate the properties of whole number addition. For instance, for the commutative property, she could compare the following two illustrations:

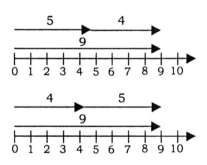

27. Severino's technique uses the associative and commutative properties of addition and the fact that zero is the additive identity:

27 + 36 =
27 + 36 + 0 =

27 + 36 + (3 − 3) =
(27 + 3) + 36 − 3 =
(30 + 36) − 3 = 66 − 3 = 63

Patricia's technique uses the commutative and associative properties of addition:

27 + 36 =
(20 + 7) + (30 + 6) =
(20 + 30) + (6 + 1 + 6) =
50 + (6 + 6) + 1 =
50 + (12 + 1) =
50 + 13 = 63

28. Remind Kayla that 7 + 3 = 10 in a *base 10* system since this is 1 long (ten) and 0 ones. Then, ask Kayla, "In base eight, how many units make up a long?" Suggest that she draw a picture of the numerals using base 8 blocks.

29. Tell Chandler that Conner used the missing addend approach; Connor found what number of girls must be added to the 9 boys to get the total number of 21 students.

30. This picture helps me visualize the different approaches to subtraction (take-away and missing addend), the models I can use to illustrate each one (set and measurement), and whether I can apply comparison to each of these.

Problems Related to the NCTM Standards and Curriculum Focal Points

1. The ideas of joining and separating sets is the beginning of the concepts of addition and subtraction.

2. Some of the understandings of subtraction are the take-away and missing-addend approaches. In conjunction with the missing addend approach students become familiar with the "four-fact families" which relate addition and subtraction facts.

3. By understanding properties such as commutative and associative, students can develop more flexible ways for doing computations mentally. For example, (7 + 5) + 3 is easier to solve after applying these properties.

Section 3.2

1. (a) 2 × 4 (b) 4 × 2 (c) 7 × 3

2. (a)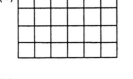

(b)

(c)

$$\boxed{(◯◯◯◯◯◯)(◯◯◯◯◯◯)}$$

$$\boxed{(◯◯◯◯◯◯)(◯◯◯◯◯◯)}$$

(d) →——→——→——→
    6   12   18   24

(e)

	e	f	g	h	i	j
a	(a,e)	(a,f)	(a,g)	(a,h)	(a,i)	(a,j)
b	(b,e)	(b,f)	(b,g)	(b,h)	(b,i)	(b,j)
c	(c,e)	(c,f)	(c,g)	(c,h)	(c,i)	(c,j)
d	(d,e)	(d,f)	(d,g)	(d,h)	(d,i)	(d,j)

3. (a) Cartesian product since the set of possibilities is {small, medium, large} × {cola, diet cola, lemon-lime, root beer, orange}: $x = 3 \cdot 5$
   (b) Rectangular array approach, since students form an array of 72 rows and 4 columns: $n = 72 \cdot 4$
   (c) Repeated addition, since the bill could be found by adding 70¢ + 70¢ + ... +70¢ where

the sum has 25 terms: $c = 25 \cdot 70$

4. (a) 39 + 39 + 39 + 39 = 156
   (b) 231 + 231 + 231 = 693
   (c) 172 + 172 + 172 + 172 + 172 = 860
   (d) 843 + 843 + 843 + 843 + 843 + 843 = 5058

5. (a) (i) No. 2 + 1 = 3 (ii) Yes
   (b) (i) No. 4 + 3 = 7; (ii) Yes

6. (a) Distributive over subtraction
   (b) Associative
   (c) Multiplicative by 0
   (d) Distributive over addition

7. (a) $3 \cdot 29 + 3 \cdot 30 + 3 \cdot 6$
   (b) $5x - 5(2y)$
   (c) $(3 + 6 - 4)a$
   (d) $(x + 3)(x + 2)$
   (e) $37 \cdot 60 - 37 \cdot 22$

8. (a) 14(20 - 1)   (b) 25(40 - 2)
   (c) 35(100 - 2)   (d) 27(1000 - 1)

9. (a) 463 × 16 + 463
   (b) 463 × 15 + 463 × 2
   (c) 463 × 16 + 10 × 16 + 463 + 10

10. (a) 8 × 85 = (8 × 5) 17 = 40 × 17 = 680
    (b) 12(125) = 3 (4 × 125) = 3 × 500 = 1500

11. (a)

×	0	1	2	3	4	5	6	7
0	0	0	0	0	0	0	0	0
1	0	1	2	3	4	5	6	7
2	0	2	4	6	10	12	14	16
3	0	3	6	11	14	17	22	25
4	0	4	10	14	20	24	30	34
5	0	5	12	17	24	31	36	43
6	0	6	14	22	30	36	44	52
7	0	7	16	25	34	43	52	61

(b) (i) 61_{eight} = 7_{eight} × ?; 7_{eight}
    (ii) 17_{eight} = 3_{eight} × ?; 5_{eight}
    (iii) 30_{eight} = 6_{eight} × ?; 4_{eight}
    (iv) 16_{eight} = 2_{eight} ×?; 7_{eight}
    (v) 44_{eight} = 6_{eight} × ? 6_{eight}

(vi) $25_{eight} = 7_{eight} \times ?; 3_{eight}$

12. (a) Sharing. The 28 students are the groups, and the 60 cupcakes are broken into 28 groups to find out how many are in each group.
    (b) Measurement. The 2 cups is how much is in each group and the solution is the number of groups you can make from 6 cups.
    (c) Sharing. The 3 shirts is the number of groups and the $45 is divided among the groups. The solution is the amount of money in each group.

13. (a) Answers will vary. Kobe has 91 jelly beans and he eats 7 jelly beans every hour. How many hours until they are all gone?
    (b) Answers will vary. Kobe has 91 jelly beans to give to 7 friends. How many jelly beans will each friend get?

14. (a) $24 = 12x$
    (b) $x = 27 \cdot 3$
    (c) $a = bx$

15. (a) 2, R = 1   (b) 0, R = 3
    (c) 7, R = 0   (d) 0, R = 1
    (e) 3, R = 0   (f) 0, R = 8

16. (a) 2, infinite
    (b) 1, infinite
    (c) 6, infinite
    (d) 23, infinite

17. None

18. 48

19. $21,000

20. $(2,348 + 7,652) \times 7,653,214 =$ $(10,000)(7,653,214) =$ $76,532,140,000$

21. No. Consider {0, 1}.

22. No. Since division by zero is not permitted, zero cannot be in the set. If any two nonzero numbers are in a set, then a proper fraction results, hence not closed.

23. 333,333,333; 777,777,777; 999,999,999. Associativity for multiplication.

24. $7 + 7^2 + 7^3 + 7^4 = 2800$ (2801 if you count the man). Only 1; the speaker was going to St. Ives.

25. The number is divisible by 1001, which equals $7 \times 11 \times 13$. (Use place value to show this.)

26. $4913 = 17^3, 5832 = 18^3$

27. The sequence of cubes.

28. Yes. The difference of n "twos" from $2n$ "ones" will be the square of n "threes."

29. (a) Dave   (b) Charlie

30. Since the sum of the ages equal to the house number does not provide a solution, there are two choices: 6,6,1 and 9,2,2. But there is an oldest child, so 9,2,2 is the answer.

31. Take a ball from the B/W box. If it's B, then the B/W box is B, the B box is W and the W is B/W. Argue similarly if the ball is W.

32. a or b must be 0. If both are nonzero, the product is nonzero.

Analyzing Student Thinking

33. There is a difference between these two approaches, but they are similar. With rectangular array approach, the product of $a \times b$ is the number of elements in a rectangular array with a rows and b columns. With the Cartesian product approach $a \times b$ is the number of ordered pairs that can be formed from a set with a elements and a set with b elements.

34. Phyllis is incorrect. The tree diagram approach can be used to model the product of any number of numbers. For example, to model the product of three numbers, $a \times b \times c$, draw a tree diagram with 3 sets of branches: a set of a branches and, for each of those a branches, draw b branches and, for each of those b branches, draw c branches. The total number of ends of the final branches will be $a \times b \times c$.

35. Maurice, this is a common misuse of the distributive property. The parentheses in the original problem indicate that we should first multiply 7 times 3 to get 21, then multiply 21 by 6, to obtain 126. The other problem will be 6 times as large, namely 756. Since the two answers are not the same, we see that multiplication does not distribute over *multiplication*. The distributive property distributes multiplication over *addition* (or *subtraction*).

36. Yes, Taylor, applying the associative property of multiplication may help make this easier to compute mentally: $6(7 \times 3) = (6 \times 7) \times 3$. This equals 42 times 3, which equals 126.

37. Breanne, recall that the number 0 is the identity for *addition* since when we add 0 to any number, a, we get a. So, the identity for *multiplication* is a number that can be multiplied by any number, a, to get a. It's not 0 since 0 times a is 0, not a. The multiplicative identity is 1 since 1 times a is equal to a.

38. Olga, the distributive property could be used to break a multiplication problem down into two problems that are easier to compute mentally, as in this example:

$$3 \times 14 = 3(10 + 4) =$$
$$3 \times 10 + 3 \times 4 =$$
$$30 + 12 = 42$$

39. If we let a be any non-zero number, $a \div 0$ could only be equal to 0 if $0 \times 0 = a$. But $0 \times 0 = 0$, and a is not zero.

40. No, "4 divided by 12" is written $4 \div 12$ and leads to a fractional answer, whereas "4 divided into 12" is written $12 \div 4$ and is equal to 3.

Problems Related to the NCTM Standards and Curriculum Focal Points

1. Some of the key underlying concepts are the different ways that multiplication can be viewed (repeated addition, rectangular array, Cartesian product) and the different ways that division can be viewed (sharing, measurement, missing factor, repeated subtraction.)

2. One very common use of the distributive property is in factoring in algebra.

3. In a problem like 4×3, which means 4 groups of 3, it is assumed that all 4 groups are equal in size. For division any problem that is sharing assumed equal sharing.

Section 3.3

1. (a) 9   (b) 64

2. $29 < 44$, $15 < 44$, $44 > 29$, $44 > 15$

3. Yes

4. (a) Yes   (b) Yes

5. (a) 4^7 (b) $3^{6.4^3}$
   (c) $2x^3y^2$ (d) a^4b^4

6. $6^2 < 5^3 < 2^7 < 3^5$

7. (a) $10 \cdot a \cdot b \cdot b \cdot b \cdot b$

    (b) $2 \cdot x \cdot 2 \cdot x \cdot 2 \cdot x \cdot 2 \cdot x \cdot 2 \cdot x$

    (c) $2 \cdot x \cdot x \cdot x \cdot x \cdot x$

8. (a) x^9 (b) a^{12} (c) $(xy)^7$

    (d) 2^7 (e) 2^4 (f) 3^{23}

9. $7^{20} = \left(\left(7^2\right)^2\right)^5 = \left(\left(7^2\right)^5\right)^2 = \left(\left(7^5\right)^2\right)^2$

10. Sometimes true. If $b = m = 1$, then $a^n \cdot 1^1 = a^n$ and $a^{n \cdot 1} = a^n$.

11. (a) 12   (b) Any whole number

    (c) 7

12. (a) 2,203   (b) 31,226   (c) 2,304

13. (a) $2 \cdot 3(3 - 2) = 6$

    (b) $\dfrac{2 \cdot 3^3}{15 - 6} = \dfrac{2 \cdot 3^3}{3^2} = 6$

    (c) $25 - 16 + 4 = 13$

    (d) $32 - 2^4 \cdot 3^4 + \left(2^3 \cdot 3^2\right)$
        $= 32 - 2 \cdot 9 = 14$

14. By agreement and because exponents can be thought of as repeated multiplication.

15. (a) $1 + 2 + 3 = 6$, $1^3 + 2^3 + 3^3 = 36 = 6^2$

    (b) $1^3 + 2^3 + 3^3 + \ldots + n^3 = (1 + 2 + 3 + \ldots + n)^2$

    (c) $1^3 + 2^3 + 3^3 + \ldots + 10^3 = (1 + 2 + 3 + \ldots + 10)^2 = 55^2 = 3{,}025$

16. $4^{14} = (2^2)^{14} = 2^{28} < 2^{30} = (2^3)^{10} = 8^{10} < 9^{10} = (3^2)^{10} = 3^{20} < 3^{22}$

17. Approximately 80,530,000 mm or 80.5 km.

18. (a) $2^7 = 128$ (b) 21

    (c) 1   (d) 7   (e) 7

19. (a) 11   (b) 1,111

(c) 111,111   (d) 11,111,111

20. Using variables, this problem is equivalent to showing that $10a + b$ divides evenly into $(10a)^2 - b^2$, or that $x + y$ divides into $x^2 - y^2$. But $x^2 - y^2 = (x + y)(x - y)$. Thus $x + y$ divides into $x^2 - y^2$ exactly $x - y$ times.

21. (a) $3 < 7$ and $3 \cdot 5 = 15 < 7 \cdot 5 = 35$.

    (b) $3 < 7$ and $3 \cdot 0 = 0 </ 7 \cdot 0 = 0$

    (c) Let $a < b$ and $c \neq 0$. By the Property of Less Than and Addition, $a + a + \cdots + a$ (c times) $< b + b + \cdots + b$ (c times).
        Thus, $ac < bc$.

    (d) If $a < b$ and c is a factor of a and b, then $a \div c < b \div c$.

22. $\dfrac{\overbrace{a \cdot a \cdots a}^{n} \cdot \overbrace{a \cdot a \cdots a}^{m-n}}{\underbrace{a \cdot a \cdots a}_{n}} = a^{m-n}$

Analyzing Student Thinking

23. Brooke, the property of less than and addition is true for any whole numbers, a, b and c. However, for less than and subtraction, if $a < b$, then $a - c < b - c$, is only true for values of c that are less than a; otherwise $a - c$ is not a whole number (the whole numbers are not closed under subtraction).

24. There is not a property of less than and division for whole numbers since the quotient of two whole numbers is not always a whole number (the whole numbers are not closed under division).

25. Jarell, use the definition of whole-number exponents to write out the meaning of the product: $3^2 \cdot 3^4 = (3 \cdot 3) \cdot (3 \cdot 3 \cdot 3 \cdot 3)$. This is 6 factors of 3 or 3^6, not 6 factors of 9.

26. Viridiana is incorrect. She has found two examples where the answers happen to be equal. We need only look at another example to see that the operations of addition and multiplication are not always the same; for instance, $2 + 3 = 5$ and $2 \cdot 3 = 6$.

27. Abbi, notice that:
$$8^5 + 2^2 = (2^3)^5 + 2^2 = 2^{15} + 2^2 =$$
$$2^{13} > 2^{12} = (2^2)^6 = 4^6 > 4^3$$

28. When Cho rewrote $(3^2)^2$ as $3^{(2^2)}$ she was correct, although this was probably due to luck since she also rewrote $(2^3)^2$ as $2^{(3^2)}$ and this can not be true: $(2^3)^2 = 2^6$ but $2^{(3^2)} = 2^9$. In general, $(a^b)^c = a^{(b^c)}$ is only true if $b \cdot c = b^c$.

29. Ayumi is incorrect. Look at an example: $2^3 \cdot 3^2 = (2 \cdot 2 \cdot 2) \cdot (3 \cdot 3) = (8)(9) = 72$ but
$(2 \cdot 3)^{3+2} = (6)^5 = 7776$.

30. Gavin, check this with an example: $(4 + 3)^2 = (7)^2 = 49$, but
$4^2 + 3^2 = 16 + 9 = 25$.

31. Baily applied the exponent (Excuse) before computing the difference within the parentheses (Please). This is incorrect.

Problems Related to the NCTM Standards and Curriculum Focal Points

1. Since the definition of ordering in Section 2.2 is based on objects in sets, it is more concrete and more appropriate for young students. The definition in section 3.3 is based on an understanding of addition which more abstract than physical objects in sets.

2. Exponential notation like 3^4 is just a simpler and more efficient way to write $3 \times 3 \times 3 \times 3$. Exercise #5 in Set B is a similar example of how exponential notation simplifies some expressions.

3. Since 2 inches is a positive whole number amount that will be added to a previous height, we know that the previous height is "less than" the new height. IF a students didn't grow, then no height would be added and last year's height would not be less than this year's height.

Chapter 4

Section 4.1

1.   (a) 520   (b) 3700   (c) 137
     (d) 270

2.   (a) 27   (b) 46   (c) 128
     (d) 263

3.   (a) 598   (b) 301   (c) 321
     (d) 104

4.   (a) 955   (b) 1900   (c) 148
     (d) 3626   (e) 248

5.   (a) 12,800,000
     (b) 72,000,000
     (c) 1,400,000,000
     (d) 150,000,000,000
     (e) 480,000,000,000
     (f) 115,000,000,000,000

6.   (a) $52 - 35$: $52 - 30 = 22$, $22 - 5 = 17$
     (b) $173 - 96$: $173 - 90 = 83$, $83 - 6 = 77$
     (c) $241 - 159$: $241 - 100 = 141$, $141 - 50 = 91$, $91 - 9 = 82$
     (d) $83 - 55$: $83 - 50 = 33$, $33 - 5 = 28$

7.   (a) $16 \times 21 = 8 \times 42 = 4 \times 84 = 2 \times 168 = 336$
     (b) $4 \times 72 = 2 \times 144 = 288$
     (c) $8 \times 123 = 4 \times 246 = 2 \times 492 = 984$
     (d) $16 \times 211 = 8 \times 422 = 4 \times 844 = 2 \times 1688 = 3376$

8.   Overestimate. For example, if her calculations show that houses with in seven miles are at risk, she should raise her estimate to ten miles to be safe.

9.   (a) (i) 12,000
         (ii) 12,000 to 14,000
         (iii) 12,700 (iv) 12,800
     (b) (i) 5,000 (ii) 5,000 to 9,000
         (iii) 6,400 (iv) 6,800
     (c) (i) 10,000
         (ii) 10,000 to 50,000
         (iii) 17,000 (iv) 19,000

10.   (a) 200,000 to 600,000
      (b) 40,000 to 100,000
      (c) 35,000,000 to 48,000,000

11.   (a) $84 \times 50 = 4,200$
      (b) $5,600 \div 80 = 70$
      (c) $2,400 \div 60 = 40$
      (d) $80 \times 80 = 6,400$
      (e) $200 \times 75 = 15,000$
      (f) $6,300 \div 90 = 70$

12.   (a) 250   (b) 600   (c) 590
      (d) 4,200   (e) 7,000

13.   (a) 2000   (b) 810,000
      (c) 720   (d) 216,000,000

14.   (a) $52 \times 40 = 2080$ and
          $50 \times 38 = 3800/2 = 1900$
      (b) $20 \times 70 = 1400$ and
          $20 \times 75 = 1500$
      (c) $90 \times 10 = 900$ and
          $90 \times 11 = 990$
      (d) $25 \times 40 = 1000$ and
          $25 \times 44 = 4400/4 = 1100$

15.   (a) <u>15</u>,000 to <u>24</u>,000 using range estimation
      (b) <u>50</u>,000 to <u>120</u>,000 using range estimation
      (c) <u>8</u>,000,000 to <u>27</u>,000,000 using range estimation

16.   (a) 9   (b) 7

17.   (a) 5^5 (b) 3^8 (c) 9^3 (d) 6^6

18.   a. Multiply 14 and 39 with the calculator and then multiply by $100 = 20 \times 5$ mentally to get 54,600.
      b. Multiply 27 and 23 with the calculator and then multiply by $1000 = 40 \times 25$ mentally to get 621,000.
      c. Multiply 647 and 89 with the calculator and then multiply by $10000 = 50 \times 200$ mentally to get 575,830,000.
      d. Multiply 91 and 173 with the calculator and then multiply by $100 = 25 \times 2 \times 2$ mentally to get 1,574,300.

19. (a) 489 R 21   (b) 2,593 R 100
    (c) 6,928 R 998   (d) 1,091 R 134

20. (a) Yes (b) Yes (c) No (d) No

21. True

22. All are true.

23. All

24. (a) 104,506   (b) 864
    (c) 31,753   (d) 161,590

25. (a) $136 \rightarrow 1^3 + 3^3 + 63^3 = 244 \rightarrow$
      $2^3 + 43^3 + 4^3 = 136$
   (b) $160 \rightarrow 1^3 + 6^3 + 0^3 = 217 \rightarrow$
      $2^3 + 1^3 + 7^3 = 352 \rightarrow$
      $3^3 + 5^3 + 2^3 = 160$
   (c) $919 \rightarrow 9^3 + 1^3 + 9^3 = 1,459$
      $\rightarrow 1^3 + 4^3 + 5^3 + 9^3 = 919$

26. 123,456,789

27. (a) 9,801
   (b) 998,00
   (c) 99,980,001

28. Row 1: 9
    Row 2: 7   4   2
    Row 3: 6
    Row 4: 362,880

29. 36×5
   (i) Special factor: $36 \times 5 =$
     $(36 \times 10) \div 2 = 180$.
   (ii) Multiplicative compensation:
     $36 \times 5 = (18 \times 2) \times 5 =$
     $18 \times (2 \times 5) = 180$.
   In (i) 360 was divided by 2 and in
   (ii) 36 was divided by 2 .

30. 27,777,777,555,555,556

31. Find $712 \cdot 864$, then affix 6 zeros
    at the end.

32. 777,777,776,222,222,223

33. $(299 + 20 + 20 + 2 + 1) \times (100 +$
    $20 + 20 + 2 + 1)$

34. 1,234,321
    23,454,321
    12,345,654,321

35. 132, 264, 385, 594, 682, 396,
    407, 649, 836

36. 121,932,631,112,635,269

37. (a) 1,649; 3,136; 2,604
   (b) $(10a + c)(10b + c)$ should be
     $100(ab + c) + c^2$ where $a + b$
     $= 10$.
     Proof: $(10a + c)(10b + c)$
     $= (10a + c)10b + (10a + c)c$
     $= 100ab + 10bc + 10ac + c^2$
     $= 100ab + 10c(b + a) + c^2$
     $= 100ab + 100c + c^2$
     $= 100(ab + c) + c^2$
     (since $a + b = 10$)

38. (b) 678,947,368,421,052,631,588

39. (i) Identify the digit in the
     place to which you are
     rounding.
   (ii) If the digit(s) in the place(s) to
     the right is (are) a 5 (and all
     zeros) and the number in the
     place to which you are
     rounding is even, change the
     5 to a zero. If the number in
     the place to which you are
     rounding is odd, increase it by
     1 and change the 5 to a zero.
   (iii) If the digit(s) in the place(s) to
     the right is (are) a 5 (and
     something other than all
     zeros), add 1 to the digit in
     rounding and change all digits
     to its right to zeros.
   (iv) If the digit in the place to the
     right is a 4, change the 4 and
     all digits to its right to 0.

40. (a) 4   (b) 4   (c) 9   (d) 9

41. If the answer is odd, the odd
    number of coins is in the left
    hand. If even, the even number of
    coins is in the left hand.

Analyzing Student Thinking

42. Yes, Jessica's method is valid. By subtracting 30 instead of 28, she got a difference that was 2 less than the original. She compensated for this by adding 2 to the 54.

43. Kalil's method works if you start with an even number since 2 divides into it evenly. However, when dividing an odd number by 2, one obtains a decimal that must then be multiplied by 10. With whole numbers, affixing zeros is equivalent to multiplying by ten.

44. Kalil's method works fine with multiples of 5. For other numbers, we must divide by 10 after multiplying by 2.

45. Yes, since $125 + 5 = (100 + 25) + 5$, and Paula used the fact that division distributes over addition *from the right*.

46. Alyssa, we can see that for the sum $158 + 547$ the answer should be between $100 + 500$ and $200 + 600$, or 600 and 800, not 600 and 700. Also, notice that the sum is $600 + 58 + 47$ which is greater than 700 since $58 + 47$ is greater than 100.

47. Jared is not correct; for example, estimating $123 + 359$ with one-column front-end estimation gives an estimate of $100 + 300 = 400$, but with two-column front-end estimation it's $120 + 350 = 470$. The two-column estimate is a *better* estimate because it is closer to the actual sum, $123 + 359 = 482$.

48. A low estimate of the product is $3000 \times 200 = 600,000$, so Nicole's answer is much too small. She left off a digit when recording her answer; she wrote 89, 248, rather than 899, 248.

49. Kysha, finding this product is not possible using your calculator, since it is capable of displaying only numbers with 10 or fewer digits. If you use a more powerful calculator, or if you do the multiplication by hand, you will be able to compute the product. Here is one way to make the computation by hand easier: multiply 987 by 123 and affix 6 zeros at the end, then multiply 654 by 123 and affix 3 zeros at the end, then multiply 321 by 123. Then add these three numbers together to obtain the result.

Problems Related to the NCTM Standards and Curriculum Focal Points

1. An example of a problem to estimate could be 21×32. A student could do this by mentally calculating 20 and 30 to get $(2 \times 3) \times (10 \times 10) = 600$. A student could also mentally calculate 14×7 as $(10 + 4) \times 7 = 70 + 28 = 98$.

2. (a) A group of 14 friends wants to go to the movie that costs $7 each. What is the total cost?
   (b) Items costing $1.28, $3.21, $2.79, and $.95 are going to be purchased. Is $10 sufficient?
   (c) Items costing $1.28, $3.21, $2.79, and $.95 are going to be purchased. What is the exact total?
   (d) This could be the same question as part c but with no access to a calculator.

3. Once a problem is understood, a person could estimate the answer before doing the computations. When the final answer is calculated, it can be compared to this estimation as a way of looking back. If the estimation and actual calculation are not close, the problem should be reexamined.

Section 4.2

1.   (a)

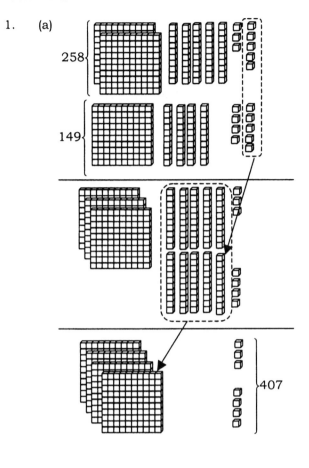

(b)

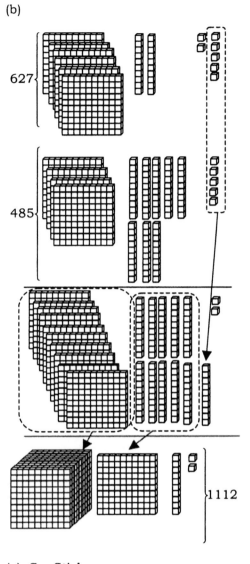

2.   (a) S = Stick
         B = Bundle of 10 sticks
         H = Bundle of 10 bundles
         BBBBSSSSSS + BBBBBSSSSS
         = BBBBBBBBBSSSSSSSSSSSS
         = BBBBBBBBBBS = HS

    (b)

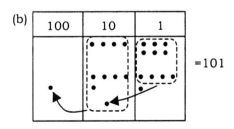

3.   Expanded form, commutative and associative properties of addition,

single-digit addition facts, expanded form, associative property of addition, distributive property of multiplication over addition, associative property and single-digit addition facts, place value.

4. (a)   4(100) + 7(10) + 8
           + 2(100) + 6(10) + 9
           = 6(100) + 13(10) + 17
           = 7(100) + 7

    (b)   1(1000) + 9(100) + 6(10) + 5
           + 0(1000) + 8(100) + 5(10) + 7
           = 1(1000) + 17(100) + 11(10) + 12
           = 2(1000) + 8(100) + 2(10) + 2

5. (a) +   347   (b) +   3538
             679   784
              16   12
              11   11
               9   12
            ────   3
            1026   ────
                                4322

    (c) More efficient, but less meaningful without the zeros.

6. (a) 856   (b) 1763   (c) 535

7. (a) 1641   (b) 10,185

8. (a) Simple, requires more writing and crossing out numbers.
    (b) Fewer symbols, more complicated due to the carry.

9.   616   There are many other
     919   correct answers.
     898
     868
     686
     989

10. Estimate: The sum is greater than 80,000.

11. (a) B A C   (b) B C A
     (c) A B C   (d) C B A

12. (a)

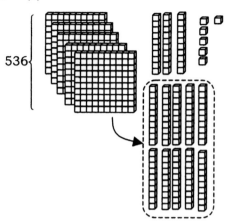

Exchange 1 flat for 10 longs.

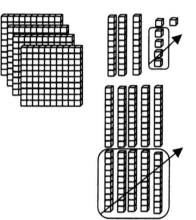

536 take away 54 leaves 482.

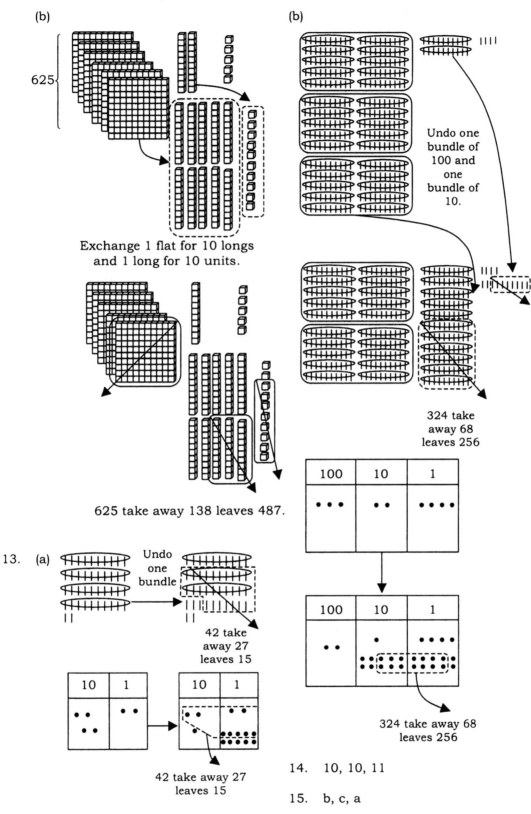

(b)

625

Exchange 1 flat for 10 longs
and 1 long for 10 units.

625 take away 138 leaves 487.

(b)

Undo one
bundle of
100 and
one
bundle of
10.

324 take
away 68
leaves 256

100	10	1
• • •	• •	• • • •

100	10	1
• •	• • • • • •	• • • •

324 take away 68
leaves 256

13. (a)

Undo
one
bundle

42 take
away 27
leaves 15

10	1
• • • •	• •

10	1
• • •	• • • • • • •

42 take away 27
leaves 15

14. 10, 10, 11

15. b, c, a

16. (a)
$$4(100) + 5(10) + 5$$
$$-2(100) + 7(10) + 8$$
$$\overline{3(100) + 14(10) + 15}$$
$$-2(100) + 7(10) + 8$$
$$\overline{1(100) + 7(10) + 7}$$

(b)
$$5(100) + 0(10) + 3$$
$$-1(100) + 4(10) + 7$$
$$\overline{4(100) + 9(10) + 13}$$
$$-1(100) + 4(10) + 7$$
$$\overline{3(100) + 5(10) + 6}$$

(c)
$$3(1000) + 4(100) + 2(10) + 6$$
$$-0(1000) + 6(100) + 5(10) + 2$$
$$\overline{2(1000) + 13(100) + 12(10) + 6}$$
$$-0(1000) + 6(100) + 5(10) + 2$$
$$\overline{2(1000) + 7(100) + 7(10) + 4}$$

17. (a) "29, 30, 40." Change is $12.
(b) "34, 35, 40, 60, 80, 100."
Change is $67.

18. (a)
```
 3479      3479
-2175    + 7824
          11303
         +    1
          1304
```

(b)
```
  6, 0 0 2, 0 0 5
- 4, 1 8 7, 2 6 9

  6, 0 0 2, 0 0 5
+ 5, 8 1 2, 7 3 0
1 1, 8 1 4, 7 3 5
+               1
  1, 8 1 4, 7 3 6
```

(c) The method with three-digit numbers is the same except the leading digit may be a zero. If so, the answer is the two-digit number that remains, plus 1.

19. (a)
```
     1               1  1
 3476            3476
- 5⁶5̶8    ⟶    - 5⁶5̶8
    18            2918
```

(b)
```
  5  ¹0, ¹0 ¹0 ¹4
-  ⁴3̶ ⁷6̶, ³2̶ ⁹8̶  9
   1  3, 7  1  5
```

(c) Yes. Because the amount that is added to the minuend is added to the subtrahend, the difference remains the same.

20. (a)

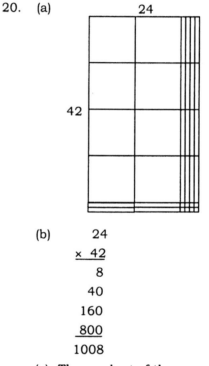

(b)
```
     24
   × 42
      8
     40
    160
    800
   1008
```

(c) The product of the ones digits, 8, is represented by the unit blocks in (a); the product of the tens and ones digits, 40 and 160, by the longs; and the product of the hundreds digits, 800, by the flats.

21.

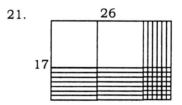

22. (a)

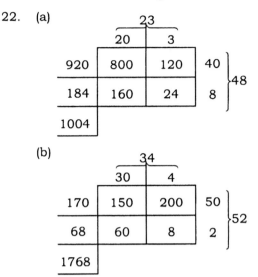

```
                23
          20      3
  920    800    120    40 ⎤
                          ⎬ 48
  184    160     24     8 ⎦
 1004
```

(b)

```
                34
          30      4
  170    150    200    50 ⎤
                          ⎬ 52
   68     60      8     2 ⎦
 1768
```

(c) The numbers within the grid are the same as the steps of the intermediate algorithm 1.

23. Expanded form, distributivity, expanded form, associativity of multiplication, place value, place value, addition

24. (a) 11,376   (b) 552,832

25. (a)
```
       276
    ×   43
      1104
    +  828
     11868
```
(b)
```
       768
    ×  891
      6144
      6912
       768
    684288
```

26. (a)
```
   44×83
   22×166
   11×332
    5×664
    2×1328
    1×2656
    3652
```
(b)
```
   31×54
   15×108
    7×216
    3×432
    1×864
    1674
```

27. (a) Left Hand: 4 up, 1 down
       Right Hand: 1 up, 4 down
                (4 + 1) × 10 + (4 × 1)
                    = 54
    (b) Left Hand: 2 up, 3 down
       Right Hand: 4 up, 1 down
                (4 + 2) × 10 + (3 × 1)
                    = 63

(c) Left Hand: 3 up, 2 down
   Right Hand: 3 up, 2 down
            (3 + 3) × 10 + (2 × 2)
                = 64

28. (a)
```
    1×43
    2×86
    4×172
    8×344
   14×43
   = (2 + 4 + 8) × 43
   = 86 + 172 + 344 = 602
```
(b)
```
    1×67
    2×134
    4×268
    8×536
   16×1072
   21×67
   = (1 + 4 + 16) × 67
   = 67 + 268 + 1072 = 1407
```
(c)
```
    1×73
    2×146
    4×292
    8×584
   16×1168
   32×2336
   43×73
   = (1 + 2 + 8 + 32) × 73
   = 73 + 146 + 584 + 2336 = 3139
```
(d) Distributive property

29. (a)
```
   22)749
     -660   30(22)
       89
      -66    3(22)
       23
      -22    1(22)
    1 + 34(22) = 749
```

(b)
```
      _____
  14 ) 3251
      -2800    200(14)
       451
       -280     20(14)
       171
       -140     10(14)
        31
        -28      2(14)
      _____
        3 + 232(14) = 3251
```

30. (a) 63   (b) Repeated
         - 9   subtraction
         ___
          54
         - 9
         ___
          45
         - 9
         ___
          36
         - 9
         ___
          27
         - 9
         ___
          18
         - 9
         ___
           9
         - 9
         ___
           0   63 ÷ 9 = 7

31. (a) 39 – 3 – 3 – 3 – 3 – 3 – 3 – 3
         – 3 – 3 – 3 – 3 – 3 – 3 = 0 so
         39 ÷ 3 = 13.
     (b) 89 – 8 – 8 – 8 – 8 – 8 – 8 – 8 –
         8 – 8 – 8 – 8 = 1 so
         89 ÷ 8 = 11 r1.
     (c) 75 – 6 – 6 – 6 – 6 – 6 – 6 – 6 –
         6 – 6 – 6 – 6 = 3 so
         75 ÷ 6 = 12 r3.
     (d) Use the calculator to do
         repeated subtraction and
         count the number of times the
         divisor is subtracted.

32. (a)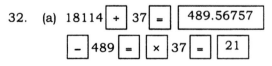

The quotient is 489 and the
remainder is 21.

(b) 381271 [+] 147 [=] [2593.680272]

[–] 2593 [=] [×] 147 [=] [100]

The quotient is 2593 and the
remainder is 100.

(c) 9346870 [+] 349 [=] [26781.86246]

[–] 26781 [=] [×] 349 [=] [301]

The quotient is 26781 and the
remainder is 301.

(d) Yes, if a is divided by b, we
    have $a = bq + r$. This method
    finds $a – bq$, which is r.

33.

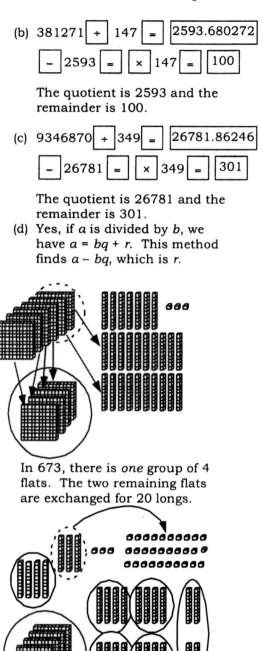

In 673, there is *one* group of 4
flats. The two remaining flats
are exchanged for 20 longs.

In the remaining 273, there are
six groups of 4 longs. The three
remaining longs are exchanged
for 30 units.

remainder

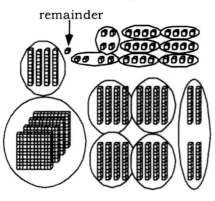

34. There is 1 flat in each of 3 groups and so there are 2 flats still to be divided (these will be grouped with the longs at the next step, making 22 longs).

35. Peter subtracted in the wrong order in 2 places. Jeff did not borrow properly. John did not need to borrow a second time in hundreds place.

36. 2, 3, 4, 5

37. (a) 631   (b) 37

38. (a) 10652 cents   (b) 10562 cents

39. (a) 12, 123, 1234,· · ·
    (b) 10 addends

40. The hundreds digit plus the ones digit is 9 and the middle digit is always 9.

41. Yes

42. All except 9.

43. Carol: 124   Steve: 96   Tracy: 44 r6

44. There is no extra dollar. 30 - 5 = 25. Also 3(9) - 2 = 25.

45. $x(x+2) + 1 = (x+1)^2$

Analyzing Student Thinking

46. We use a concrete model such as base-ten pieces to help students develop a deeper understanding of the usual procedures, such as "carrying," involved in addition.

47. While it is fine for a student to use the lattice method, it is usually more efficient to use the standard algorithm.

48. 123 – 67 = (100 – 60) + 10 + (10 – 7) + 3 = (40) + 10 + (3) + 3 = 66. Some students may find the subtract-from-the-base algorithm easier and faster than the standard subtraction algorithm since they only need to know the addition facts and differences from 10.

49. Advantage: base ten blocks provide a concrete model as a first step in learning the standard multiplication algorithm, with intermediate multiplication algorithms assisting in the transition from the concrete model to the abstract standard algorithm. Disadvantage: the 4 sections of the rectangle formed by the base 10 blocks to represent a product correspond more closely to the subproducts in the intermediate multiplication algorithms than the standard algorithm; the complexity of the standard algorithm is difficult to model concretely.

50. Nicholas, we look at different algorithms for subtractions to help you better understand the process. If you want to focus on learning just one of these, you can choose the one that makes the most sense to you. The standard algorithm is usually the most efficient.

51. This case, discussed in Robert Davis's book, *Learning Mathematics: The Cognitive Science Approach to Mathematics Education,* involved a student who believed that you could not "borrow" from a zero place.

Therefore, each time she needed to borrow, she went directly to the 4 and borrowed from it without changing the zeros. She subtracted 7 from 15 and got 8, and she subtracted 3 from 10 and got 7. But both times she borrowed from the 4, which became a 3 and then a 2.

52. Natasha, the lattice method is very simple compared to the standard multiplication algorithm—simply multiply each pair of digits and add down the diagonals.

53. Yes, Andres's method will always work--he used expanded form and the distributive property.

54. Show Dylan a set of 6 flats, 2 longs, and 1 unit and ask him to share these among 3 groups. Each group will have 2 flats and 7 units, or 207.

Problems Related to the NCTM Standards and Curriculum Focal Points

1. When adding or subtracting multidigit numbers, the addition or subtraction of the hundreds, thousands, or millions can always be boiled down to adding or subtracting single digit numbers. Thus, having quick recall of the addition and subtraction facts allows one to focus on the principles of place value essential to understanding these multidigit operations.

2. Maintaining an understanding of the meaning of division is valuable in developing a solid understanding of the algorithm. If $21 \div 7$ is only the memorized fact of 3 and not seen as 21 broken into 7 groups or groups of size 7, then confusion in the steps of the algorithm is likely.

3. Some students naturally think of doing the operations from right to left instead of left to right. This

method can be as effective if the student has a solid understanding of the expanded form of numbers as well as place value and the distributive property. For example, some students may compute 27×12 as $27 \times 10 = 270$ and $27 \times 2 = 54$ to get 324.

Section 4.3

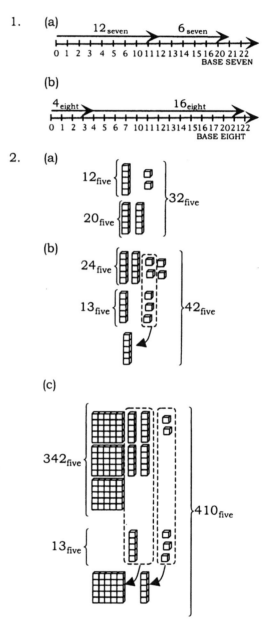

1. (a)

(b)

2. (a)

(b)

(c)

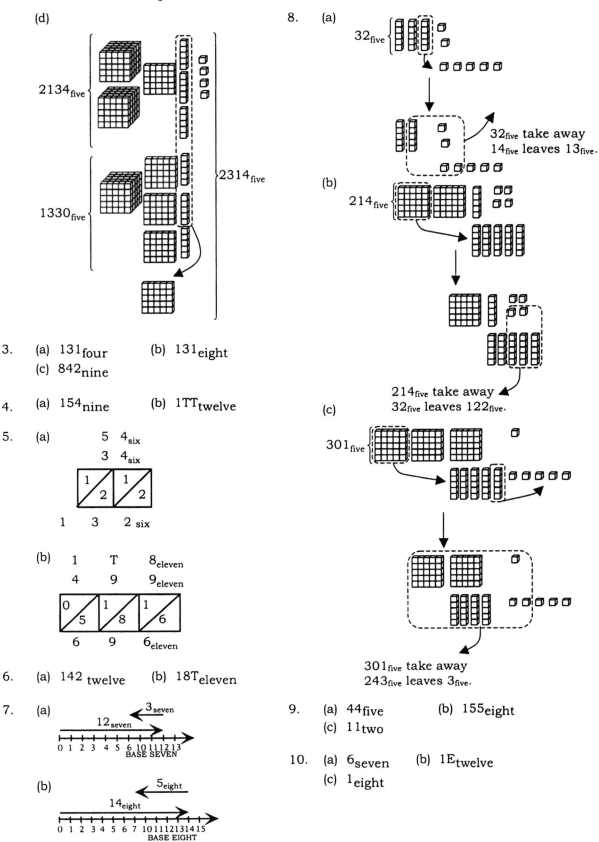

(d)

2134_{five}

1330_{five}

2314_{five}

8. (a)

32_{five}

32_{five} take away
14_{five} leaves 13_{five}.

(b)

214_{five}

214_{five} take away
32_{five} leaves 122_{five}.

(c)

301_{five}

301_{five} take away
243_{five} leaves 3_{five}.

3. (a) 131_{four} (b) 131_{eight}
    (c) 842_{nine}

4. (a) 154_{nine} (b) $1TT_{twelve}$

5. (a)
      5   4_{six}
      3   4_{six}

      | 1 / 2 | 1 / 2 |

      1   3 2_{six}

    (b)
      1   T 8_{eleven}
      4   9 9_{eleven}

      | 0 / 5 | 1 / 8 | 1 / 6 |

      6   9 6_{eleven}

6. (a) 142_{twelve} (b) $18T_{eleven}$

7. (a)
      3_{seven}
      12_{seven}
      0 1 2 3 4 5 6 10 11 12 13
      BASE SEVEN

    (b)
      5_{eight}
      14_{eight}
      0 1 2 3 4 5 6 7 10 11 12 13 14 15
      BASE EIGHT

9. (a) 44_{five} (b) 155_{eight}
    (c) 11_{two}

10. (a) 6_{seven} (b) $1E_{twelve}$
    (c) 1_{eight}

11. $1001010_{two} - 111001_{two} =$
      $1001010_{two} + 110_{two}$
      $- 1000000_{two} + 1_{two} =$
      10001_{two}

12.   (a)

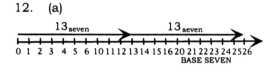

13_{seven} 13_{seven}

0 1 2 3 4 5 6 10 11 12 13 14 15 16 20 21 22 23 24 25 26
BASE SEVEN

   (b)

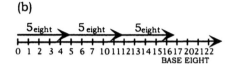

5_{eight} 5_{eight} 5_{eight}

0 1 2 3 4 5 6 7 10 11 12 13 14 15 16 17 20 21 22
BASE EIGHT

13.   (a) 13_{six}

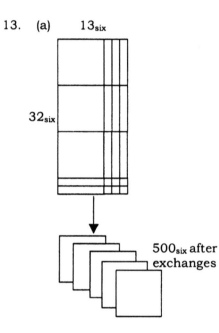

32_{six}

500_{six} after exchanges

   (b) 34_{seven}

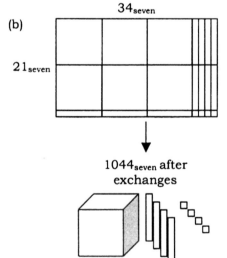

21_{seven}

1044_{seven} after exchanges

14.   (a) 101011111_{two} (b) 969_{twelve}
      (c) 65601_{seven}

15.   (a)

3_{seven} 3_{seven} 3_{seven} 3_{seven} 3_{seven}

0 1 2 3 4 5 6 10 11 12 13 14 15 16 20 21 22 23
BASE SEVEN

   (b)

5_{eight} 5_{eight} 5_{eight}

0 1 2 3 4 5 6 7 10 11 12 13 14 15 16 17 20 21 22 23 24
BASE EIGHT

16.   (a) 3_{five} (b) 121_{six}
      (c) 143_{seven}

17.   (a) 6_{seven} (b) 8_{nine}
      (c) T_{twelve}

18.

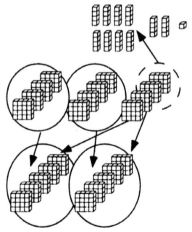

Since there is not a group of size 11_{four} cubes, the three cubes are exchanged for flats.

There are two groups of flats of size 11_{four}. The remaining two flats are exchanged for longs.

(continued on next page)

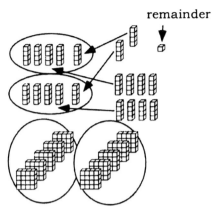

remainder

There are two groups of longs of size 11_{four} with no longs left over. There are no groups of units of size 11_{four}, but there is one unit remaining. Thus the quotient is 220_{four} with remainder 1.

19. eight

20. Betty has $6; Tom has $2.

21. 10

22. Assume n is even. Then n can be expressed as $2m$ where m is a whole number. Then $n^2 = (2m)^2 = 4m^2$ which is even. This contradicts the given information, so n must be odd.

Analyzing Student Thinking

23. Antolina, studying algorithms in other bases can help you understand the base ten algorithms better, as well as clarify the meanings of place value and regrouping. Plus, working with algorithms in other bases is just good exercise for your mind.

24. Ralph, go ahead and use the addition table—this will likely help you memorize it.

25. No, a base-four system uses only the digits 0, 1, 2, and 3, so we would not write the number 413_{four}.

26. Geoff, the standard algorithm involves just as many steps as the intermediate algorithm, the difference is that we record all of these steps on our paper when we use the intermediate algorithm. The standard algorithm requires you to do a lot of this work mentally. You may want to write out the steps until you are comfortable doing them in your head.

27. First, look at the student's work to see if you can identify the trouble he is having or ask him to explain what part he is having a hard time with. It may help to start with a model, such as the base 5 number line, showing how to use repeated subtraction to find a simple quotient. Then, demonstrate an intermediate algorithm, such as the scaffold method, and discuss the connections between this method and the standard algorithm.

28. Sherry, remember that 12_{six} in expanded form $1(6) + 2(1)$, or 8 in base 10. Thus, when you subtract 5_{six} from 12_{six}, you get 3_{six}.

Problems Related to the NCTM Standards and Curriculum Focal Points

1. When adding in other bases like base 6, for example, you are forced to always look for groups of 6 because any group of 6 units, longs, or flats can be exchanged for 1 long, flat or cube respectively. Thus, the relationships of numbers that add to 6 become more important. The thinking required in base 6 is identical to that in base 10 so working in one base system builds on the understanding of another.

2. When doing multidigit addition in base 7, for example, you may need to know what $5_{seven} + 5_{seven}$ is before you can make the decision

whether or not to carry. By first
building a table of addition facts,
you can refer to the table to see
that the sum is 13_{seven} and then
think about how the "carrying"
procedure might work. Thus, the
table of addition facts in base
seven is needed because you likely
don't have quick recall of those
facts.

3.   When finding the product 27×63,
      you will need to know the
      individual products of 7×3, 2×3,
      7×6, and 2×6 before the desired
      product can be found. Thus
      having quick recall of the
      multiplication facts, makes it
      easier to focus on whether you are
      multiplying by a 2 or 20 and
      whether you should carry or not.
      Thus, fluency of multidigit
      multiplication is enhanced.

Chapter 5

Section 5.1

1. Multiples of 2 in columns 2, 4, and 6; multiples of 3 in columns 3 and 6; multiples of 5 on diagonal; multiples of 7 on diagonals

2. (a) $2^6 \times 3$

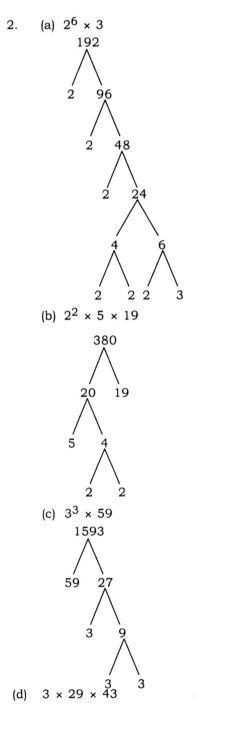

(b) $2^2 \times 5 \times 19$

(c) $3^3 \times 59$

(d) $3 \times 29 \times 43$

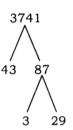

3. (a) 3×13 (b) $3 \times 13 \times 29$
   (c) 5×11 (d) $5 \times 11 \times 17$
   (e) $11 \times 13 \times 23$ (f) $3 \times 13 \times 151$

4. (a) 7   (b) 10   (c) 3×18
   (d) $2 \times 5 \times 7$
   (e) $2^3 \times 3 \times 7^3 \times 13^5$
   (f) $2^2 \times 3^9 \times 5^6 \times 17^8$
   (g) $2^{17} \times 3^{16} \times 5^{86} \times 29^{37}$
   (h) 2×11
   (i) $p^2 q^8 r^6 s^2 t^{27}$
   (j) $(5 \times 3 + 2)$

5. 1,2,3,4,6,8,12, and 24

6. (a) 114 ends in 4; $x = 57$
   (b) $3 + 3 + 6 = 12$ which is divisible by 3; $x = 112$

7. (a) 3, 4, 9
   (b) 3, 9

8. (a) $9 + 5 + 4 = 18$, $4 + 1 + 2 = 7$, $18 - 7 = 11$. Since $18 \mid 11$, $11 \mid 945, 142$.
   (b) $6 + 2 + 4 + 1 = 13$, $2 + 7 + 5 = 14$, $14 - 13 = 1$. Since $11 \nmid 1$, $11 \nmid 6, 247, 251$.
   (c) $3 + 5 + 2 = 10$, $8 + 6 + 7 = 21$, $21 - 10 = 11$. Since $11 \mid 11$, $11 \mid 385, 627$.

9. (a)   3,709,069 ⟶

    $-$ 18 $= 2 \times 9$

          370,888 ⟶

    $-$ 16 $= 2 \times 8$

          37,072 ⟶

    $-$ 4 $= 2 \times 2$

          3,703 ⟶

    $-$ 6 $= 2 \times 3$

          364 ⟶

    $-$ 8 $= 2 \times 2$

          28

    $7 \mid 28$ so $7 \mid 3,709,069$

    (b)   275,555 ⟶

    $-$ 10 $= 2 \times 5$

          27,545 ⟶

    $-$ 10 $= 2 \times 5$

          2,744 ⟶

    $-$ 8 $= 2 \times 4$

          266 ⟶

    $-$ 12 $= 2 \times 6$

          14

    $7 \mid 14$ so $7 \mid 275,555$

    (c)   39,486 ⟶

    $-$ 12 $= 2 \times 6$

          3,936 ⟶

    $-$ 12 $= 2 \times 6$

          381 ⟶

    $-$ 2 $= 2 \times 1$

          36

    $7 \nmid$ so $7 \nmid 39,486$

10. (a) F. Try 24.
    (b) F. Try 12.

11. (a) False $2 \mid 18$ and $6 \mid 18$ but $12 \nmid 18$
    (b) False $6 \mid 4 \cdot 15$ but $6 \nmid 4$ and $6 \nmid 15$

12. (a) T. $8 \mid 608$ and
        $3 \mid (3 + 2 + 5 + 6 + 8)$.
    (b) F. $9 \nmid (1 + 3 + 7 + 5)$
    (c) T. $40 \mid 800$
    (d) T. $4 \mid 16$ and
        $9 \mid (6+7+7+9+1+6)$

13. All are composite.
    (a) even
    (b) a multiple of 127
    (c) a multiple of 3

14. 2, 3, 5, 7, 11, 13, 17, 19, 23. No other primes need to be checked.

15. (a) Yes   (b) No

16. Let $r = a \cdot 10^3 + b \cdot 10^2 + c \cdot 10 + d$ be any 4 digit number.
    Rewrite:
    $r = a(999+1) + b(99+1) + c(9+1) + d$
    $= a \cdot 999 + a + b \cdot 99 + b + c9 + c + d$
    $= (a \cdot 111 + b \cdot 11 + c)9 + (a + b + c + d)$
    Since $9 \mid 9$ it also divides $(a \cdot 111 + b \cdot 11 + c) \cdot 9$. Thus, if $9 \mid (a + b + c + d)$, it is true that $9 \mid r$.

17. Observe that $4 \mid 10^n$ for $n \geq 2$ and that $8 \mid 10^n$ for $n \geq 3$. Then make a proof modifying the proof for divisibility by 2.

18. $9! - 8! + \ldots + 1! = 326981 = 79 \times 4139$

19. (a) 31, 37, 41, 43, 47, 53, 59
    (b) 53, 59, 61, 67, 71 (and others)
    (c) 101, 103, 107, 109 (and others)

20. Yes, we have checked all primes p such that $p^2 \leq 211$.

21. False. When $n = 41$, $n^2 - n + 41 = 41^2 - 41 + 41 = 41^2$, a composite.

22. $2^3 - 1 = 7$, a prime;
    $2^5 - 1 = 31$, a prime;
    $2^7 - 1 = 127$, a prime;
    $2^{13} - 1 = 8191$, a prime.

23. Every number can be expressed as one of the following: $6n$, $6n + 1$, $6n + 2$, $6n + 3$, $6n - 2$, or $6n - 1$. But $6 \mid 6n$, $2 \mid (6n + 2)$, $3 \mid (6n + 3)$, and $2 \mid (6n - 2)$. Thus the only ones that could be primes are $6n + 1$ or $6n - 1$.

24. No, sum of two odd numbers is even. All evens, except 2, are composite.

25. Answers will vary.

26. 3,5,7 is the only prime triple. For suppose p, $p + 2$, $p + 4$ is another prime triple. Then p *is* not a multiple of 3, so (i) $p = 3k + 1$ or (ii) $p = 3k + 2$. If $p = 3k + 1$, then $p + 2 = 3k + 1 + 2 = 3k + 3$, which is a multiple of 3, hence not prime. If $p = 3k + 2$, then $p + 4 = 3k + 2 + 4 = 3k + 6$, which again is a multiple of 3. Thus p, $p + 2$, and $p + 4$ can all be prime only when $p = 3$.

27. (a) $17 - 5$
    (b) $43 - 23$
    (c) $41 - 13$
    Note: Each part has many possible answers.

28. One possible solution:
    Row 1 - 67, 1,43;
    Row 2 13,37,61;
    Row 3 - 31, 73,7

29. No - according to Fundamental Theorem of Arithmetic, there is exactly one way to write any number as a product of prime

30. 16, 25

31. $2^3 \times 3 \times 5 \times 7 = 840$

32. $2^4 \times 3^2 \times 5^2 \times 7 \times 11 \times 13 \times 17 \times 19 \times 23$

33. 5. Proof: $n + (n +1) + (n +2) + (n +3) + (n +4) = 5n + 10 = 5(n + 2)$.

34. Yes; for example, consider a 4-digit number, n, in expanded form: $n = 1000a + 100b + 10c + d$. Reversing the digits and adding to n gives:
    $$1000a + 100b + 10c + d$$
    $$\underline{1000d + 100c + 10b + a}$$
    $$1001a + 110b + 110c + 1001d$$
    $= 11(91a + 10b + 10c + 91d)$, a multiple of 11. A similar argument can be made for an number with an even number of digits.

35. (a) 9
    (b) 99
    (c) 9

36. True. This can be proved using the test for divisibility by 3.

37. $16.22 or $5.11

38. (a) 2
    (b) 24
    (c) 248

39. 428571

40. 6 and 66 years old.

41. True. Let n = any whole number. Then
    $$n + (n +1) + (n +2) + ... + [n +(m-2)] + [n +(m -1)] = mn + \frac{(m-1)m}{2} = m[n + \frac{(m-1)}{2}].$$
    Therefore (since m is odd, $n + m$-1 is a whole number) the m consecutive whole numbers beginning with n are divisible by m.

42. 349 at $1.73

43. (a) 9   (b) 10

44. Numbers that have a multiple of six 9s as digits.

45. 27,374,985

46. Yes

47. Let x and y be any two consecutive numbers in the Fibonacci sequence. Then, the next eight numbers are $x + y$, $x + 2y$, $2x + 3y$, $3x + 5y$, $5x + 8y$, $8x + 13y$, $13x + 21y$, and $21x + 34y$. The sum of these ten numbers is $55x + 88y$, a multiple of 11.

48. This table should be created on a spreadsheet.

n	p(n)	n	p(n)
1	43	11	173
2	47	12	197
3	53	13	223
4	61	14	251
5	71	15	281
6	83	16	313
7	97	17	347
8	113	18	383
9	131	19	421
10	151	20	461

Analyzing Student Thinking

49. Yes, Courtney, you can use the Sieve of Eratoshenes to find the composite numbers—if you followed the algorithm for finding primes, the composite numbers are all those that you crossed off.

50. No, the student is not correct; for example, $3 \mid (2 + 4)$, but 3 does not divide 2 or 4.

51. Yes, Christa is correct; since $10 = 9+1$, $100 = 99+1$, $1000 = 999+1$ and so forth, each power of 10 is 1 more than a multiple of 9 as well as one more than a multiple of 3. Because of this similarity between powers of 10 and multiples of 3 or 9, the divisibility tests are also similar.

52. Yes, that's right, Brooklyn, you checked all the prime numbers whose square is less than or equal to 113.

53. $a \mid b$ is a statement about the relationship between the numbers a and b; for instance, to say that 4 divides 12, or $4 \mid 12$, means there exists a whole number, namely 3, that can be multiplied by 4 to get 12. However, a/b is the quotient of the numbers a and b—it is equal to the answer you get when dividing a by b; for example, $12/4 = 3$. It is true to say that, if $a \mid b$, then b/a is an integer.

54. Kelby, in your first example, 2 and $9 = 3 \times 3$ have no common factors, so their product divides 36. However, in your second example, $4 = 2 \times 2$ and $6 = 2 \times 3$ have a common factor of 2. Thus, the product of $4 \times 6 = 24 = 2 \times 2 \times 2 \times 3$ has one more factor of 2 than does $36 = 2 \times 2 \times 3 \times 3$ and 24 does not divide 36. Notice that 12 is a number that is smaller than 24 but also a multiple of both 4 and 6. It does divide 36.

55. Lorena, 357 does happen to be divisible by 7 since $357 = 51 \times 7$, but your test for divisibility by 7 does not always work; for instance 27 has 7 as its last digit, but 27 is not divisible by 7.

56. No, 354 is not divisible by 4 or 6.

Problems Related to the NCTM Standards and Curriculum Focal Points

1.   In order to determine whether a number is prime or composite, one must look at the number and then think through their division facts to know if it has any whole number divisors. This may also be done by thinking through the multiplication facts to see if any two numbers multiplied together are equal to the number of interest.

2. Which is bigger 3/7 or 39/91? When determining the fractions that are equivalent to 3/7, one must use the multiples of 3 and 7. To simplify a fraction like 39/91 one must determine the prime factorizations of both numerator and denominator in order to see the common factors that can be divided out. Either of these methods could be used to see that these fractions are the same.

Section 5.2

1. (a) 9 (b) 16 (c) 2016
    (d) 45
    (e) 24 factors: 1, 11, 11^2, 11^3, 11^4, 11^5, 13, 13^2, 13^3, 11×13, 11×13^2, 11×13^3, $11^2 \times 13$, $11^2 \times 13^2$, $11^2 \times 13^3$, $11^3 \times 13$, $11^3 \times 13^2$, $11^3 \times 13^3$, $11^4 \times 13$, $11^4 \times 13^2$, $11^4 \times 13^3$, $11^5 \times 13$, $11^5 \times 13^2$, $11^5 \times 13^3$

2. (a) $120 = 2 \times 2 \times 2 \times 3 \times 5$
    (b) 2, 3, 4 = 2 × 2, 5,
        6 = 2 × 3, 8 = 2 × 2 × 2,
        10 = 2 × 5, 12 = 2 × 2 × 3,
        etc.
    (c) Same factors, not used more times than in (a)
    (d) Prime factors of n are 11 and/or 13, not more than 5 factors of 11 and 3 factors of 13.

3. (a) Factors of 24: {1, 2, 3, 4, 6, <u>8</u>, 12, 24}
        Factors of 16: (1, 2, 4, <u>8</u>, 16}
        GCF(24, 16) = 8
    (b) Factors of 48: {1, 2, 3, 4, 6, 8, 12, <u>16</u>, 24, 48}
        Factors of 64: {1, 2, 4, 8, <u>16</u>, 32, 64}
        GCF(48, 64) = 16
    (c) Factors of 54: {1, 2, 3, 6, 9, <u>18</u>, 27, 54}
        Factors of 72: {1, 2, 4, 3, 6, 8, 9, 12, <u>18</u>, 24, 36, 72}
        GCF(54, 72) = 18

4. (a) 18 (b) 1 (c) 17

5. (a) 6 (b) 111 (c) 3 (d) 1

6. (a) 22 (b) 9 (c) 2

7. (a) 2 (b) 6
    (c) 8 (d) 169

8. (a) check 2, 4
    (b) check 13
    (c) check 3, 11

9. (a) Multiples of 15: {15, 30, 45, 60, <u>90</u>,...}
        Multiples of 18: {18, 36, 54, 72, <u>90</u>, ...}
        LCM(15, 18) = $2 \times 3^2 \times 5$ = 90
    (b) Multiples of 26: {26, 52, <u>78</u>, ...}
        Multiples of 39: {39, <u>78</u>, ...}
        LCM(26, 39) = 78
    (c) Multiples of 36: {36, 72, 108, <u>144</u>, ...}
        Multiples of 45: {45, 90, <u>144</u>, ...}
        LCM(36, 45) = 144

10. (a) 105 (b) 70
    (c) 300 (d) 910

11. (a) 357 (b) 1443 (c) 1125

12. (a) 1 (b) 2 (c) 69
    (d) 17 (e) $5^3 \cdot 7^3 \cdot 13^4$
    (f) $3^3 \cdot 7^2$

13. (a) 60 (b) 225
    (c) $3^4 \cdot 5^5 \cdot 7^6 \cdot 11^4$
    (d) $2^4 \cdot 3^8 \cdot 5^4 \cdot 11^3 \cdot 13^7$

14. (a) $1260 = 2^2 \cdot 3^2 \cdot 5 \cdot 7$
    (b) $59,400 = 2^3 \cdot 3^3 \cdot 5^2 \cdot 11$
    (c) $36,036 = 2^2 \cdot 3^2 \cdot 7 \cdot 11 \cdot 13$

15. (a) GCF(a, b) = 7; $a \cdot b = 4116$;
        LCM(a, b) = 4116 ÷ 7 = 588
    (b) $5^3 \cdot 7^4$
    (c) $a = 2^7 \cdot 5^5 \cdot 7^5 \cdot 11^4$, $b = 5^3 \cdot 7^4$
        and
        $a = 2^7 \cdot 5^3 \cdot 7^4$, $b = 5^4 \cdot 7^5 \cdot 11^4$

16. (a) (i)

     (ii) GCF (30, 24) = $2 \cdot 3$
           LCM (30, 24) = $2 \cdot 2 \cdot 2 \cdot 3 \cdot 5$

     (b) (i)

     (ii) GCF(4, 27) = 1
           LCM(4, 27) = $2 \cdot 2 \cdot 3 \cdot 3 \cdot 3$

     (c) (i)

     (ii) GCF(18, 45) = $3 \cdot 3$
           LCM(18, 45) = $2 \cdot 3 \cdot 3 \cdot 5$

17. LCM(a, b) except when $a = b$, in
     which case they are equal.

18. (a) abundant   (b) perfect
     (c) abundant   (d) deficient

19. (a) No; 1648:
          $1 + 2 + 4 + 8 + 16 + 103 + 206$
          $+ 412 + 824 = 1576$
          1576:
          $1 + 2 + 4 + 8 + 197 + 394 +$
          $788 = 1394$
     (b) Yes ; 2620:
          $1 + 2 + 4 + 5 + 10 + 20 + 131 +$
          $262 + 524 + 655 + 1310 =$
          2924
          2924:
          $1 + 2 + 4 + 17 + 34 + 43 + 68 +$
          $86 + 172 + 731 + 1462 = 2620$
     (c) 18, 416

20. (a) No; 248:
          $2 + 4 + 8 + 31 + 62 + 124 =$
          231
          231:
          $3 + 7 + 11 + 21 + 33 + 77 =$
          152

     (b) Yes; 1050:
          $2 + 3 + 5 + 7 + 10 + 14 + 15 +$
          $21 + 25 + 30 + 35 + 42 + 50 +$
          $70 + 75 + 105 + 150 + 210 +$
          $350 + 525 = 1925$
          1925:
          $5 + 7 + 11 + 25 + 35 + 55 + 77$
          $+ 175 + 275 + 385 = 1050$
     (c) Yes; 1575:
          $3 + 5 + 7 + 9 + 15 + 21 + 25 +$
          $35 + 45 + 63 + 75 + 105 + 175$
          $+ 315 + 525 = 1648$
          1648:
          $2 + 4 + 8 + 16 + 103 + 206 +$
          $412 + 824 = 1575$

21. (a) 3:   1,3   2
          4:   1,2,4   3
          5:   1,5   2
          6:   1,2,3,6   4
          7:   1,7   2
          8:   1,2,4,8   4
          9:   1,3,9   3
          10: 1,2,5,10   4
          11: 1,11   2
          12: 1,2,3,4,6,12   6
          13: 1,13   2
          14: 1,2,7,14   4
          15: 1,3,5,15   4
          16: 1,2,4,8,16   5
     (b) prime numbers
     (c) perfect square

22. (a) p
     (b) p^2
     (c) pq or p^3
     (d) p^4
     (e) p^5 or p^2q
     (f) p^{11}, p^5q, p^3q^2, $p^2q\,r$

23. (a) b is a multiple of a
     (b) a is a multiple of b
     (c) both a and b are 1
     (d) The only common factor of a
          and b is 1, i.e. GCF (a, b) =
          1.

24. GCF(x^2, y^2) = 1. The prime
     factorizations of x and y share no
     primes. In x^2 and y^2 those same
     primes occur, just twice as often,
     so still none are common.

25. 496 is the sum of the cubes of 1,3,5, and 7. 8128 is the sum of the cubes of the odd numbers 1 through 15.

26. 5, 6

27. 136 miles

28. LCM(3, 4, 5) = 60 so 60 minutes after 11 was the first time all 3 dogs barked together again.

29. 90 since 90 = $2^1 \times 3^2 \times 5^1$, there are $(1+1)(2+1)(1+1) = 12$ factors.

30. 60 has 12 factors.

31. $23 \cdot 28 \cdot 33 = 21,252$

32. $494 \div 13 = 38$. $100a + 10b + a = 100a + 10(13 - a) + a = 91a + 10 \times 13 = (7a + 10)13$

33. $4 + 9 + 3 + 7 + 7 + 7 + 5 = 42$, $4,937,775 = 5 \times 5 \times 3 \times 65,837$, and $5 + 5 + 3 + 6 + 5 + 8 + 3 + 7 = 42$.

34. (a) 4
    (b) 8
    (c) $(\dfrac{m + n}{GCF(m, n)} - 1) \times GCF(m, n)$

35. $1729 = 12^3 + 1^3 = 10^3 + 9^3$

36. 377 and 233. Any pair of consecutive Fibonacci numbers beyond the 12th one. Other answers are possible.

Analyzing Student Thinking

37. No, Colby is not correct. In order to determine the number of factors, he needs to first write $8^3 9^4$ in its prime factorization form: $8^3 9^4 = 2^9 3^8$ has $(9+1)(8+1) = 90$ factors.

38. Eva, the LCM(a, b) is the smallest number that both a and b will divide. Thus, LCM(a, b) ≥ both a and b. However, the GCF(a, b) is the greatest number that divides both a and b; hence GCF(a, b) ≤ both a and b. So, LCM(a, b) ≥ GCF(a, b).

39. LCD: least common denominator
    GCD: greatest common divisor

40. Ask Brett to consider the following whole numbers that have exactly three factors: 4, 9, 16, 25, 49, ... Can you see anything special about these numbers? They are all perfect squares.

41. Yes, he is correct in both cases. To write a fraction a/b in simplest form (i.e. "reduce" the fraction), one divides a and b by GCF(a, b). When finding a common denominator between two fractions, in order to add or subtract them, say, one usually uses the LCM of the denominators of the two fractions.

42. Both the Set Intersection method and the Prime Factorization method are important to learn. Using Set Intersection helps us to understand the meaning of the GCF, but it is more cumbersome to use this method. The Prime Factorization method is often more efficient to use.

43. Yes, the student is correct. This does not invalidate the theorem because, in the proof, it is assumed that p is the largest prime; 13 is clearly not the largest prime.

Problems Related to the NCTM Standards and Curriculum Focal Points

1. By knowing the division facts you can quickly identify factors of a number and can then see common factors of multiple numbers in order to find the GCF. Similarly, quick recall of multiplication facts help in finding multiples of numbers and thus the LCM is easier to find.

2.   When adding or subtracting
      fractions, a lowest common
      denominator is often needed. The
      LCM is the same as the lowest
      common denominator. Simplifying
      fractions requires dividing out
      common factors between the
      numerator and denominator. Thus
      the GCF can be used to simplify
      fractions.

3.   When you need to solve equations
      like $x^2 - 6x - 91 = 0$, knowing
      whether or not 91 is prime or can
      be factored and what the
      factorization might be is critical.
      As mentioned before, LCMs and
      GCFs are also used in working
      with fractions in algebra.

Chapter 6

Section 6.1

1.   (a) 5/8   (b) 3/10
     (c) 4/5   (d) 5/12

2.   (a) (i)

      (ii)

  (b) (i)

      (ii)

  (c) (i)

      (ii)

  (d) (i)

      (ii)

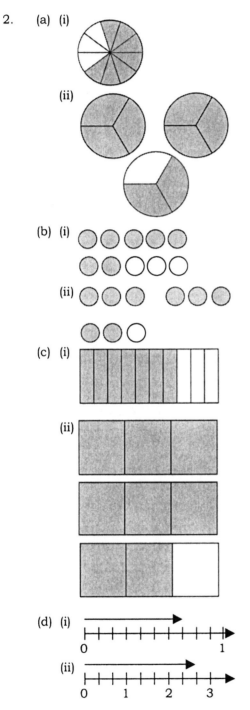

3.   (a)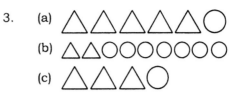

    (b)

    (c)

4.   Yes. The shaded rectangles represent ½ and the shaded triangles represent ¼. Thus, the shaded region represents ¾.

5.   (a) 9/40   (b) 5/40   (c) 7/40

6.   (a) False, total days not the same for each month
    (b) True
    (c) False, each part (month) not equivalent size

7.   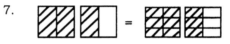

  The same amount is shaded in both figures.

8.   (a) F   (b) F
    (c) T   (d) T

9.   (a) and (d)

10.   (a) 21/17   (b) 14/3
     (c) 5/7   (d) 29/2

11.   (a) $5\dfrac{28}{111}$ (b) $62\dfrac{1}{3}$

12.   (a) Since a 13th < an 11th < a 9th,
     $\dfrac{5}{13} < \dfrac{5}{11} < \dfrac{5}{9}$.
    (b) Since a 9th < an 8th < a 7th,
     $\dfrac{6}{7} < \dfrac{7}{8} < \dfrac{8}{9}$

13.   (a) 7/13 < 14/25 < 4/7
    (b) 2/9 < 3/11 < 5/18 < 7/23

14. $\dfrac{ad + bc}{2bd}$ is midway between $\dfrac{a}{b}$ and $\dfrac{c}{d}$ since it is the average of the two.

15. Only fractions in (a) are equal.

    In (b) $\dfrac{1516}{2312} < \dfrac{4196}{5202} < \dfrac{2653}{2890}$.

    In (c) $\dfrac{516}{892} < \dfrac{1892}{3268} < \dfrac{1376}{2376}$

16. (a) $\dfrac{20}{230}, \dfrac{9}{100}$ (b) $\dfrac{4}{20}, \dfrac{20}{100}$

    (c) $\dfrac{17}{230}, \dfrac{7}{100}$ (d) $\dfrac{7}{17}, \dfrac{41}{100}$

17. Both

18. Mr. Roberts's class

19. There are many correct possibilities. One is shown for each case.

    (a)

    (b)

    (c)

    (d)

    (e)

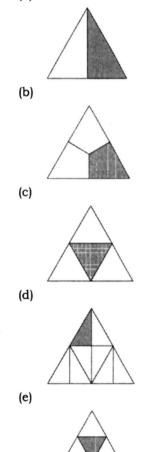

20. (a) (i) $\dfrac{16}{64} = \dfrac{1}{4}$ (ii) $\dfrac{19}{95} = \dfrac{1}{5}$

   (iii) $\dfrac{26}{65} = \dfrac{2}{5}$

   (iv) $\dfrac{199}{995} = \dfrac{1}{5}$

   (v) $\dfrac{26666}{66665} = \dfrac{2}{5}$

   (b) Answers will vary here, but some examples are:

   $\dfrac{1666}{6664}, \dfrac{2666666}{6666665}, \dfrac{1999}{9995}$

21. Yes, this process can continue. No, there is no smallest fraction greater than 0.

22. The size of the unit is different so comparison cannot be made.

23. (a) 672   (b) 11,193

24. Greater than - the fraction is always closer to one.

25. For example, 2001/6000, 2002/6000,..., 2999/6000

26. $80,000,000,000

27. 8/17

28. $2,800

29. Approximately 9.3 km

30. (a) In order, from nearest to farthest: Kelly, Janet, Cathy, Rose, Ann

    (b) 2.5 K

31. (a)

    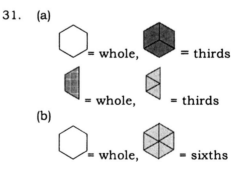

    (b)

    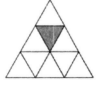

(c)

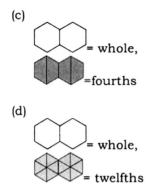

= whole,

=fourths

(d)

= whole,

= twelfths

32. These activities highlight that the wholes can be different shapes and the parts are always equal; and, most importantly, they provide a bridge from the concrete representation of a picture to the abstract representation of numerals.

Analyzing Student Thinking

33. David's statement is true since proper fractions are less than 1, while improper fractions are greater than 1.

34. It's true that multiplying the top and bottom of a fraction by the same number does not change the value of the fraction, by definition of fraction equality. However, adding the same number to the top and bottom of a fraction changes its value; for instance $\frac{1}{2} \neq \frac{1+2}{2+2} = \frac{3}{4}$.

35. Help Brandon find equal fractions with like denominators as follows: 3/4 = 15/20 and 3/5 = 12/20, so 13/20 or 14/20 would be between 3/4 and 3/5.

36. Rafael, to compare two fractions, first write them with a common denominator. Since $\frac{1}{4} = \frac{1 \cdot 2}{4 \cdot 2} = \frac{2}{8}$, we see the two fractions are actually equal.

37. Collin is correct in the case that the denominators of the two fractions are equal; for instance 4/5 is larger than 3/5 since 4 is larger than 3. However, if the two fractions do not have a common denominator, the one with the larger numerator may or may not be the larger fraction; for instance, 7/20 is not larger than 1/2, even though 7 is larger than 1.

38. Show the student that 3/2 would mean that the circle is divided into 2 equivalent parts, and 3 such parts are shaded—this requires two circles.

39. Hailey is incorrect; for example, 2 × 3 < 1 × 8, but 2/3 is not less than 1/8. What we can say is: if $ab < cd$, then either $a/c < d/b$ or $a/d < c/b$.

Problems Related to the NCTM Standards and Curriculum Focal Points

1. Three possible ideas are: 1) the denominator represents the number of pieces a whole is cut into, 2) those pieces are all of equal size, and 3) the numerator represents how many of those pieces are of interest.

2. One possible representation is an area model cut into equally sized pieces with a certain number of them shaded. Another representation is a set of objects where some of the objects have different attributes than the rest. A number line is also a possible representation. Answers may vary.

3. "Parts of unit wholes" is shown in Set A #1a. A "part of a collection" is shown in Set A #1c. A location on a number line is represented in Set A #2. An example of division of

whole numbers occurs when one thinks of dividing 3 brownies evenly among 4 people. More abstractly, this is dividing 3 by 4.

Section 6.2

1. (a)

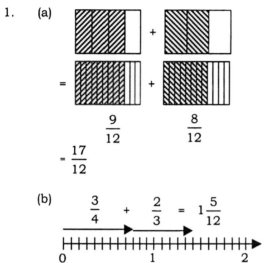

$$= \frac{17}{12}$$

(b)

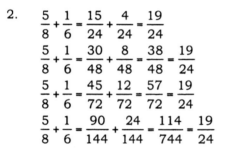

$$\frac{3}{4} \quad + \quad \frac{2}{3} \quad = \quad 1\frac{5}{12}$$

2. $$\frac{5}{8} + \frac{1}{6} = \frac{15}{24} + \frac{4}{24} = \frac{19}{24}$$
    $$\frac{5}{8} + \frac{1}{6} = \frac{30}{48} + \frac{8}{48} = \frac{38}{48} = \frac{19}{24}$$
    $$\frac{5}{8} + \frac{1}{6} = \frac{45}{72} + \frac{12}{72} = \frac{57}{72} = \frac{19}{24}$$
    $$\frac{5}{8} + \frac{1}{6} = \frac{90}{144} + \frac{24}{144} = \frac{114}{744} = \frac{19}{24}$$

Other correct answers are possible.

3. (a)

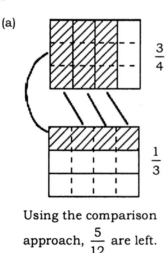

Using the comparison approach, $\frac{5}{12}$ are left.

(b)

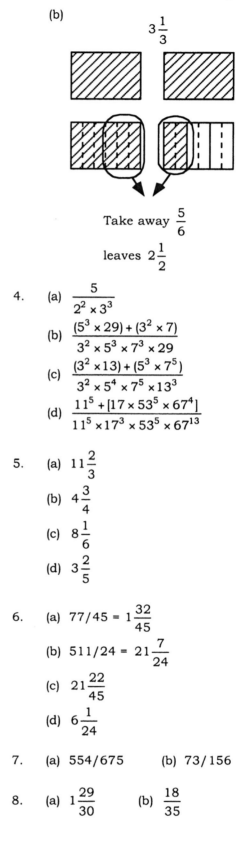

$3\frac{1}{3}$

Take away $\frac{5}{6}$

leaves $2\frac{1}{2}$

4. (a) $\dfrac{5}{2^2 \times 3^3}$

(b) $\dfrac{(5^3 \times 29) + (3^2 \times 7)}{3^2 \times 5^3 \times 7^3 \times 29}$

(c) $\dfrac{(3^2 \times 13) + (5^3 \times 7^5)}{3^2 \times 5^4 \times 7^5 \times 13^3}$

(d) $\dfrac{11^5 + [17 \times 53^5 \times 67^4]}{11^5 \times 17^3 \times 53^5 \times 67^{13}}$

5. (a) $11\frac{2}{3}$

(b) $4\frac{3}{4}$

(c) $8\frac{1}{6}$

(d) $3\frac{2}{5}$

6. (a) $77/45 = 1\frac{32}{45}$

(b) $511/24 = 21\frac{7}{24}$

(c) $21\frac{22}{45}$

(d) $6\frac{1}{24}$

7. (a) $554/675$ (b) $73/156$

8. (a) $1\frac{29}{30}$ (b) $\frac{18}{35}$

9. (a) 5/12 + 4/12

0   9/12   1

(b) 1/5 + 7/15

0   2/3

(c) 1/3 + 5/12

0   3/4   1

10. (a) (i) 3/8   (ii) 1/24
     (b) Associativity

11. (a) $1\dfrac{32}{45}$ (b) $6\dfrac{1}{24}$

12. (a) $1\dfrac{25}{126}$ (b) $\dfrac{73}{156}$

13. (a) $\dfrac{17}{30}$ (b) $\dfrac{18}{35}$

14. By cross multiplication: $\dfrac{2}{5} < \dfrac{5}{8}$

since $2 \cdot 8 < 5 \cdot 5$.

Using common denominators:

$\dfrac{2}{5} < \dfrac{5}{8}$ since

$\dfrac{2}{5} = \dfrac{2 \cdot 8}{5 \cdot 8} = \dfrac{16}{40} < \dfrac{25}{40} = \dfrac{5 \cdot 5}{8 \cdot 5} = \dfrac{5}{8}$

15. (a) $1\dfrac{5}{8}$

     (b) $3\dfrac{2}{15}$

     (c) $9\dfrac{2}{11}$

16. (a) $5\dfrac{4}{9} - 3 = 2\dfrac{4}{9}$

     (b) $9\dfrac{2}{6} - 3 = 6\dfrac{1}{3}$

     (c) $21\dfrac{5}{7} - 9 = 12\dfrac{5}{7}$

(d) $5\dfrac{8}{11} - 3 = \dfrac{8}{11}$

17. (a) (i) 11 to 13   (ii) 12

     (b) (i) 1 to 2   (ii) $1\dfrac{1}{2}$

     (c) (i) 17 to 20   (ii) 18

18. (a) $6 + 6\dfrac{1}{2} = \dfrac{1}{2}$

     (b) $8 - 5\dfrac{1}{2} = 2\dfrac{1}{2}$

     (c) $8 + 2\dfrac{1}{2} + 7 = 17\dfrac{1}{2}$

19. $\sim 4 \cdot 6 = 24$

20. 8

21. 8

22. 52 bags

23. 45 minutes

24. $35'\dfrac{1}{2}"$

25. Amy: $2\dfrac{1}{2}$ Robert: $\dfrac{7}{15}$
Review simpler problems, meaning of mixed numbers, use diagrams.

26. (a) $8^2 + 15^2 = 17^2$, 17

     (b) (i) $\dfrac{1}{7} + \dfrac{1}{9} = \dfrac{16}{63}$,
            $16^2 + 63^2 = 65^2$

        (ii) $\dfrac{1}{11} + \dfrac{1}{13} = \dfrac{24}{143}$,
            $24^2 + 143^2 = 145^2$

        (iii) $\dfrac{1}{19} + \dfrac{1}{21} = \dfrac{40}{399}$,
            $40^2 + 399^2 = 401^2$

     (c) The third number, c, is two more than the denominator of the sum.

     (d) $\dfrac{1}{2n-1} + \dfrac{1}{2n+1} = \dfrac{4n}{4n^2 - 1}$ and
       $(4n)^2 + (4n^2 - 1)^2 = (4n^2 + 1)^2$

27. 11/23

28. (a) 7/8, 15/16, 31/32,
    (b) 7   (c) 1

29. (a) 1/5 - 2/5 is not a fraction
    (b) 3/4 - 1/4 ≠ 1/4 - 3/4
    (c) (4/5 - 3/5) - 1/5 ≠
        4/5 - (3/5 - 1/5)

30. (a) $\dfrac{1}{6}$ $\dfrac{1}{30}$ $\dfrac{1}{60}$ $\dfrac{1}{60}$ $\dfrac{1}{30}$ $\dfrac{1}{6}$

    $\dfrac{1}{7}$ $\dfrac{1}{42}$ $\dfrac{1}{105}$ $\dfrac{1}{140}$ $\dfrac{1}{105}$ $\dfrac{1}{42}$ $\dfrac{1}{7}$

    (b) The first number in the nth
        row is $\dfrac{1}{n}$.
    (c) Each fraction in the triangle is
        the sum of the two fractions
        directly below it. For example,
        $\dfrac{1}{30} + \dfrac{1}{20} = \dfrac{1}{12}$.

31. (a) 5/12 - 1/3 = 1/12 and
        11/12 - 1/3 = 7/12
    (b) 6/12 - 1/6 = 1/3 and
        2/3 - 6/12 = 1/6

32. One way would be to use an area
    model for fraction addition.

33. This rearrangement is impossible.

Analyzing Student Thinking

34. Yes, Cristobal is correct—any
    common multiple of the
    denominators of the fractions will
    suffice as a common denominator;
    however, using the LCD often
    makes computations easier since
    the numbers involved will
    generally be smaller.

35. Ask Whitley to demonstrate her
    method. Chances are she is using
    a common denominator without
    being aware of it or she is using
    an invalid method.

36. You can change the fractions to
    improper fractions first, but it's
    not necessary. Another way is to
    write the fraction parts of the
    mixed numbers with a common
    denominator and then add the
    whole number parts and the
    fraction parts together:
    $$3\frac{1}{4} + 5\frac{2}{7} = 3\frac{7}{28} + 5\frac{8}{28} = 8\frac{15}{28}.$$

37. Yes, Kalil applied the
    commutative and associative
    properties of fraction addition.

38. You might start by agreeing with
    the Marcos that in the real world
    the word *fraction* often means a
    small part. However, when we are
    writing numerical fractions, they
    can be quite large. For example,
    how big is 5/2? That's bigger
    than 1. 99/100 is a proper
    fraction, but it is much closer to 1
    than to 1/2 or 0.

39. Show Brenda an example such as
    1/2 and 1/3. In order to add or
    subtract these two fractions, we
    need to change them both to
    sixths so we can add the
    appropriate parts of the same-
    sized unit.

    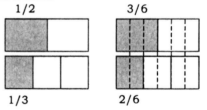

40. No, Marilyn needs to have the
    same unit (either both 8" or 12"
    inch pizzas). Also, saying 5/12 of
    a pizza does not refer to which size
    pizza, which is a problem.
    Another approach is to compute
    the area of the pizzas. If she ate
    1/4 of the smaller pizza, she ate
    1/4(8²) = 16 square inches. If she
    ate 1/6 of the larger pizza, she ate
    1/6(12²) = 24 square inches. This
    is 16 + 24 = 40 square inches of
    pizza. The total amount of pizza is

64 + 144 = 208 square inches, and 40 is not 5/12(208).

Problems Related to the NCTM Standards and Curriculum Focal Points

1. One important concept in adding fractions is recognizing the need for the two fractions being added or subtracted to have the same size pieces. Having the same size pieces is the same as having a common denominator.

2. One possible meaning is for students to be able to sketch an area, set or number line model to represent each fraction. They can then combine or compare the representations of the individual fractions to find the sum or difference.

3. From the student's experience, they should have or develop a good sense of whether a fraction is close to a half or one. This knowledge can then be used to estimate addition and subtractions of fractions by rounding to the nearest half or whole.

Section 6.3

1. (a)

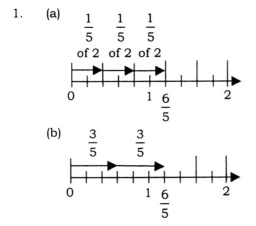

(b)

2. (a)

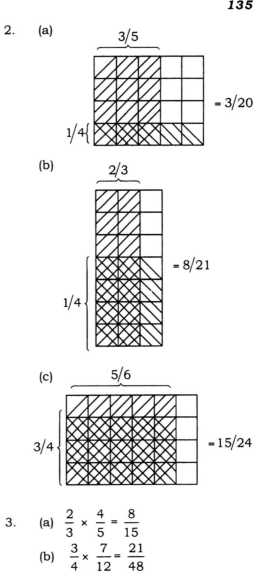

(b)

(c)

3. (a) $\dfrac{2}{3} \times \dfrac{4}{5} = \dfrac{8}{15}$

    (b) $\dfrac{3}{4} \times \dfrac{7}{12} = \dfrac{21}{48}$

4. (a) 4/13   (b) 4/13

5. (a) 3/16, 5/8, 9/10, 7/5
    (b) 5/7, 10/9, 8/5, 16/3
    (c) They are reversed.

6. (a) Distributive
    (b) Associative
    (c) Commutative and Associative

7. (a) 4/15   (b) 3/5
    (c) 77/1,000,000
    (d) 8/9
    (e) 34/35   (f) 103/105
    (g) 26/35   (h) $41\dfrac{8}{35}$

8. (a) 3/4   (b) 15/7

9. (a) $31\dfrac{7}{20}$ (b) $104\dfrac{5}{24}$

    (c) $114\dfrac{32}{45}$

10. (a) Yes   (b) No

11. (a)

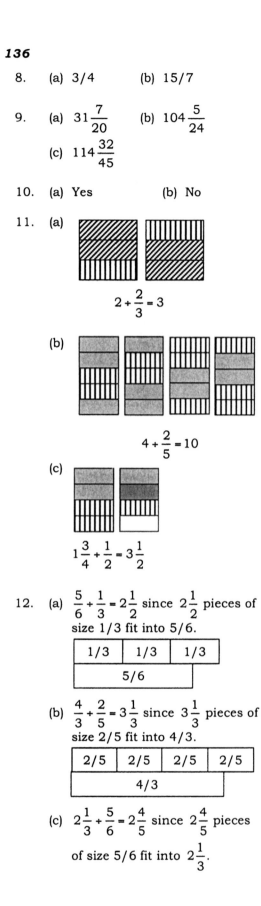

$2 + \dfrac{2}{3} = 3$

    (b)

    $4 + \dfrac{2}{5} = 10$

    (c)

    $1\dfrac{3}{4} + \dfrac{1}{2} = 3\dfrac{1}{2}$

12. (a) $\dfrac{5}{6} \div \dfrac{1}{3} = 2\dfrac{1}{2}$ since $2\dfrac{1}{2}$ pieces of size 1/3 fit into 5/6.

1/3	1/3	1/3
5/6		

    (b) $\dfrac{4}{3} \div \dfrac{2}{5} = 3\dfrac{1}{3}$ since $3\dfrac{1}{3}$ pieces of size 2/5 fit into 4/3.

2/5	2/5	2/5	2/5
4/3			

    (c) $2\dfrac{1}{3} \div \dfrac{5}{6} = 2\dfrac{4}{5}$ since $2\dfrac{4}{5}$ pieces of size 5/6 fit into $2\dfrac{1}{3}$.

5/6	5/6	5/6
1	1	1/3

13. (a) $\dfrac{5}{8} \div \dfrac{3}{8} = \dfrac{5}{3}$

    (b) $\dfrac{12}{13} \div \dfrac{4}{13} = \dfrac{12}{4} = 3$

    (c) $\dfrac{13}{15} \div \dfrac{28}{30} = \dfrac{26}{30} \div \dfrac{28}{30} = \dfrac{26}{28} = \dfrac{13}{14}$

14. (a) $\dfrac{12}{15} \div \dfrac{4}{5} = \dfrac{3}{3} = 1$

    (b) $\dfrac{18}{24} \div \dfrac{9}{6} = \dfrac{2}{4} = \dfrac{1}{2}$

    (c) $\dfrac{30}{39} \div \dfrac{6}{13} = \dfrac{5}{3} = 1\dfrac{2}{3}$

    (d) $\dfrac{28}{33} \div \dfrac{14}{11} = \dfrac{2}{3}$

15. (a) $\dfrac{3}{4} \div \dfrac{6}{9} = \boxed{}$ so

    $\dfrac{6}{9} \times \boxed{} = \dfrac{3}{4}$

    $\dfrac{9}{6} \times \dfrac{6}{9} \times \boxed{} = \dfrac{9}{6} \times \dfrac{3}{4}$

    $\boxed{} = \dfrac{27}{24} = 1\dfrac{1}{8}$

    (b) $\dfrac{10}{7} \div \dfrac{8}{11} = \boxed{}$ so

    $\dfrac{8}{11} \times \boxed{} = \dfrac{10}{7}$

    $\dfrac{11}{8} \times \dfrac{8}{11} \times \boxed{} = \dfrac{11}{8} \times \dfrac{10}{7}$

    $\boxed{} = \dfrac{110}{56} = 1\dfrac{27}{28}$

    (c) $\dfrac{5}{6} \div \dfrac{2}{3} = \boxed{}$ so

    $\dfrac{2}{3} \times \boxed{} = \dfrac{5}{6}$

    $\dfrac{3}{2} \times \dfrac{2}{3} \times \boxed{} = \dfrac{3}{2} \times \dfrac{5}{6}$

    $\boxed{} = \dfrac{15}{12} = 1\dfrac{1}{4}$

16. (a) $\dfrac{4}{3}$ (b) 2

(c) $\dfrac{15}{4}$ (d) 24/35

$\dfrac{16}{56} < \dfrac{20}{56} < \dfrac{21}{56}$

17. (a) 27/22   (b) 1700/9
    (c) 9/10

27. 125.4 billion

18. (a) 1/18   (b) 18

28. 270 bottles

19. (a) $1\dfrac{77}{445}$ (b) $\dfrac{183}{328}$ (c) $1\dfrac{53}{156}$

29. $4\dfrac{1}{2}$yards, $2\dfrac{1}{4}$yards

20. (a) 1   (b) 88/217

30. $2100, $3200

21. (a) $52(1/2) = 26$

31. $1\dfrac{1}{3}$pounds

   (b) $\dfrac{5}{8} + \left(\dfrac{2}{5} + \dfrac{3}{5}\right) = \dfrac{5}{8} + 1 = 1\dfrac{5}{8}$

32. $0.50

   (c) $\left(\dfrac{3}{7} \times \dfrac{7}{3}\right) \times \dfrac{1}{9} = 1 \times \dfrac{1}{9} = \dfrac{1}{9}$

33. 1/3

34. 3/4

   (d) $7 + 23\left(\dfrac{3}{7} + \dfrac{4}{7}\right) = 7 + 23(1) = 30$

35. Abigail: 4/12 = 1/3
    Harold: 24/20 = 6/5

22. (a) $20 \times 5\dfrac{1}{2} = 110$

36. (a) 96 eggs   (b) 12 days
    (c) 9 chickens

   (b) $75 \div 25 = 3$
   (c) $56 \div 8 = 7$
   (d) $25 \times 4 = 6$

37. Top row: $2\dfrac{2}{3}$

   Second row: $2\dfrac{1}{2}$, $3\dfrac{1}{2}$, 1/4

23. (a) 36   (b) 27

   Third row: 1/2

24. (a) $50 \times 246 = \dfrac{24,600}{2} = 12,300$

   Bottom row: $15\dfrac{5}{9}$

   (b) $84,602 \times 50$

38. $x + y = 18$ $x\, y = 40$

     $= \dfrac{8,460,200}{2}$

   $\dfrac{1}{x} + \dfrac{1}{y} = \dfrac{y + x}{xy}$

     $= 4,230,100$

   $(x + y)^2 = x^2 + 2x\,y + y^2$
   (a) 18/40 = 9/20
   (b) $18^2 = x^2 + y^2 + 80$, thus

   (c) $75 \times 848 = \dfrac{3}{4} \times 84,800$

       $x^2 + y^2 = 244.$

     $= 3 \times 21,200$

     $= 63,600$

   (d) $420 \times 75 = 42,000 \times \dfrac{3}{4}$

39. (a) $6 + 1\dfrac{1}{5} = 6 \times 1\dfrac{1}{5}$

     $= 10,500 \times 3$

       $7 + 1\dfrac{1}{6} = 7 \times 1\dfrac{1}{6}$

     $= 31,500$

   (b) Using a variable, check to see

25. (a) 15/14   (b) 5/2
    (c) 7/2   (d) 3/50

       that $x + 1\dfrac{1}{x} = x \times 1\dfrac{1}{x}$.

26. $\dfrac{2}{7} < \dfrac{2+3}{7+8} < \dfrac{3}{8}$and

40. (a) $\frac{a}{b} < \frac{c}{d}$ means for some

nonzero $\frac{m}{n}$, $\frac{a}{b} + \frac{m}{n} = \frac{c}{d}$ and

$\frac{c}{d} < \frac{e}{f}$ means for some

nonzero $\frac{p}{q}$, $\frac{c}{d} + \frac{p}{q} = \frac{e}{f}$.

Replacing $\frac{c}{d}$ in the second

equation yields $(\frac{a}{b} + \frac{m}{n}) + \frac{p}{q}$

$= \frac{e}{f}$, or $\frac{a}{b} + (\frac{m}{n} + \frac{p}{q}) = \frac{e}{f}$,

where $\frac{m}{n} + \frac{p}{q}$ is a nonzero

fraction, so $\frac{a}{b} < \frac{e}{f}$ by the
alternative definition.

(b) $\frac{a}{b} < \frac{c}{d}$ means for some

nonzero $\frac{m}{n}$, $\frac{a}{b} + \frac{m}{n} = \frac{c}{d}$, so

$\frac{c}{d} + \frac{e}{f} = (\frac{a}{b} + \frac{m}{n}) + \frac{e}{f} =$

$(\frac{a}{b} + \frac{e}{f}) + \frac{m}{n}$. Thus

$\frac{a}{b} + \frac{e}{f} < \frac{c}{d} + \frac{e}{f}$, by the
alternative definition.

(c) As in parts (a) and (b), show

that $\frac{a}{b}\frac{e}{f} + \frac{m}{n}\frac{e}{f} = \frac{c}{d}\frac{e}{f}$, thus

$\frac{a}{b}\frac{e}{f} < \frac{c}{d}\frac{e}{f}$.

41. 60

42. (a) 2 3/4 + 5 7/8 = 2 + 3/4 + 5 +
         7/8 = 2 + 7/8 + 5 + 3/4 = 2
         7/8 +5 3/4
     (b) (2 + 3/4) × (5 + 7/8) ≠
         (2 + 7/8) × (5 + 3/4)

Analyzing Student Thinking

43. Devonnie is not correct. To
     multiply fractions, you only need

to multiply the numerators and
multiply the denominators. You
could find a common denominator
when multiplying fractions, but
this just makes unnecessary work.

44. Yes, Cameron simplified each
     fraction and then multiplied the
     fractions. Another way to do this
     problem is: multiply the fractions
     before simplifying, then simplify
     the product.

45.

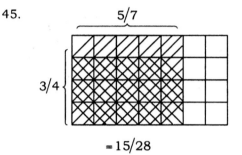

$= 15/28$

46.

Start by drawing eight rectangles
and divide each into four equal
parts. Then shade three out of
every four of the smaller
rectangles. Count the number of
groups of three smaller rectangles
(each one represents 3/4). There
are <u>ten</u> groups of size 3/4 in the 8
original rectangles, and another
<u>two of the three parts</u> needed to
make another group of size 3/4;

that is $8 + \frac{3}{4} = 10\frac{2}{3}$.

47. Yes, this works except for the case
     when either of the divisors is zero.

48. Katrina, for $6 \div \frac{1}{2}$ the answer is 12

since there are 12 one-halves in 6
(two halves for each of the 6
units).

49. There is no one estimation method
     that is always preferred—the
     method you choose will depend,
     for instance, on how close to the

actual answer you need your
estimate to be.

**Problems Related to the NCTM
Standards and Curriculum Focal Points**

1.   One possible example is the
      representation in Figure 6.23
      which shows the division of
      fractions from a sharing
      perspective. Answers may vary.

2.   When using the common
      denominator method for division
      of fractions, you may need to first
      get both fractions in terms of a
      common denominator. Rewriting
      fractions with a common
      denominator requires an
      understanding of equivalent
      fractions. Answers may vary.

3.   From the student's experience,
      they should have or develop a
      good sense of whether a fraction is
      close to a half. This knowledge can
      then be used to estimate
      multiplication by fractions close to
      a half by just dividing by 2.
      Answers may vary.

Chapter 7

Section 7.1

1.   (a) 70.05003   (b) 3000.89
    (c) 0.025001

2   (a) (i) $5(\frac{1}{10}) + 2(\frac{1}{100}) + 5(\frac{1}{1000})$

        (ii) $\frac{525}{1000}$

    (b) (i) $3 \times 10 + 4 + \frac{7}{1000}$

        (ii) $\frac{34007}{1000}$

    (c) (i) $5 + \frac{102}{100000}$

        (ii) $\frac{50102}{10000}$

3.   (a) 0.000746
    (b) 746,000.000746
    (c) 746,000,000.746

4.   (a) Seventy-eight billionths.
    (b) Seven thousand five hundred eighty-nine and twelve thousand three hundred forty-five hundred thousandths.
    (c) One hundred eight-seven thousand two hundred thirteen and two thousand three hundred thousandths
    (d) One billion one million two thousand three and one hundred thousand two ten hundred millionths.

5.   Either it is read "point zero five nine" or "fifty-nine thousandths."

6.   (a) and (c)

7.   (a) R   (b) T, 4 places
    (c) T, 9 places   (d) T, 23 places
    Explanation: Highest power of 2 and/or 5.

8.   (a) 3.078, 3.08, 3.087, 3.80
    (b) 8.0019929, 8.010019, 8.01002
    (c) 0.5, 0.5005, 0.505, 0.55

9.   (a) 5/7, 10/13, 4/5
    (b) 4/11, 2/5, 3/7
    (c) 7/13, 5/9, 11/18
    (d) 17/29, 3/5, 11/18

10.   (a) $\frac{1}{2} < \frac{5}{8} < \frac{17}{23}$

    (b) $\frac{2}{3} < \frac{3}{4} < \frac{13}{16}$

    (c) $\frac{8}{5} < \frac{50}{31} < \frac{26}{15}$

11.   No

12.   (a) $7 \times 10 = 70$
    (b) 26.58 - 9 = 17.58
    (c) 0.00491
    (d) 6 + 6.16 = 12.16
    (e) 5.7 + 8 = 13.7
    (f) 67,320
    (g) 639
    (h) 72 + 6 = 78

13.   (a) $230 \times 1/10 = 23$
    (b) $36 \times 1/4 = 9$
    (c) $82 \times 1/2 = 41$
    (d) $125 \times 4/5 = 100$
    (e) $175 \times 1/5 = 35$
    (f) $3/5 \times 35 = 21$

14.   (a) 1264.16
    (b) 0.00000078752
    (c) 8.25×10^{27}
    (d) 8.25×10^{13}

15.   (a) $30 \times 3 = 90$ to $40 \times 4 = 160$, $35 \times 4 = 140$
    (b) 39
    (c) 60, 60 to 140
    (d) 10

16.   (a) $125 \div 5 = 25$
    (b) $90 \times 8 = 720$
    (c) $400 \div 5/4 = 320$
    (d) $350 \times 2/5 = 140$
    (e) $1/4 \times 48 = 1200$
    (f) $3600 \div 3/5 = 3600 \times 5/3 = 6000$

17.   (a) 321.09   (b) 12.162
    (c) 4.009   (d) 2.0
    (e) 2.00

18. (a) Change 1.4 to 0.6.
    (b) Magic

19. D = 5, O = 2, N = 6, A = 4, L = 8, G = 1, E = 9, R = 7, B = 3, T = 0

Analyzing Student Thinking

20. Joseph did not read the number correctly; the word "and" is used only for the decimal point.

21. Brigham, this method for determining whether or not a decimal will repeat works only if the fraction under consideration has been written in simplest form first. 42/150 can be simplified to 7/25. The factors of the denominator, 25, are limited to 2's and 5's (in this case only 5's), so it is a terminating decimal, 0.28.

22. Mary Lou, we can see that 12/17 is indeed a fraction since it is written in the form a/b, where a and b are whole numbers. Also, since the denominator has factors other than 2 and 5, it must have a repeating decimal representation—the repetend is longer than your calculator is capable of displaying. Doing the division by hand will give you the entire repetend but you might have to go out at least 17 decimal places.

23. Camille, . 0.45 means 45/100 and 0.5 = 0.50 means 50/100. Thus, 6.45 < 6.50 since 45 < 50.

24. Caroline's method is incorrect; 19.67472 is less than halfway between 19.67 and 19.68, so the nearest hundredth is 19.67.

25. It appears that Amir thinks the "round a 5 up" rule has a corresponding "round a 4 down" rule; an explanation similar to the one given to Caroline above could help him see why he is incorrect.

26. Merilee, since the denominator of 2/3 has factors other than 2 and

5, it must have a repeating decimal. If you divide 2 by 3 you get 0.6666..., but your calculator rounded the last 6 in the display to a 7 since the next digit is greater than 5 (it's a 6).

27. Alondra, recall that there are infinitely many fractions between any two fractions, and since decimals are fractions, there must be infinitely many decimals between 0.19 and 0.20; some examples are 0.191, 0.192, and 0.1901.

Problems Related to the NCTM Standards and Curriculum Focal Points

1. Just as the place values to the left of the decimal point represent 1, 10, 100, 1000, and so forth, the place values to the right represent 10ths, 100ths, 1000ths etc. In this way non-whole numbers are represented using fractions with denominators that are powers of ten.

2. Any finite decimal representation can be rewritten as a fraction with a denominator which is a power of 10.

3. Fractions can be compared by first converting them to their decimal representation and then comparing the decimal numbers.

Section 7.2

1. (a) 101.782   (b) 28.135
   (c) 0.2034   (d) 21.901

2. (a) 45.92   (b) 0.1248
   (c) 148   (d) 31.2

3. (a) 23,278.9504   (b) 390.009

4. (b) and (c)

5. (a) 8.6×10^2
   (b) 4.52×10^3

(c) 2.6×10^7
(d) 3.15×10^5
(e) 1.084×10^9
(f) 5.4×10^{13}

6. (a) 3.85×10^9 sec
    (b) 4.73×10^9 sec
    (c) 154,500,000,000 sec
    One hundred fifty-four billion
    five hundred million seconds

7. (a) 8.05×10^6
    (b) 6.278×10^{10}

8. (a) 5.9×10^{23} (b) 9.431×10^4
    (c) 8.3×10^4

9. (a) 3.468×10^{40} (b) 9.5×10^{14}
    (c) 4.6656×10^{55}

10. 19.522 kilometers

11. (a) 1.2×10^{14} kilograms
     (b) 2.48×10^{18} dollars
     (c) About 290,000 times.
     (d) About $29,000 per person.
     Note: In 2001, we owed
     $21,500 each – a 35%
     increase!

12. (a) $0.3\overline{50}$____   (b) $0.\overline{14}$
     (c) $0.45\overline{31596}$

13. (a) 0.317431743174
     (b) 0.317400000000
     (c) 0.115912311591

14. (a) 5/9
     (b) 78/99 = 26/33
     (c) 123/999 = 41/333
     (d) 123/990 = 41/330
     (e) 177/9900 = 59/3300
     (f) 123,333/999,000 =
          41,111/333,000

15. Not equal,
     $0.2\overline{525} = 0.25252525$ is smaller
     than $0.2\overline{525} = 0.2525525525$
     from the 100-thousandths place.

16. *x, z, y*

17. (a) 24.3, 27.5
     (b) 92.1984, 129.07776
     (c) 0.000555, 0.0005555
     (d) 9.6, 14.5____
     (e) $0.8\overline{3}$, $0.85714\overline{2}$

18. (a) (i) 2 steps   (ii) 3 steps
          (iii) 1 step   (iv) 8 steps
     (b) Many answers are possible.
          One answer is 4.87.

19. (a) (i) 1/9   (ii) 1/99
          (iii) 1/999
          (iv) 1/9999
     (b) 1/999,999,999
     (c) 0.01

20. 1. Since $1/3 = 0.\overline{3}$, three times
        both sides of this equations yields
        $1 = 0.\overline{9}$.

21. (a) $a_{n+1} = a_n + 9/10^{n+1}$ and
          $1 = a_{n+1} + 1/10^{n+1}$
     (b) Since $1 = a_{100} + 1/10^{100}$,
          $1 - a_{100} = 1/10^{100}$.
          Therefore, $1 - a_n < 1/10^{100}$
          whenever $n > 100$.
     (c) Use idea in part (b).
     (d) Essentially $0.\overline{9}$ is greater than
          any number less than 1 and
          $0.\overline{9}$ does not exceed 1, hence
          $0.\overline{9} = 1$.

22. (a) $0.\overline{142857}$, $0.\overline{285714}$,
          etc. The repetends have 6
          digits and they share the same
          digits.
     (b) The repetends for 1/13, 3/13,
          4/13, 9/13, 10/13, 12/13
          use same digits and the rest
          use same digits. All have
          repetends with 6 digits.

23. $\dfrac{y}{10^n} + \dfrac{x}{99999} \cdot \dfrac{1}{10^n} = \dfrac{99999y + x}{(99999)(10^n)}$,
     where $0 \le y < 10^n$ and
     $1 \le x \le 99,998$

24. $999 \div 22 = 45$ with 9 remaining, so the 999th digit is 7.

25. (a) 1   (b) 7

26. After taking 1/2 of 16 1/2, the final correct step is to find 1/2 of 12, not 1/2 of 12 1/2.

27. (a) 28.6650 g   (b) 28.6749 g

28. (a) 257.6 mi   (b) 7.8 in.

29. $2528.24

30. $43.71

31. 55 mph

32. $3,750

33. $31.63

Analyzing Student Thinking

34. Bhumi simply lined up the numbers as if they were whole numbers, like this:

    $$\begin{array}{r} 6.45 \\ 2.3 \\ \hline 6.68 \end{array}$$

    To help her understand her misconception, you could have Bhumi write the numbers as fractions with denominator 100:
    $$\frac{645}{100} + \frac{230}{100} = \frac{875}{100} = 8.75.$$

35. Kaisha put the decimal point in the wrong place; $72 \times 35 = 2520$ and, since there are a total of two decimal places in the original problem (7.2×3.5), the final answer will have two also. Thus, 25.20 is the correct answer. Likely, Kaisha did not count the 0 when counting over two decimal places.

36. Yes, it appears Tyler used compensation to compute the product mentally (he divided and

then multiplied by 0.01): 50×4.68
$= (50 \div 100) \times (4.68 \times 100)$
$= 0.5 \times 468 = 234$.

37. The student is incorrect since 0.33 is not equal to 1/3. The correct answer is $0.33 \times 24 = 7.92$, so the student's answer of 8 was a good estimate of the actual answer.

38. Show Henry that he needs to multiply by 1000 (since the repetend is 3 digits long) in order to get the numbers to line up for subtraction. If he does that, he will get $999n = 7445$, or $n = \frac{7445}{999}$.

39. Lauren could be correct since the ones could repeat indefinitely. Thus, one needs to ask Lauren what she was thinking. It appears that the pattern implied by the "..." is that, after each occurrence of a 2, the number of 1's increases by one and is then followed by a 2. If this is the case, the decimal never repeats.

40. Ask the student to tell you how she knows her claim is true. She might offer an argument such as the following: first, we know that every repeating decimal has a fraction representation. We also know the sum of two fractions is a fraction (closure property of fraction addition.) Thus, the sum of two repeating decimals must be a repeating decimal. Of course this is wrong, as can be seen in the sum of the two repeating decimals whose fraction forms are 1/3 and 2/3, since $1/3 + 2/3 = 1$, a nonrepeating decimal.

41. Show Barry that he can multiply 1,275 by 3,987 on his calculator and then affix $10 + 6 = 16$ zeros at the end of the answer he gets. Additionally, show Barry how to enter the product on a scientific calculator, using scientific notation.

Problems Related to the NCTM Standards and Curriculum Focal Points

1. When adding whole numbers it is important to add tens to tens and hundreds to hundreds. Similarly, when adding decimal numbers, tenths need to be added to tenths and hundredths to hundredths. This is done by lining up the decimal point.

2. When multiplying 0.43 and 0.7, these number could be rewritten as the fractions $\frac{43}{10^2} \times \frac{7}{10^1}$. The exponents on the denominators indicate how many digits are to the right of the decimal. Thus, the denominators would be multiplied together by adding the exponents of the powers of ten which the same as counting the number of digits to the right of the decimal.

3. Because our numeration system is base ten, multiplying by a power of 10 is equivalent to moving the decimal point. Thus if the product 3.7×10^7 were computed, the decimal would be moved 7 places to the right yielding 37,000,000.

Section 7.3

1. (a) 2:5   (b) 6.18:100   (c) 3:4
   (d) 5:1   (e) 1:2   (f) 9:16

2. Each is an ordered pair. For example, (a) measures population density.

3. (a) 1/7   (b) 2/7   (c) 25/17

4. (a) No   (b) No

5. (a) $\frac{32}{29}$ (b) $\frac{37}{86}$
   (c) Mandarin : Hindi/Urdu
   (d) $\frac{167}{500}$ (e) $\frac{507}{1000}$

6. (a) 2 1/2   (b) 1
   (c) 320   (d) 5.1

7. (a) 56   (b) 116.67
   (c) $\frac{2}{3}$ (d) 96
   (e) $\frac{30}{17}$ or ≈1.76   (f) $\frac{24}{11}$ or ≈ 2.18

8. $\frac{35 \text{ mi}}{87.5 \text{ mi}} = \frac{2 \text{ hrs}}{5 \text{ hrs}}$,
   $\frac{2 \text{ hrs}}{35 \text{ mi}} = \frac{5 \text{ hrs}}{87.5 \text{ mi}}$,
   $\frac{87.5 \text{ mi}}{35 \text{ mi}} = \frac{5 \text{ hrs}}{2 \text{ hrs}}$

9. (a) 26:6 = 52:12 = 104:24
   (b) 84:6 = 42:3 = 210:15
   (c) 40:12 = 10:3 = 30:9
   (d) 27.50:1.5 = 55:3 = 110:6
   (e) 750:12 = 250:4 = 1000:16

10. 88 kph

11. (a) 60 oz for 29 cents
    (b) $45 for 10 yards
    (c) 18 oz for 40 cents

12. Model *XL*

13. About 148 minutes

14. About 87 gallons.

15. About $2085

16. Just over 7 weeks.

17. (a) 105 miles, 350 miles, 35*n* miles
    (b) About 28 3/5 inches

18. 8572 seeds

19. About 2.3 miles

20. (a) 5 1/2 cups
    (b) 5 gallons
    (c) 6 liters
    (d) $2.71/lb

21. About 206.1 mph

22. (a) 134   (b) 70

23. (a) 6.48 runs
    (b) About 29 runs

24. (a) 11/32 inch
    (b) 29,500 miles

25. (a) A and C
    (b) 20 : 21
    (c) 12 : 11
    (d) No, adding using equivalent
        ratios does not give same
        result.

26. 6 inches

27. (a) F = 170 2/3, D = 576,
        A = 864, E = 1296, B = 1944
    (b) D = 288, E = 324, F = 341
        1/3, G = 384, A = 432, B = 486
    (c) 1.125 = 9/8
    (d) 1.333 = 4/3

28. Ferne - 39
    Donna - 21
    Susan - 12

29. 54 feet

30. 31 eggs

31. No. Consider the following:
    Joleen bats 1 for 10 and Maureen
    bats 0 for 1. Then Joleen bats 1
    for 1 and Maureen bats 1 for 2. At
    the end of the season, Joleen's
    average is 1/11 and Maureen's is
    1/3.

32. 4, 7, 28, $3n - 2$

33. 9:4

Analyzing Student Thinking

34. Carlos, consider the following
    diagram that represents 3 parts oil
    (shaded) to 4 parts vinegar. Oil
    makes up 3/7 of the bottle of
    salad dressing, not 75%.

35. Scott, a ratio of 5:4 means there
    will be 5 boys for every 4 girls in
    your class. So, there might be 5
    boys and 4 girls, but there also

could be 10 boys and 8 girls, or 15
boys and 12 girls.

36. Yes, Ashlee is correct, provided
    $c \neq 0$. We can use cross-
    multiplication to show this. If
    $\dfrac{a}{b} = \dfrac{c}{d}$, then $ad = bc$. And, if $ad =$
    bc, then $\dfrac{a}{c} = \dfrac{b}{d}$.

37. No; if 0.25 cm. = 12 miles, then
    100 cm. = 4800 miles, not 48
    miles.

38. Micala does not understand that,
    to have the same flavor, she needs
    to keep the same ratio of OJ to
    water. Using 2 cans of OJ would
    require 6 cans of water, since 1:3
    = 2:6.

39. Sabrina is incorrect; if 60% of the
    class is girls, then 40% is boys
    and that is a ratio of 6:4 or 3:2.

40. The problem is mismatched units.
    The proportion needs to be
    $\dfrac{\text{feet}}{\text{feet}} = \dfrac{\text{feet}}{\text{feet}}$ or $\dfrac{\text{inches}}{\text{inches}} = \dfrac{\text{feet}}{\text{feet}}$ or
    $\dfrac{\text{feet}}{\text{inches}} = \dfrac{\text{feet}}{\text{inches}}$. This latter
    proportion yields $\dfrac{4}{15} = \dfrac{\text{tree}}{144}$, or the
    height of the tree is 38.4 feet.

**Problems Related to the NCTM
Standards and Curriculum Focal Points**

1. The student is looking at the
   problem additively instead of
   multiplicatively. He thinks that
   because there are 2 more cans of
   OJ, then there should be 2 more
   cans of water. However, in order to
   be proportional, he needs to see
   that there are 3 times as many
   cans of OJ so there needs to be 3
   times as many cans of water.

2. In Problem Set B #13 and #14,
   rates are used. In #13, the rate is
   kilometers per minute or

kilometers per hour and in #14 the rate is gallons per week or gallons per year. Answers may vary.

3. When mixing orange juice, there are typically 3 cans of water for each can of orange juice so the scale is 3. If 4 cans of OJ are used, then the scale of 3 will help determine that $3 \times 4 = 12$ cans of water are needed. Answers may vary.

Section 7.4

1. (a) 44%, .44, 11/25
    (b) 97%, .97, 97/100
    (c) 124%, 1.24, $1\frac{6}{25}$

2. $\frac{6666}{10000}$, 0.6666; $\frac{3}{1000}$, 0.3%;

    0.025, 2.5%; $\frac{1}{20}$, 5%; $\frac{160}{100}$, 0.016;

    0.01, 1%; $\frac{1}{100000}$, 0.001%;

    $\frac{17}{200000}$, 0.000085

3. (a) 400, 350, 25%, 250
    (b) $1.00, $15.00, $40.00
    (c) 0.06, 0.36, 0.03, 0.45

4. (a) 98   (b) 61   (c) 50%
    (d) 1462   (e) 125%   (f) 142
    (g) 500   (h) 0.1%   (i) 350

5. (a) 1.6   (b) 10   (c) 30
    (d) 150   (e) 6   (f) 44
    (g) 7.5   (h) 360

6. (a) 90
    (b) 11
    (c) $3/4 \times 320 = 240$
    (d) $1/3 \times 210 = 70$
    (e) $2/5 \times 250 = 100$
    (f) $1/8 \times 400 = 50$
    (g) $2/3 \times 660 = 440$
    (h) $1/5 \times 120 = 24$

7. (a) $1/5 \times 35 = 7$

    (b) $2/5 \times 60 = 24$
    (c) $1/4 \times 60 = 15$
    (d) $200\% \times 85 = 170$
    (e) $15\% \times 42 = 6.3$
    (f) $10\% \times 430 = 43$
    (g) $1/2 \times 26 = 13$
    (h) $2/5 \times 150 = 60$

8. (a) $1.65   (b) $2.25
    (c) $5.25   (d) $3.60

9. (a) What percent of 95 is 67?
    (b) 18.4 is 112% of what number?
    (c) What is $16\frac{2}{3}\%$ of $3\frac{1}{2}$?
    (d) 2.8 is what percent of 0.46?
    (e) 0.05% of what number is 4200?
    NOTE: Other answers are possible.

10. (a) 370.8   (b) 41.0%
    (c) 216.7%   (d) 350
    (e) 2400   (f) 75.6%

11. (a) 4400   (b) 22%
    (c) 1250   (d) 125
    (e) 650%

12. (a) 30.6   (b) 90.72
    (c) 190   (d) 62.5
    (e) $101.70   (f) $105.60

13. (a) $194.05   (b) $111.48
    (c) $1011.88   (d) $312.88

14. 68.75%
    Enter 80 as the whole and 55 as the part.

15. $12.91
    Guess and Test. By entering a value for the Whole and 70 for the Percent, we can add the Part and the Whole searching for a sum of $21.95. The best guess on the eManipulative is $12.90.

16. 66%

17. $11\frac{2}{3}\%$

18. $349.50

19. Rent, Utilities $2320, Tuition $2100, Food $1520, Other $660, Transportation $640, Clothes, Health $400, Books, Supplies $360

20. 36.1%

21. 150 games

22. (a) About 71%
    (b) About 99.6%

23. $1600

24. $7.80 to $12.00

25. (a) 12.1%   (b) 18.4%
    (c) No, gas consumption increased at a higher rate as the number of less efficient SUV's on the road increased.

26. $795

27. Both

28. (a) (i) $237.22   (ii) $799.56
    (iii) $187.74
    (b) $4505

29. 750%

30. 4% less

31. 49%

32. (a) $4515   (b) $174,418.61
    (c) $78,070.18
    (d) 202,272.73 pounds

33. At least 12 passes

34. They are equal.

35. 1 pencil, 9 erasers, 90 paper clips

36. Use Guess and Test; Tom = 7 and Carol = 13

37. 3. Cut open all of the links of one chain and use them to link the remaining chains together.

38. 1111

39. 20. Yes. $n \rightarrow n + 20 \rightarrow 10(n+20) \rightarrow 2(n+20) \rightarrow n + 20 \rightarrow 20$

40. $133,156.49

41. (a) Investment (2) - at 6.1% compounded annually.
    (b) He must invest $3553.28 at the rate in (a).

42. (a) Net loss $5.50
    (b) Net loss $2.00
    (c) Strategy b

43. 15%

44. 45

Analyzing Student Thinking

45. That's incorrect, Martina. Notice that $\frac{60}{40}$($27.88)=$41.82. Since you can't save more than the original price of the shirt, you have made an error.

46. No; 7/50 and 13/25 are easy, too, since 50 and 25 are divisors of 100:

    $7/50 = (7 \cdot 2)/(50 \cdot 2) = 14/100 = 14\%$
    $13/25 = (13 \cdot 4)/(25 \cdot 4) = 52/100 = 52\%$

47. Yes, because Bertrand set up a proportion of the form:

    $$\frac{percent}{100} = \frac{part}{whole}.$$

48. No; the student simply computed the amount of savings, a dollar amount, $199 − 159.20 = $39.80. To determine the percent saved, he could solve the following proportion:

    $$\frac{percent}{100} = \frac{part}{whole}$$
    $$\frac{x}{100} = \frac{39.80}{199}$$

49. No. The amount of money at the end of the first year is $1000 ×

1.03 (that's 100% + 3% of $1000). Since the money is invested for 10 years, the total amount of money in the account with compound interest will be $1000 × (1.03)^{10} = $1343.92.

50. No, since the selling price of the car after a 20% mark-up would be: $17,888 × 1.20 = $21,465.60, but marking this down 20% would give a selling price of: $21465.60 ×0 .80 = $17,172.48, which is less than the dealer paid for the car.

51. Jerry took 35% of the sale price, rather than of the original price. Since you don't know the original price, you need to remember that if you saved 35% off the original price, you paid 65% of the original price. You can find the original price by dividing the sale price by 0.65. The original price was $210.77.

Problems Related to the NCTM Standards and Curriculum Focal Points

1. If you answered 27 out of 40 questions correct on a test and wanted to find the percent correct, a proportion could be set up as follows:

$$\frac{27}{40} = \frac{x}{100}$$

Solving this proportion would yield 67.5%. Answers may vary.

2. Some possible commonly used fractions, decimals and percents are:

$$\frac{1}{2} = 0.5 = 50\%$$

$$\frac{3}{4} = 0.75 = 75\%$$

$$\frac{3}{8} = 0.375 = 37.5\%$$

$$\frac{4}{5} = 0.8 = 80\%$$

3. It means that regardless of what is given in a problem – fraction, decimal or percent – a student could use it or convert it to the most convenient form for solving the problem.

Chapter 8

Section 8.1

1. 556 is the only integer; 3/4 and 556 are positive and -252/5 is negative.

2. (a) 1   (b) - 4   (c) 5   (d) - 3

3. (a) RRR

-3   0

(b) BBBBBB

0   6

4. (a) $-a$ (b) b
   (c) $-(a + b)$ (d) $b - a$

5. (a) {-1, -2, -3, -4,...}
   (b) {1, 2, 3, 4,...}   (c) W

6. (a) BBBBRRRRRRR = -3

-3   0   4

(b) RRR RRRRR = -8

-8   0

7. (a) 14 + (-6) = (8 + 6) + (-6) =
   8 + [6 + (-6)] = 8 + 0 = 8
   (b) 21 + (-41) = 21 + [(-21) + (-20)]
   = [21 + (-21)] + (-20) = 0 + -20
   = -20

8. 17. Top: 42; Second: 16 26;
   Middle: -6 22 4

9. Only (d) is true.

10. (a) Associative Property for Integer Addition
    (b) Additive Identity

11. (a) 3117   (b) 33

12. (a) -7   (b) -13

(c) 9   (d) -3

13. (a) Start with RRR and add 3 zero pairs to obtain BBBRRR RRR. Take away 6 reds to get BBBR̶R̶R̶R̶R̶R̶ = 3
    (b) Start with 0 and add 4 zero pairs to obtain BBBBRRRR. Take away 4 red to get BBBBR̶R̶R̶R̶ = 4

14. (a) -14   (b) 52
    (c) 14   (d) 6

15. (a) -231   (b) -56
    (c) 986   (d) -555

16. (a) opposite of negative five
    (b) Ten minus the opposite of negative two
    (c) opposite of p

17. (a) 3   (b) 7   (c) $-x$
    (d) $-x$ (e) x (f) x

18. (a) Gained 9 yards
    (b) Loss of 2 points
    (c) Gained $200

19. (b)

20. Philadelphia: 28   Cheyenne: 44
    Bismarck: 11

21. The result $-a$ represents "the opposite of a". Thus, when a is negative, $-a$ is positive.

22. 98 -28

23. (a) -8, 3   (b)   -7, 4
    (c) 0, 8

24. Top: 9; Third 25 -15 14;
    Bottom: 33 -8 -7 21

25. (a) (i) 1 2 3 4 ...
    (ii) 1 2 3 4 . . .
         -1 -2 -3 -4. . .
         0 1 2 3 . . .
    (iii) . . . 6 4 2 0 1 3 5 . . .
    . . . -3 -2 -1 0 1 2 3 . . .

(b) These sets have same number of elements

26.

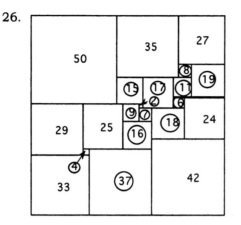

27. Most people recognize that the word "unique" means "one of a kind." But in the phrase *"there is a unique integer"* there is also a guarantee that every integer has an additive inverse. So the phrase means that every integer has "at least one and at most one" additive inverse.

Analyzing Student Thinking

28. Yes, Jarell, theoretically we could continue indefinitely to create new representations for any integer. For instance, take a pair of one red and one black chip from a (theoretically) infinite pile of chips and add these to any collection of chips representing the integer to obtain a new representation of the integer.

29. No, Brandi is incorrect; integer addition has one property that whole-number addition does not: the Additive Inverse Property.

30. If the student subtracts the numbers as they stand, the problem will become 4 - (-6) which equals 10. This is incorrect. What was intended (but not said) was that one should find the difference between the two numbers, neglecting the minus

sign. Thus, 6 - 4 = 2, so the answer is -2.

31. Chandler, your answer is correct; now please explain why.

32. No; for example, 1 + (-2) = -1, a negative number.

33. The symbol $-n$ means "the opposite of n." So, the sign of $-n$ depends on the sign of n. If n is positive, say 5, its opposite is $-n = -(5) = -5$, a negative number. But, if n is negative, say -5, then its opposite is $-n = -(-5) = 5$, a positive number. And, if $n = 0$, then $-n = -(0) = 0$, which is neither a positive nor a negative number.

34. Yes. Each pair of one red and one black chip represents a zero and, since the integer is negative, there must be some red chips that are not paired with a black chip.

Problems Related to the NCTM Standards and Curriculum Focal Points

1. Problem 1: At 10:00 pm the temperature was 7 degrees and it dropped 15 degrees overnight. What is the new temperature in the morning?
Problem 2: Reno gained 17 yards on his first run of the football game and lost 5 yards on his second run of the game. How many yards did he gain in his first two carries?
Answers may vary.

2. Rule: When adding numbers with the same sign, the absolute values of the numbers can be added and the common sign will the sign of the sum.
Context: In the context of temperature change, if the temperature decreases twice, you know that the total change will have to be a decrease so the sum of two negative numbers has to be negative.

Section 8.2

1. (a)

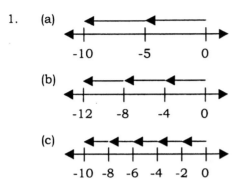

    (b)

    (c)

2. (a) $-5 \times (-1) = 5$ $-5 \times (-2) = 10$
    $5 \times (-3) = 15$
    (b) $-8 \times (-1) = 8$ $-8 \times (-2) = 16$
    $-8 \times (-3) = 24$
    Negative times negative equals positive

3. (a) -30   (b) 420
    (c) -230   (d) 0

4. (a) B̶B̶B̶B̶   B̶B̶B̶B̶   B̶B̶B̶B̶
    RRRR   RRRR   RRRR = -12
    (b) RRRR RRRR = -8
    (c) BB R̶R̶ = 2

5. Distributivity, additive inverse, multiplication by 0

6. (a) $-6x - 12$ (b) $-5x + 55$
    (c) $-3x + 3y$ (d) $xa - xb$
    (e) $-xa + xb$ (f) $x^2 - x - 6$

7. (a) -1872   (b) 8134
    (c) 224,409   (d) -243,984

8. (a) -34   (b) 907

9. (a) 0   (b) 4   (c) 36

10. (a) -31   (b) 123
    (c) -58   (d) -1

11. No

12. (a) Negative   (b) Positive
    (c) Negative   (d) Positive
    (e) Positive   (f) Negative
    (g) Positive   (h) Negative

13. Always positive: c, d, e
    Always negative: f

14. (a) $\dfrac{1}{16}$ (b) $\dfrac{1}{32}$ (c) $\dfrac{1}{343}$

15. (a) $\dfrac{1}{729}$ (b) $\dfrac{1}{729}$ (c) 15,625
    (d) Yes

16. (a) $\dfrac{1}{512}$ (b) $\dfrac{1}{512}$ (c) $\dfrac{1}{50625}$
    (d) Yes

17. (a) 5^5 (b) 3^{16}
    (c) 4^5 or 2^{10} (d) $\dfrac{1}{6^4}$

18. (a) 0.000009
    (b) 0.000000000000126

19. (a) 6.91×10^{-7}
    (b) 3.048×10^{-13}
    (c) 8.071×10^{-20}

20. (a) 2.6936×10^{-20}
    (b) 4.4×10^{23}
    (c) 3.93×10^{-20}
    (d) 5.4×10^{-14}
    (e) 2.046×10^{-9}
    (f) 1.6×10^{-9}

21. (a) $-7 + 4 = -3$ (b) $-6 + 11 = 5$
    (c) $-23 + 6 = -17$

22. (a) <   (b) >   (c) >
    (d) >   (e) >   (f) >
    (g) =   (h) <

23. (a) <   (b) <

24. Second row: 8, 18
    Third row: -2
    Bottom row: 2, -2, -9
    Also,
    Second row: -8, -18
    Third row: 2
    Bottom row: -2, 2, -9

25. (a) -3, -2, and -1   (b) No
    (c) -3

26. (a) No, no, yes (-1), no
     (b) Yes (0), no, no, yes (1)

27. (a) $pq = -|p||q|$
     (b) $pq = |p||q|$

28. (a) $p/q = -|p|/|q|$
     (b) $p/q = |p|/|q|$

29. No; $-3 < -2$, but $(-3)^2 > (-2)^2$.

30. Yes; $x < y$ means $y = x + p$ for
     some $p > 0$, $z - y = z - (x + p) =$
     $z - x - p$. Therefore, $z - y + p =$
     $z - x$ which means $z - y < z - x$.

31. 8.38×10^{-26} grams

32. 6.508×10^{-7} meter

33. (a) 1.1×10^{-22} kilograms
     (b) Approximately 1.62×10^{-27}
         kilograms.

34. (a) 2.31×10^6 corpuscles
     (b) About 1.08×10^7 seconds or
         125 days.

35. True. From problem 23 in part A,
     squares must be a multiple of 3 or
     one more than a multiple of 3. If
     neither x nor y is a multiple of 3,
     then $x^2 + y^2 = (3m + 1) +$
     $(3n + 1) = 3(m + n) + 2 = z^2$. But
     z^2 must be of the form $3r$ or $3r +$
     1. Thus, one of x or y must be a
     multiple of 3.

36. 1806

37. If $(a - b)c = 0$, then $a - b = 0$ or $c =$
     0. Because c was assumed to be
     nonzero, $a - b = 0$, or $a = b$.

Analyzing Student Thinking

38. Olga, the number $-xyz$ is not
     necessarily negative; this number
     has the opposite sign of the
     number xyz.

39. In general, this equation is false.
     If we multiply $(a + b)(a + b)$ using
     the distributive property, we get
     the answer $a^2 + 2ab + b^2$. So the
     problem becomes "When does
     $a^2 + b^2 = a^2 + 2ab + b^2$?" That
     reduces to "When does $2ab = 0$?"
     The Zero Divisors Property tells us
     that this is true when $a = 0$ or $b =$
     0. So the conclusion is that the
     equation is rarely, but sometimes,
     true.

40. No; $-a + -b = a/b$, and the sign of
     a/b can be positive, negative, or
     neither, depending on the signs of
     a and b.

41. Yes; $-a + -b = \dfrac{-a}{-b} = \dfrac{(-1)a}{(-1)b} = \dfrac{a}{b}$.

42. No; multiplying by 10^{-7} would
     move the decimal point in 3.47
     seven places to the left. Thus,
     there should only be six zeros
     between the decimal point and the
     3 since .000000347 has the
     decimal point seven places to the
     left of 3.47.

43. Ask Tonya if she knows how to
     check her answer. Once she
     checks and sees that she is
     incorrect, remind her that the rule
     she is trying to apply to this
     problem states that "when you
     multiply or divide both sides of an
     inequality by a negative, reverse
     the inequality." But she was
     dividing both sides by 7, a
     positive, so the inequality remains
     unchanged.

44. Joe's calculator squared 7, then
     gave the opposite of that number,
     -49—this is the order of operations
     indicated by -7^2. Misha's
     calculator squared the opposite of
     7, or $(-7)^2$.

**Problems Related to the NCTM
Standards and Curriculum Focal Points**

1. Rule: A positive number multiplied
    by a negative number is a negative
    number.
    Context: For 5 consecutive hours,
    the temperature changes by -3
    degrees each hour. What is the
    total temperature change after the
    5 hours? It can be seen that this is
    just 5 groups of -3 degrees which
    would be -15. Answers may vary.

2. When writing very large numbers,
    positive powers of 10 can be used
    instead of writing many zeros.
    Similarly very small numbers can
    be represented using negative
    powers of 10 because they are the
    same as $\dfrac{1}{10}$ to positive powers.
    Thus a number like
    0.0000000057, which is
    $\dfrac{57}{10,000,000,000}$, can be rewritten
    as 5.7×10^{-9}. Answers may vary.

3. Using integers to compare
    temperatures is common. For
    example, which is colder -5 or -7
    degrees? Similarly, which is
    warmer -4 or 2 degrees? Answers
    may vary.

Chapter 9

Section 9.1

1. (a) 7 and -3 are integers

    (b) $7\frac{1}{8} = \frac{57}{8}$ and 57 and 8 are integers.

    (c) $-3 = \frac{-3}{1}$; -3 and 1 are integers.

2. (a) *I* and *Q*   (b) *F* and *Q*

3. -5/-6, - (-5/6), - (5/-6)

4. (a) True   (b) False

5. (a) -2/3   (b) 5/7
   (c) -4/9   (d) -8/9

6. (a) -1/2   (b) -41/36
   (c) -2/3   (d) 1/24

7. (a) 17/23   (b) 6/29

8. (a) 2/7   (b) 5/16

9. (a) -164/837   (b) -243/245

10. (a) *F, I, N, Q*   (b) *I* and *Q*

11. (a) Identity property of rational number addition

    (b) Additive inverse property of rational number addition

12. (a) 2/3   (b) -33/28
    (c) 29/36   (d) -1/12

13. (a) -19/528   (b) 79/60

14. (a) None   (b) *I* and *Q*

15. (a) -2/7   (b) -1
    (c) 3/2   (d) -1/3

16. (a) 8/5   (b) 0
    (c) 5/6   (d) -23/27

17. (a) 1139/826   (b) 25/72

18. (a) *F* and *Q*   (b) *F, I, N, Q*

19. (a) Associative property of rational number multiplication

    (b) Commutative property of rational number addition

20. (a) (i) $(-43)^2(-36)^3 =$ $(1849)(-46,656) =$ $-86,266,944$

    (ii) $(43)^2(36)^3 =$ $(1849)(46,656) =$ $86,266,944$. The final answer is negative since (neg.)$^{\text{even power}}$ (neg.)$^{\text{odd power}}$ = (pos.)(neg.) = neg.

    (b) (i) $\left(-\frac{18}{25}\right)\left(\frac{-45}{-91}\right)\left(\frac{28}{-81}\right) =$ $\left(-\frac{-810}{-2275}\right)\left(\frac{28}{-81}\right) =$ $\left(-\frac{-22680}{184275}\right) = \left(\frac{22680}{184275}\right)$

    (ii) $\left(\frac{18}{25}\right)\left(\frac{45}{91}\right)\left(\frac{28}{81}\right) =$ $\left(\frac{810}{2275}\right)\left(\frac{28}{81}\right) = \left(\frac{22680}{184275}\right)$. The final answer is positive since (neg.)(pos.)(neg.) = (neg.)(neg.) = pos.

21. (a) -4   (b) -3/5
    (c) 8/9   (d) 2/3

22. (a) -1207/627   (b) 9/5

23. (a) (i) $\frac{(-1111)(-23)(49)}{-77} =$ $\frac{(25553)(49)}{-77} =$ $\frac{1252097}{-77} = -16261$

    (ii) $\frac{(1111)(23)(49)}{77} =$ $\frac{(25553)(49)}{77} =$ $\frac{1252097}{77} = 16261$

    The final answer is negative since

$$\frac{(neg.)(neg.)(pos.)}{neg.} =$$

$$\frac{(pos.)(pos.)}{neg.} =$$

$$\frac{pos.}{neg.} = neg.$$

(b) (i) $$\frac{(-35)(-91)}{(-36)(-24)} \div \left(\frac{49}{-144}\right) =$$

$$\frac{3185}{-864} \div \left(\frac{49}{-144}\right) =$$

$$\frac{3185}{-864} \times \frac{-144}{49} =$$

$$\frac{-458640}{-42336} = \frac{458640}{42336}$$

(ii) $$\frac{(35)(91)}{(36)(24)} \div \left(\frac{49}{144}\right) =$$

$$\frac{3185}{864} \div \left(\frac{49}{144}\right) =$$

$$\frac{3185}{864} \times \frac{144}{49} = \frac{458640}{42336}$$

The final answer is negative since

$$\frac{(neg.)(neg.)}{(neg.)(neg)} \div \left(\frac{pos.}{neg.}\right) =$$

$$\frac{(pos.)}{(pos.)} \div (neg.) =$$

$$(pos.) \div (neg.) = neg.$$

24. (a) >   (b) <
    (c) =   (d) <

25. (a) $$\frac{475}{652} < \frac{-308}{-421}$$

    (b) $$\frac{372}{487} < \frac{-261}{319}$$

26. (a) Property of Less Than and Addition
    (b) Property of Greater Than and Multiplication by a Negative

27. (a) $x < -18/35$ (b) $x > -43/35$

28. (a) $x < -5/2$ (b) $x < -35/16$

29. (a) $x > 5/2$ (b) $x < -56/15$

30. (a) $-113/217 < -163/314$, $-92/177$
    (b) $-545/522 < -812/779$, $-1357/1301$

31. There are many possible solutions
    (a) For example, $-11/9$, $-16/13$, and $-21/17$.
    (b) For example, $-2/21$, $-3/31$, and $-3/32$.

32. (a) $a/b + c/d = (ad + bc)/bd$

      (definition of addition) = $(bc + ad)/bd$ (commutativity of integer addition) = $bc/bd + ad/bd$ (definition of addition with a common denominator) = $c/d + a/b$ (simplification)
    (b) An argument similar to part (a)

33. (a) holds.
    (b) $3 - 1 \neq 1 - 3$
    (c) $(4 - 2) - 1 \neq 4 - (2 - 1)$
    (d) $a - 0 = a$, but $0 - a \neq a$.
    (e) There is no inverse since there is no identity.

34. Add $-a/b$ to both sides of the equation so that $0 = a/b + (-a/b)$. Thus, by definition, the opposite of $-a/b$ is a/b; in other words, $-(-a/b) = a/b$.

35. (a), (c), and (d) are true; (b) is false; $1/3 - 1/2 = -1/6$.

36. $(a/b)(c/d - e/f)$
    $= (a/b)[c/d + (-e/f)]$
    $= (a/b)(c/d) + (a/b)(-e/f)$
    $= (ac)/(bd) + (-ae)/(bf)$
    $= (ac)/(bd) - (ae)/(bf)$
    $= (a/b)(c/d) - (a/b)(e/f)$

37. For simplicity, assume that the denominators are positive. First get common denominators. Then $adf/bdf < cbf/bdf$ and $cbf/bdf < ebd/bdf$. Thus $adf < cdf$ and $cbf < ebd$. Therefore, $adf/bdf < ebd/bdf$, or $a/b < e/f$.

38. (a) $ad < bc$ and $ef > 0$. By

Properties of Ordering Integers
$adef < bcef$ and thus
$a/b \times e/f < c/ \times e/f$ by the
Cross Multiplication Property
of Inequality.

(b) Similar argument

39. If $\dfrac{a}{b} < \dfrac{c}{d}$ then $\dfrac{ad}{bd} < \dfrac{bc}{bd}$ so
$ad < bc$. Thus, $ad + 1 \le bc$ and
$2ad + 2 \le 2bc$, so $2ad + 1 < 2bc$.
Hence
$$\frac{ad}{bd} = \frac{2ad}{2bd} < \frac{2ad+1}{2bd} < \frac{2bc}{2bd} = \frac{bc}{bd} \text{ So}$$
$\dfrac{e}{f} = \dfrac{2ad+1}{2bd}$ is one fraction that

satisfies $\dfrac{a}{b} < \dfrac{e}{f} < \dfrac{c}{d}$.

40. Let n be an odd number, the first
of the Pythagorean triple. Then n^2
is its square. Next, $(n^2 - 1)/2$ is
the second number and
$(n^2 - 1)/2 + 1$ is the third.
$n^2 + [(n^2 - 1)/2]^2 =$
$n^2 + (n^4 - 2n^2 + 1)/4 =$
$(n^4 + 2n^2 + 1)/4$ and
$[(n^2 - 1)/2 + 1]^2 = [(n^2 + 1)/2]^2 =$
$(n^4 + 2n^2 + 1)/4.$

41. The sum $\dfrac{3}{7} + \dfrac{2}{5}$ is $\dfrac{3 \times 5 + 7 \times 2}{7 \times 5}$, or

$\dfrac{29}{35}$, which has integers as its
numerator and denominator and a
nonzero denominator since both 7
and 5 are nonzero. Thus,
$\dfrac{29}{35}$ satisfies the definition of a
rational number.

Analyzing Student Thinking

42. Yes, Rock, fractions have the form
a/b, where a and b are whole
numbers. 2/3 fits this definition,
but -2/3 does not since -2 is not a
whole number. However, -2/3
does fit the definition of a rational

number: a number of the form
a/b, where a and b are integers.

43. Yes, Maria, 10/3 is the simplest
form of the rational number. Karl
is also correct, and he wrote his
answer as a mixed number, where
the fractional part is in simplest
form.

44. Cody is incorrect. Rational-
number addition has one property
that fraction addition does not: the
Additive Inverse Property.

45. Kelsey, let's write a fraction that is
equivalent to -3/-4 =
(-1)(3)/(-1)(4) = 3/4; this is a
positive number. The quotient of
two negative numbers is positive.

46. Yes. First, Pierce found a
common denominator. To
subtract two fractions with like
denominators, just subtract their
numerators: -45 – (-24) = -45 + 24
= -21. His answer of -21/216 is
correct, though not in simplest
form since the denominator he
used, 216, is not the least possible
common denominator, which is
72.

47. Marina is incorrect. It looks like
she made a mistake in applying
the distributive property. To apply
this property, she'd need to do the
following:
2/5 × 1/7 – 2/5 × 3/7 =
2/5 × (1/7 – 3/7) =
2/5 × (-2/7) = -4/35.

48. Yes, Duncan is correct, $a/b + c/d$
is equal to $(a + c)/(b + d)$. This
method worked fine for computing
the quotient of these two fractions
since (-2) is a divisor of 12 and 7 is
a divisor of 35. However, for
instance, , the following
computation is not as simply done
using Duncan's method:
2/3 + 3/4. The standard invert-
and-multiply algorithm simplifies
the problem.

Problems Related to the NCTM Standards and Curriculum Focal Points

1. With rational numbers you can take the properties of addition and multiplication of integers and combine them with the properties of addition of fractions to add negative and positive non-integer rational numbers. For example,

$$\frac{-3}{4}+\frac{2}{3}=\frac{-3\cdot 3}{4\cdot 3}+\frac{2\cdot 4}{3\cdot 4}$$ applies the

concept of finding a common denominator with fractions and

$$\frac{-3\cdot 3}{4\cdot 3}+\frac{2\cdot 4}{3\cdot 4}=\frac{-9+8}{12}=\frac{-1}{12}$$ applies

the properties of integer multiplication and addition to find the sum. Answers may vary.

2. Example 1: The problem

$$-6\left(\frac{2}{3}+\frac{5}{6}\right)=-4+-5=-9$$ applies the

distributive property to eliminate the fractions before adding.
Example 2: The problem

$$\frac{2}{5}+\left(-5+\frac{-2}{5}\right)=\left(\frac{2}{5}+\frac{-2}{5}\right)+-5=-5$$

applies the commutative and associative properties to add compatible numbers first and simplify the problem. Answers may vary.

3. "Develop algorithms" means to use your understanding of the meaning of the operations and the properties of the numbers to develop strategies for doing algorithms that make sense and are efficient for each student. Answers may vary.

Section 9.2

1. (a) Rational (b) Irrational
    (c) Rational (d) Irrational
    (e) Rational (f) Irrational
    (g) Rational (h) Irrational

2. The number 1.414 is a rational number approximately equal to $\sqrt{2}$.

3. (a) $\sqrt{10}$ (b) $\sqrt{13}$
    (c) $\sqrt{18}=3\sqrt{2}$

4. (a) $\sqrt{8}=2\sqrt{2}$
    (b) $\sqrt{9}=3$
    (c)

5. (a) $x=\sqrt{13}$, $y=\sqrt{8}=2$
    (b) $a=\sqrt{20}=2\sqrt{5}$,
        $b=\sqrt{24}=2\sqrt{6}$,
        $c=\sqrt{33}$

6. (a) $2\sqrt{10}$ (b) $4\sqrt{5}$
    (c) $6\sqrt{5}$

7. (a) 56 (b) 71

8. (a) $4\sqrt{3}-\sqrt{3}=(4-1)\sqrt{3}=3\sqrt{3}$
        Distributive Property

    (b) $5\sqrt{7}+\left(\sqrt{35}+7\sqrt{7}\right)=$
        $5\sqrt{7}+\left(\sqrt{5}\sqrt{7}+7\sqrt{7}\right)=$
        $\left(12+\sqrt{5}\right)\sqrt{7}$

        Distributive Property

    (c) $\sqrt{32}+\sqrt{50}=$
        $4\sqrt{2}+5\sqrt{2}=9\sqrt{2}$
        Distributive Property

9. (a) 6 (b) 9 (c) $12\sqrt{5}$
    (d) $-4\sqrt{2}$ (e) $7\sqrt{2}$ (f) $4\sqrt{5}$

10. (a) 5 (b) 4

(c) $7/2$ (d) $3/5$

11. $0.\overline{876} < 0.8766876667... <$
$0.\overline{8766} < 0.87\overline{6} <$
$0.876787667788... <$
$0.876787677876... < 0.87\overline{6}$

12. For example,
$0.577757777577777...$.

13. $\sqrt{5}$, $\sqrt{6}$, $\sqrt{7}$, $2.373373337...$ for example.

14. (a) $2.2^2 < 5 < 2.3^2$
$2.23^2 < 5 < 2.24^2$
$2.236^2 < 5 < 2.237^2$
$\sqrt{5} \approx 2.24$

(b) $4.3^2 < 19.1 < 4.4^2$
$4.37^2 < 19.1 < 4.38^2$
$4.370^2 < 19.1 < 4.371^2$
$\sqrt{19.1} \approx 4.37$

(c) $0.2^2 < 0.05 < 0.3^2$
$0.22^2 < 0.05 < 0.23^2$
$0.223^2 < 0.05 < 0.234^2$
$\sqrt{0.05} \approx 0.22$

(d) Because 0.05 and 5 differ by a factor of 100, $\sqrt{0.05}$ and $\sqrt{5}$ differ by a factor of 10.

15. $r_1 = 5$
$s_1 = 24 \div 5 = 4.8$
$r_2 = \dfrac{r_1 + s_1}{2} = 4.9$
$s_2 = 24 \div 4.9 \approx 4.8979591$
$r_3 \approx 4.8989795$
$s_3 \approx 4.8989794$
$r_3 - s_3 = 0.00000001$
so $\sqrt{24} \approx 4.898979$

16. No.

17. (a) $0.5041 < 0.71$
(b) $0.9604 < 0.98$
The squares of numbers between 0 and 1 are smaller than the number.

18. (a) 6   (b) 27   (c) 9
(d) -8   (e) 27   (f) 729

19. (a) -2   (b) -6
(c) Does not exist

20. (a) 1.5874 (rounded)
(b) 2.1746 (rounded)
(c) 344.061 (rounded)
(d) 6.36 (rounded)

21. (a) $\sqrt[5]{7^2}$ (b) π to the $\sqrt{2}$ power

22. (a)

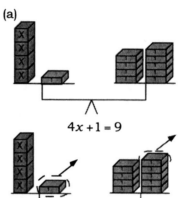

$$4x + 1 = 9$$

$$4x + 1 - 1 = 9 - 1$$

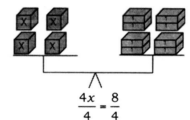

$$\frac{4x}{4} = \frac{8}{4}$$
$$x = 2$$

(b)

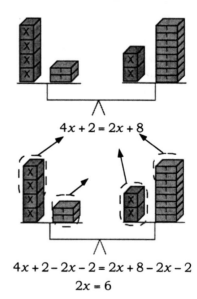

$$4x + 2 = 2x + 8$$

$$4x + 2 - 2x - 2 = 2x + 8 - 2x - 2$$
$$2x = 6$$

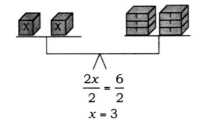

$$\frac{2x}{2} = \frac{6}{2}$$

$$x = 3$$

23. (a) $-4\sqrt{6}$ (b) $9\sqrt{3} + \sqrt{2}$
     (c) $\sqrt{3}$ (d) $-5/\pi$

24. (a) $x = -14$ (b) $x = 1/12$
     (c) $x = 13/3$ (d) $x = 3$
     (e) $x = 5$ (f) $x = 12$

25. (a) $x > 9/6 = 1.5$ (b) $x \geq -7/2$
     (c) $x \leq 4$ (d) $x < 5$

26. True. Reason, by analogy, from the proof that $\sqrt{2}$ is irrational.

27. Let $\sqrt{6} = a/b$. Then $6b^2 = a^2$ or $2 \times 3 \times b^2 = a^2$. If we consider the number of times the prime factor 2 occurs on both sides we arrive at a contradiction.

28. Assume it is rational. Simplify and then count factors of q on both sides.

29. Let $\sqrt[n]{2} = a/b$. Then $2b^n = a^n$. The prime factor 2 occurs a multiple of n times on the right, but 1 more than a multiple of n times on the left. This is a contradiction of the Fundamental Theorem of Arithmetic

30. (a) Irrational. If $\sqrt[3]{p} = a/b$, the $b^3 \cdot p = a^3$ for integers a and b. But a^3 has a multiple of 3 factors of p whereas b^3p has one more than a multiple of 3 factors of p. This is contridiction since they are equal.
     (b) Irrational. Justification is similar to that in (a).

31. (a) (i) Irrational. Proof: If $r + p$ is rational, say $r + p = t$ for some rational number t. Then $p = t - r$, which states that p is rational because $t - r$ is the difference of two rationals. A contradiction.
         (ii) Rational if $r = 0$. Irrational otherwise.
         (iii) Rational. $(\sqrt{2} + (-\sqrt{2}) = 0)$ or irrational $(\sqrt{2} + \sqrt{2} = 2\sqrt{2})$.
         (iv) Rational $(\sqrt{2} \times \sqrt{2} = 2)$ or irrational $(\sqrt{2} \times \sqrt{3} = \sqrt{6})$.
     (b) In (ii), $r = 0$ yields a rational number.

32. (a) 0.10110111...+ 0.20220222... = 0.30330333...
     (b) 0.10110111...+ 0.01001000... = 0.11111111...
     (c) $\sqrt{2} \times \sqrt{3} = \sqrt{6}$
     (d) $\sqrt{2} \times \sqrt{2} = 2$

33. (a) No   (b) No
     (c) No   (d) No

34. (a) They are equal.
     (b) $a + (1 - a)$ are the two numbers. Show that $a^2 + (1 - a) = (1 - a)^2 + a$.

35. (a) C = 261.63, C# = 277.19, D = 293.67, D# = 311.13, E = 329.63, F = 349.23, F# = 370.00, G = 392.00, B = 493.88, C = 523.25
     (b) Ratio is within 0.002 of 1.5
     (c) Within 0.002

36. Build the school at town A.

37. The sums are always the same.

38. 3 and 1/3, or -3 and -1/3

39. $47, $33, $13, $1
     There are other possible answers; for example, $282, $198, $78, $6.

40. 33

Analyzing Student Thinking

41. Sadi, to say the set of rational numbers is closed under addition means that the sum of two numbers inside that set (two rational numbers) will have a sum inside that set (also a rational number). It says nothing about the sum of two numbers outside the set, namely two irrationals. The following example shows the sum of two irrationals may be rational: 0.121121112... + 0.212212221... = 0.33333333...=1/3.

42. One way to explain would be to use the method for changing repeating decimals to fractions, but Ramona might be convinced by other methods as well. For example, if she agrees that 0.3333333... is equal to 1/3, then ask what 3 times 0.3333333... would be, and what 3 times 1/3 would be.

43. Lars is partially correct. It's true that, since $(-3)^2 = 9$, -3 is one of the two square roots of 9.

    However, the symbol $\sqrt{9}$ indicates the principal, or positive, square root of 9, so this is 3. To indicate the negative square root of 9, or -3, we'd write $-\sqrt{9}$.

44. Ian, a negative exponent indicates that it is applied to the reciprocal of the base: $27^{-5/3} = (1/27)^{5/3}$. Since the base, 27, is positive, so is its reciprocal.

45. Show Fatima any non-repeating, non-terminating decimal, such as 0.34334333433334...

46. Zachery, the negative exponent indicates that it is applied to the reciprocal of the base, not the reciprocal of the exponent itself.

47. 3-4-5, 5-12-13, 7-24-25, and 8-15-17 are four such examples.

Problems Related to the NCTM Standards and Curriculum Focal Points

1. A balance scale is a common model to illustrate solving equations. It helps to emphasize the concept of maintaining equality in the equation.

2. A mathematical expression might be something like $2x$ or $\frac{2}{3}x - \sqrt{5}$ but an equation has an equal sign in it like $2x = \frac{2}{3}x - \sqrt{5}$.

3. If the square root of a positive number, x, is computed and then the result is squared, the original number, x, will be the final output. These are inverses because one function undoes the other.

Section 9.3

1. (a) {(a, t), (a, s), (i, t), (i, f), (i, s), (o, f), (o, s)}
   (b) {(a, b), (b, a), (a, c), (c, a), (b, c), (c, b)}
   (c) {(8, 7), (8, 5), (8, 4), (8, 3), (8, 2), (8, 1), (6, 7), (6, 5), (6, 4), (6, 3), (6, 2), (6, 1), (4, 7), (4, 5), (4, 3), (4, 2), (4, 1), (7, 1), (5, 1), (3, 1), (2, 1)}
   (d) {(3, 6), (3, 9), (3, 12), (3, 15), (6, 12)}

2. (a)

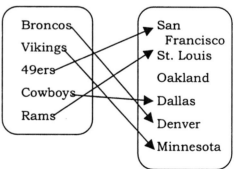

(b)
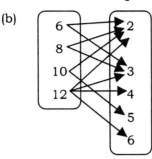

3. (a) "was the king of"
   (b) "is the square root of"

4. (a) transitive only
   (b) symmetric only
   (c) All. Equivalence relation.

5. (a) symmetric only
   (b) equivalence relation
   (c) reflexive only
   (d) symmetric only

6. (a) All. Equivalence relation.
      Every set in the partition has
      triangles of the same shape.
   (b) Reflexive and transitive
   (c) All. Equivalence relation. The
      partition contains 50 sets
      consisting of all people whose
      primary residence is in that
      state.

7. (a) Function.
   (b) Not a function. 1 has no
      image.
   (c) Not a function. 2 has two
      images.
   (d) Function.

8. (a) Function.
   (b) Not a function. Some cities
      have more than one zip code.
   (c) Function.
   (d) Not a function. Some pet
      owners have more than one
      pet.

9. (a) Not a function. Sue paired
      with both s and m.
   (b) Function.
   (c) Function.
   (d) Function.

(e) Not a function. 2 paired with
    both 1 and 3; 3 paired with
    both 1 and 3.

10. (a) (0, 4), (1, 6), (2, 12)
       Range: {4, 6, 12}
    (b) (7, 81), (2, 16), (1, 9)
       Range: {9, 16, 81}
    (c) (2, 1), (3, 5)
       Range: {1, 5}

11. (a) 1000   (b) 18
    (c) 5   (d) 3

12. (a) $f(x) = x + 3$ for $x \in \{1, 5, 8\}$
       {(1, 4) (5, 8) (8, 11)}

x	$f(x)$
1	4
5	8
8	11

    (b) $f(x) = \dfrac{1}{x}$ for $x \in \{\dfrac{1}{2}, 1, 3, 4\}$

    $\{(3, \dfrac{1}{3}), (4, \dfrac{1}{4}), (1, 1), (\dfrac{1}{2}, 2)\}$

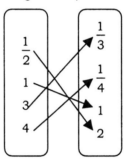

    (c) $f(x) = 3x$ for $x \in \{2, 4, 7\}$

n	$T(n)$
2	6
4	12
7	21

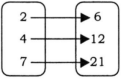

(d) {(2, 1) , (3, 4) , (4, 9) , (5, 16)}

x	f(x)
2	1
3	4
4	9
5	16

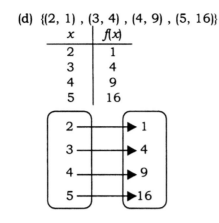

13. (a) {1, 7}, {1, 2, 3, 4, 6, 12}
     (b) (4, 2), (21, 19)
     (c) {7, 8, 9, 10, . . .},
          {951, 952, 953, . . .}
     (d) {3, 4, 5}, ∅

14. (a) 6, 11, 26, 10
     (b) One possibility:

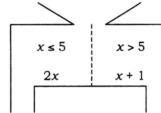

$x \le 5$ $x > 5$

$2x$ $x + 1$

15. (a) $40
     (b) $59.35
     (c) $260.95

16. f(0) = f(2) = -3
     f(-1) = f(3) = 0
     f(-2) = f(4) = 5
     Answers will vary. This is not
     consistent with the definition of a
     function because it is 2 *x*-values
     mapping to 1 *y*-value. It would
     not be a function if there were 1 *x*-
     value mapping to 2 *y*-values.

17. (a) Geometric, 10, $5(10^{199})$
     (b) Geometric, 2, $8(2^{199})$
     (c) Arithmetic, 11, 199(11) + 12 =
          2201
     (d) Neither.

18. 5112

19. 153

20. (a) 27; 125; 1331   (b) 4; 6; 14

21. (a) $1102.50; $1276.28; $1628.89
     (b) 15 years

22. (a) F(x) = 125(x + 10) + 295x
                = 420x + 1250
     (b) $6,080 The total cost of the
          fencing is $6,080 when the
          cost of fencing for the sides
          and back is $11.50 per foot.
     (c) $18.45 per foot for the sides
          and back, $28.45 per foot for
          the front.

23. (a) r = 3
     (b) 4, 12, 36, 108, 324, 972,
          2916

24. (a)

x	f(x)
1	12
2	19
3	26
4	33
5	40
6	47
7	54
8	61

     (b) Arithmetic, *a* = 12, *d* = 7
     (c) T(n) = 12 + (n - 1)7 = 7n + 5
     (d) T(25) = 180,
          T(200) = 1405
     (e) Domain: {1,2,3,4, . . . }
          Range: {12,19, 26, . . . }

25. (a)

Year	Increase in Population	Population of Mexico
1990	0	88,300,000
1991	2,207,500	90,507,500
1992	2,262,688	92,770,188
1993	2,319,255	95,089,443
1994	2,377,236	97,466,679
1995	2,436,667	99,903,346
1996	2,497,584	102,400,930
1997	2,560,023	104,960,953
1998	2,624,024	107,584,977
1999	2,689,624	110,274,601
2000	2,756,866	113,031,466
2001	2,825,787	115,857,253
2002	2,896,431	118,753,683

(b) Geometric, $r = 1.025$

(c) 113,031,465
127,884,728

(d) $P(n) = 88,300,000(1.025)^n$

26. 11

27. 6,210,001,000 is the only solution.

28. Two equations are equivalent if they have the same solution set. Let E_1 and E_2 represent two equations and E_1 be related to E_2 if they have the same solution set. Then this relation is an equivalence relation.

Analyzing Student Thinking

29. Alfonso is incorrect. Since there is no common ratio (a number, r, by which each successive term in the sequence is multiplied) it is not a geometric sequence. A geometric sequence has the form a, ar, ar^2, ar^3, ar^4,...

30. Iris, since the rate is 75 cents per quarter mile and m is the number of miles traveled, the number of quarter miles traveled is $4m$.

31. Luke is correct; a graph of the three points shows that they are not in a straight line.

32. One possibility is: 1, 3, 9, 27, ... This is a geometric sequence with a common ratio of 3. Another possibility is: 1, 3, 6, 10, ... We first add 2, then add 3, then add 4, and so on.
Infinitely many answers are possible.

33. Nicha is incorrect; a relation is defined to be a set of ordered pairs, and this example fits that definition. However, her reasoning justifies that this relation is not a *function*.

34. Arielle, consider the relation "less than" on the set of real numbers—this relation is not reflexive since a number is not less than itself. As another example, for the set $A = \{1, 2, 3\}$, the relation $\{(1, 2), (2, 2), (1, 3)\}$ is not reflexive since the ordered pair $(1, 1)$ is not an element of the relation.

35. Hayden is incorrect. The definition of function requires that no first coordinate be paired with two different second coordinates. It is okay for elements in the domain of function to be paired to the same element in the range.

Problems Related to the NCTM Standards and Curriculum Focal Points

1. Example 2.18 contains 4 examples where equations are used to represent real world problems.

2. Words: The second number is the sum $1 + 2$. The third number is the sum $1 + 2 + 3$. The fourth number is the sum $1 + 2 + 3 + 4$ and so forth.
Table:

Term #	Term
1	1
2	3
3	6
4	10
5	15
6	21
7	28

Graph:

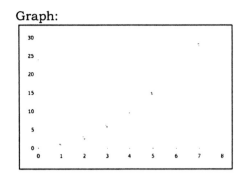

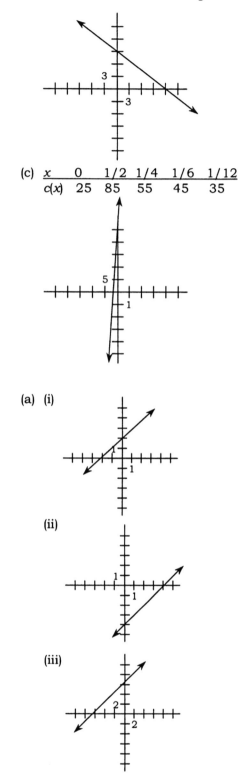

3. Any arithmetic sequence is a function with a constant rate of change and any geometric sequence is a function with a varying rate of change. A constant rate of change occurs when adding the same amount at each step. A varying rate of change occurs when adding different amounts or multiplying by the same amount at each step.

(c)

x	0	1/2	1/4	1/6	1/12
$c(x)$	25	85	55	45	35

Section 9.4

1. (a) x-axis   (b) I   (c) II
    (d) y-axis   (e) III   (f) IV

2. (a) II   (b) I
    (c) I and IV

3. $\{(x, y) \mid 1 \leq x \leq 3 \text{ and } -2 \leq y \leq 2\}$

4. (a)

x	0	1	-1	2	-2
$f(x)$	-2	1	-5	4	-8

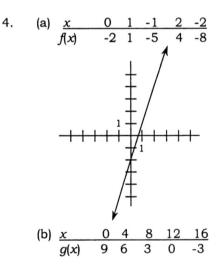

    (b)

x	0	4	8	12	16
$g(x)$	9	6	3	0	-3

5. (a) (i)

    (ii)

    (iii)

(iv)

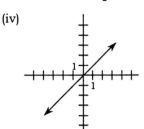

(b) The constant term determines where the graph intersects the *x*-axis

6. (a) A straight line going up to the right that passes through the origin.

(b) The value of *b* is where the line hits the *y*-axis. As *b* changes, the graph moves up or down with the same slope.

7. (a) (i)

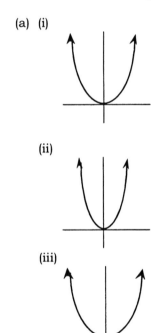

(ii)

(iii)

(iv)

(b) Positive coefficients greater than one have the effect of narrowing the graph. Positive coefficients between 0 and 1 have the effect of broadening

the graph. Multiplying by -1 has the effect of reflecting the graph in the *x*-axis. Thus the coefficient -3 would narrow the original graph and reflect it in the *x*-axis.

(c) The 5 makes the parabola in (i) 'narrower'. The 1/3 makes the parabola in (i) 'wider' and the 2 shifts it to the right 2 units.

8. (a) The parabola narrows.
(b) A horizontal line.
(c) The parabola opens down instead of up.

9. (a) (i)

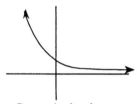

Same in both cases.

(ii)

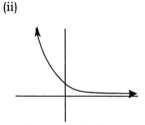

Same in both cases.

(iii)

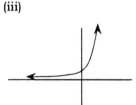

Same in both cases.

(b) Their graphs are the same because they represent the same function.

10. (a) It's a lot steeper on the right.
(b) It is a horizontal line *y*=1.
(c) The graph decreases to the right.

11. (a)

x	-2	-1	0	1	2
f(x)	-2	2	0	-2	2

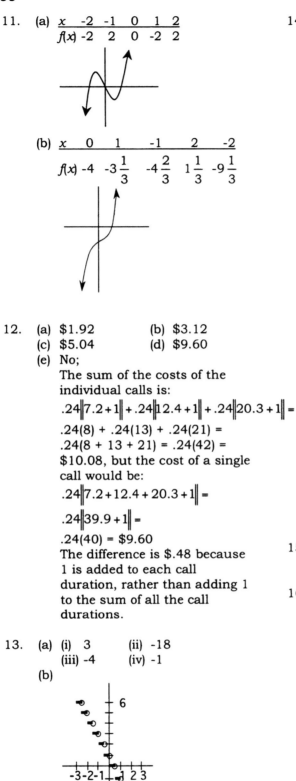

(b)

x	0	1	-1	2	-2
f(x)	-4	$-3\frac{1}{3}$	$-4\frac{2}{3}$	$1\frac{1}{3}$	$-9\frac{1}{3}$

12. (a) $1.92   (b) $3.12
     (c) $5.04   (d) $9.60
     (e) No;
         The sum of the costs of the
         individual calls is:
         $.24\|7.2+1\|+.24\|12.4+1\|+.24\|20.3+1\|=$
         .24(8) + .24(13) + .24(21) =
         .24(8 + 13 + 21) = .24(42) =
         $10.08, but the cost of a single
         call would be:
         $.24\|7.2+12.4+20.3+1\|=$
         $.24\|39.9+1\|=$
         .24(40) = $9.60
         The difference is $.48 because
         1 is added to each call
         duration, rather than adding 1
         to the sum of all the call
         durations.

13. (a) (i)   3   (ii) -18
         (iii) -4   (iv) -1
     (b)

14. (a)

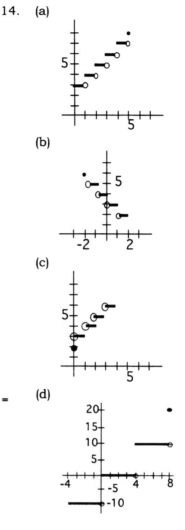

(b)

(c)

(d)

15. (a) linear   (b) step
     (c) quadratic   (d) exponential

16. (a) Function
         Domain: $-5 \le x \le 4$
         Range: $-2.5 \le y \le 4$
     (b) Not a function
     (c) Function
         Domain: All real numbers
         except 0
         Range: All real numbers except
         0
     (d) Function
         Domain: $-4 \le x < 2$ and
         $2 \le x \le 4$
         Range: $-3.5 < y \le 3$

17. (a) (i) 1   (ii) 2   (iii) 3
     (b) Domain: $-2 \le x \le 6$
         Range: {1, 2, 3, 4}

(c) $2 \le x < 3$; none.
(d) Step function

18. (a) Quadratic
     (b) $A(4) \approx 12.57$
          $A(12) \approx 113.1$

     (c)
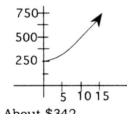

     (d) The diameter, d, must be positive.

19. (a) The distance varies according to time.
     (b) $D(8) = 1.5$. $D(8)$ is the number of miles to the lightning if 8 seconds have elapsed.
     (c) $D(t) = (3/16)t$

20. (a)
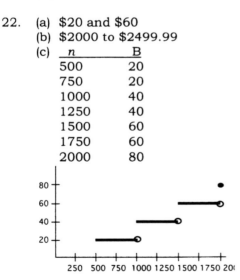

     (b) About $342
     (c) About 16.5 years
     (d) About 11 years

21. (iii)

22. (a) $20 and $60
     (b) $2000 to $2499.99
     (c)

n	B
500	20
750	20
1000	40
1250	40
1500	60
1750	60
2000	80

(d) $B(n) = 20 \left\| n/500 \right\|$

23. $T(n) = \dfrac{n}{4} + 4$

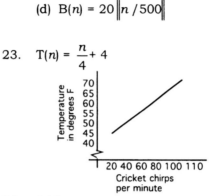

24. $1/3$

Analyzing Student Thinking

25. Yes, Millicent, that's right. To see why this is true, look at a table for a general arithmetic sequence:

0	1	2	3
a	$a+d$	$a+2d$	$a+3d$

The nth term of the sequence is of the form $dn + a$; in other words, it's a linear function with slope d.

26. Each successive y value is increased by a multiple of 3 and the value of y can be expressed as $2(3^{x-1})$. Thus, the graph will be that of an exponential function.

27. If the common difference of the arithmetic sequence were negative, then the line would slope downward. For example, consider the sequence 6, 4, 2, 0, -2, . . . where the common difference is -2. If the common ratio of the geometric sequence were a positive fraction less than one, the curve would move downward; for example, consider the sequence 20, 10, 5, 2.5, 1.25, . . . where the common ratio is 0.5. As a point of interest, if the common ratio of a geometric sequence is negative, the graph does not proceed downward in an orderly fashion, but bounces back and forth between positive and negative values. For example, the sequence 20, -10, 5, -2.5, 1.25,... is geometric with common ratio -0.5.

28. Braxton, the difference between successive output values of a linear function will equal the slope value, as long as the difference in the input values is 1.

29. Yes, Cassidy, that everyday expression comes from the fact that exponential functions grow very quickly as the value of the input increases.

30. Mikaila is incorrect; for instance, her claim is not true for the function $f(x) = x^2$, since $f(-2) = 4$ and $-f(2) = -4$.

31. Yes, Easton, many functions have this property. For instance, any function of the form $f(x) = x^2 + c$ satisfies $f(x) = f(-x)$ since the square of a number is equal to the square of its opposite. Similarly, functions of the form $f(x) = x^n + c$, where n is even, have this property. Such functions are said to be "even."

Problems Related to the NCTM Standards and Curriculum Focal Points

1. Three common ways of representing linear equations are tables, graphs, and equations. Students should be comfortable with all three representations and be able to move flexibly between them.

2. Example 9.15 involves a linear equation about a base salary with additional commission. The y-intercept of $1200 represents the base salary that a salesman will make regardless of the number of sales. The slope is the percent commission, 5%, of the sales. If the percent commission were larger, the slope of the graph would be steeper.

3. With a linear equation, for each change of 1 unit of the x variable, the y variable will change by the same fixed amount depending on the slope. With an exponential equation, however, each change of 1 unit of the x variable will yield a different change in the y variable. Thus, when the x variable changes from 1 to 2 both the linear equation and exponential equation may change by 4 units in the y variable. However, when the x variable changes from 4 to 5, the y variable of the linear equation will still change by 4 units but the exponential equation may change by 4000 units.

Chapter 10

Section 10.1

1. (a) 45, 56, 64, 71, 73, 74, 76, 82, 83, 83, 84, 85, 87, 91, 92, 92, 92, 95, 96
    (b) 45, 96
    (c) 92
    (d)
    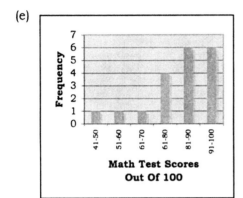
    (e)

    (f)
    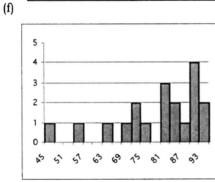

2. (a) 12.| 15 25 40 45 50 50 50 80 80 85
    (b)

12.0	
12.1	5
12.2	5
12.3	
12.4	0 5
12.5	0 0 0
12.6	
12.7	
12.8	0 0 5
12.9	

    (c) The plot in part (b) since it shows the spread of the data better.

3. (a)
    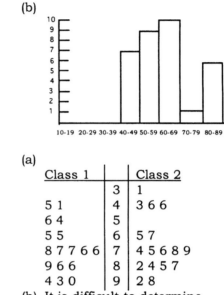
    (b)
    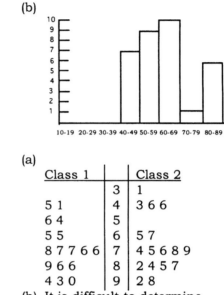

4. (a)

Class 1		Class 2
	3	1
5 1	4	3 6 6
6 4	5	
5 5	6	5 7
8 7 7 6 6	7	4 5 6 8 9
9 6 6	8	2 4 5 7
4 3 0	9	2 8

    (b) It is difficult to determine which class is better in this case.

5. (a) Yes, no   (b) Yes, no
    (c) Vertical scale does not begin at 0

6. (a)

    (b) Look for the shortest bar, which means the best braking. It is the Lincoln Mark VII.

7. (a)

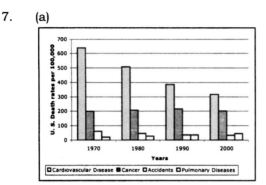

(b) Cardiovascular diseases and accidents

(c) Most resources should be targeted for cardiovascular diseases and cancer.

8. (a) $0, $21, $47.50, $112.50, $188.50, $275.50, $373.50, $481.50

(b)

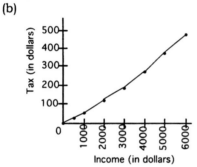

9. (a) 108°   (b) 72°
    (c) 54°   (d) $1800, $600, $600

10. (a) (i)   29%   104°
        (ii) 38%   137°
        (iii) 15%   55°
        (iv) 18%   64°

(b)

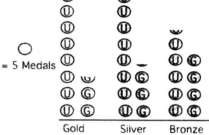

11. (a) About 2 million

(b) About 6.6 million
(c) About 5.5 million
(d) The height of all of the bars would be cut in half.
(e) The range from 4,000 to about 6.6 million makes it difficult to have an amount for the symbol to represent.

12.

U.S.A and Germany medal count for Sydney 2004

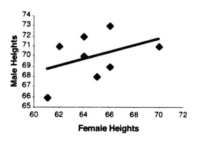

13. (a) and (c)

Dating Heights

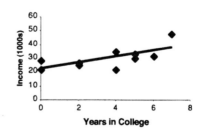

(b) There are not any outliers.
(d) There is no change since there are no outliers.

14. (a) and (b)

Education vs. Income

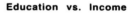

(c) Answers may vary depending on the method used to sketch your regression line in part (b).

15. (a) and (b)

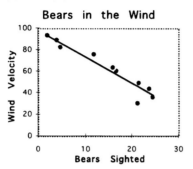

(c) It should look similar but may look slightly different depending on the strategy used to find it by hand.

16. (a) and (b)

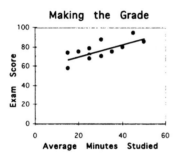

(c) It should look similar but may look slightly different depending on the strategy used to find it by hand.

17. (a) Approximately 1150
    (b) Approximately 1400

18. (a)

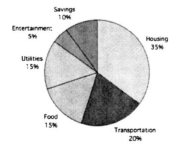

(b) The sector representing savings almost doubles and the rest of the sectors are smaller to accommodate it.

(c) $300

19. (a) Circle graph because the values are parts of a total or bar graph because it allows for comparison.
    (b) Bar graph:

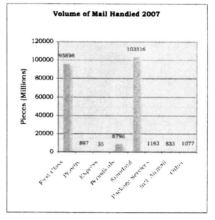

20. (a) Multiple circle because parts make up the whole population or multiple bar graphs for comparison.
    (b) Multiple bar graph:

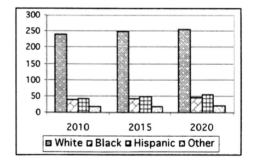

21. (a) Circle graph because values are parts of a whole or bar graph for comparison.
    (b) Circle graph:

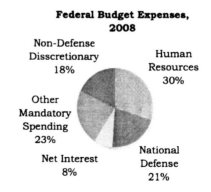

22. (a) Line graph to show trend.
     (b)

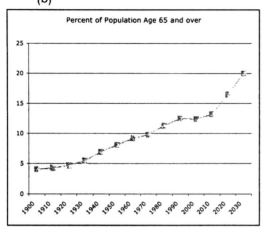

23. (a) Pictograph, bar graph, or line
         graph to show trend and
         comparisons.
     (b) Line graph:

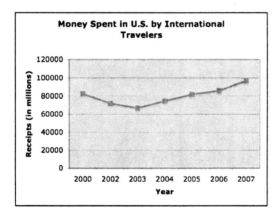

24. (a) Circle graph to show
         percentages
     (b) Circle graph:

25. (a) and (b)

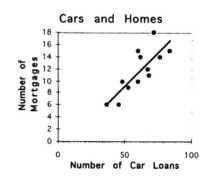

     (c) About 9 home mortgages

26. About $203,889,000,000

27. (a) 298
     (b) 5010
     (c) $\frac{1}{101} - \frac{1}{102} = \frac{1}{10302}$

28. 102,564

Analyzing Student Thinking

29. Yes. It sounds like Angela made a
     histogram (a type of bar graph)
     where the stems represent the
     interval lengths and the number of
     leaves show the frequency in each
     interval.

30. Ginger, a zig-zag or squiggle mark
     on the axis of a graph is used to
     show that part of the axis is not
     shown. It may be more
     convenient, or make for a more
     attractive graph, to do this. If you
     just crop the axis of your graph,
     but do not use the zig-zag to
     indicate this, you may deceive
     your reader.

31. No, Kevin has these two reversed.
     A circle graph is useful for
     showing relative amounts because
     it displays parts of a whole, while
     a line graph is useful for showing
     trends because it shows changes
     over time.

32. That's right, Chance. By comparing multiple circle graphs, one can see how relative amounts change.

33. Since line graphs are useful for showing changes over time, this type of graph is not appropriate for the categorized data Shawn collected. As Rosa suggests, a circle graph would work since each favorite color could be represented by one sector of the circle, showing the relative number of classmates with that favorite color.

34. Yes, Shawn, a bar chart would be an appropriate type of graph for this data, too, since it would allow you to make comparisons between the categories (each favorite color) by comparing the height of the bars (the number of classmates with that favorite color). However, neither a circle graph nor a bar chart would be "best". They are both okay.

35. No, Violet's method will not work since 60 + 70 + 30 + 50 + 90 = 300, but the sum of the measures of the central angles of a full circle is 360 degrees.

36. Vince, a regression line is very useful: it can help you see a general trend in the points you've graphed, indicates a possible relationship between the two variables, and allows you to estimate the value of one of the variables, given the value of the other.

Problems Related to the NCTM Standards and Curriculum Focal Points

1. When constructing a stem and leaf plot, the stem is one place value and the leaves are the next smaller place value(s).

2. Double Bar - Section 10.1 Set A #7 is a good example of data for a double-bar graph because for each city, you can construct two bars, one for each year, and compare them.

   Ordered pairs – Ordered pairs are graphed on a scatterplot. Thus, any pair of data that might be correlated are good for ordered pairs. For example a person's height and arm span are an ordered pair of data.

3. A histogram is used when the data set is a continuous set of numbers that are listed with different frequencies.

Section 10.2

1. (a)

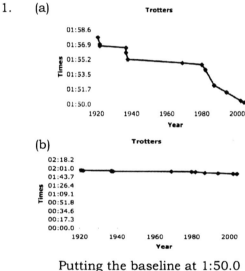

   (b)

   Putting the baseline at 1:50.0 as opposed to 0 makes the changes more dramatic.

2. (a)

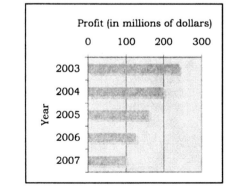

(b) Use the graph in figure 10.24 to emphasize the decrease in profits. Use the graph in part (a) to de-emphasize the decrease. Both are accurate, but the choice of which to use depends on the feeling one wants to convey to the reader.

3. (a) Oil companies want the increase to appear less dramatic so the range of the y-axis is larger.

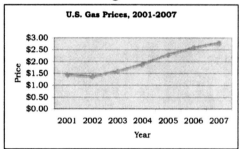

(b) Consumer groups want the increase to appear more dramatic, so the range of the y-axis is small.

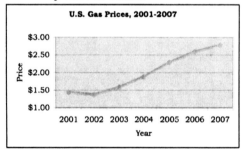

4.

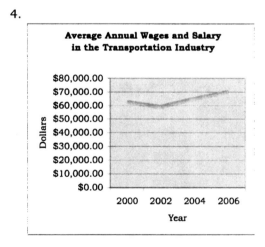

5.

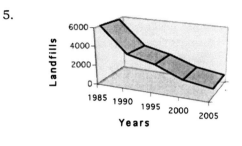

6.

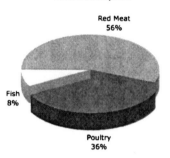

7. Because of the perspective, sectors B and D appear to be significantly larger than sectors A and C.

8.

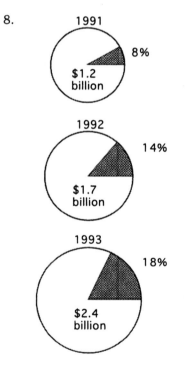

9.

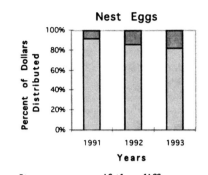

It appears as if the difference between 1992 and 1993 is small.

10. If the length of the bars (lasagna noodles) is measured from the right side of the fork and we assume that the "less often" bar is accurate, then the "once/twice a month" bar should be about 15%, the "once/twice a week" bar should be about 35%, and the "three times a week" bar should be about 29%. If the length of the bars is measured from the left side of the fork, then the bars are even less accurate at representing their corresponding percents.

11. No, the graph is not accurate. The radius has been tripled making the areas 9 times larger.

12. Exploding a sector; changing 3D perspective; incomplete labels; sectors don't add to 100%. Answers may vary.

13. Population-1000 coins in chest; Sample-20 coins taken from top.

14. Population-students taking mathematics classes; Sample-the 82 students in the three classes.

15.

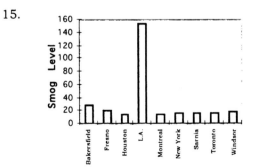

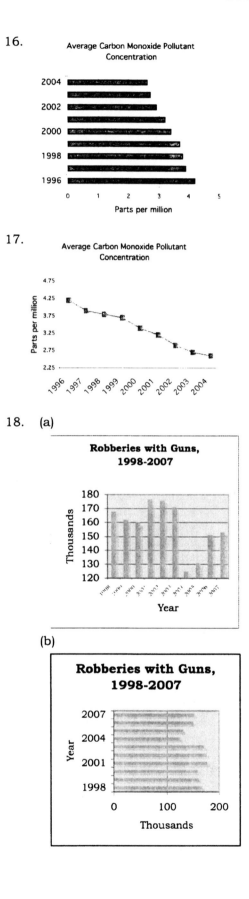

16.

17.

18. (a)

(b)

19. (a)

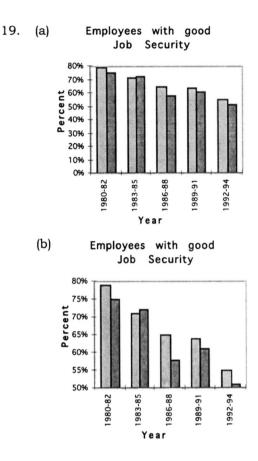

Employees with good
Job Security

(b)   Employees with good
         Job Security

20. Population-all of the professor's students; Sample-the students in the selected class; Bias- (i) the professor selected the class, (ii) the students would be discouraged from writing their true feelings because of his presence.

21. Population-all of the student body; Sample-the students at the coffee house and the gym; Bias-the students at the coffee house are participating in a social activity and the students at the gym are participating in a sporting activity so they are likely to choose candidates Johnson and Jackson respectively.

Analyzing Student Thinking

22. Siope is correct. Depending on the situation, the vertical axis of a vertical bar graph can be cropped as long as there is some

indication, like a "squiggle" mark, that the axis has been cropped.

23. Help Cesar convert the time he spends doing each activity into a percent by dividing by 24. As long as he accounts for all of the 24 hours, the percents will add up to 100 and a circle graph can be constructed.

24. No, when the length, width and height of a three-dimensional bar are doubled, the resulting bar is $2 \times 2 \times 2 = 8$ times greater in volume than the original.

25. Joel, there may be no intention to mislead. Nonetheless, it is important to be aware of the ways in which such a graph may be misleading, giving greater emphasis to differences among the data.

26. No, Otis, increasing only one dimension of the pencil icon by 3 times will result in a pencil that is 3 times larger than the original, representing 3 times the quantity represented by 1 pencil. That's accurate, not deceptive.

27. Anita, surveying only people at the park introduces a source of bias in your sample. In order to have a sample that is representative of the city's population, you need to include non-park users, too.

Problems Related to the NCTM Standards and Curriculum Focal Points

1. If a survey of 50 people is conducted in a school of 800 students, and 15 people responded in a certain way, then the proportion $\frac{15}{50} = \frac{x}{800}$ can be used to estimate how many students in the school feel the same way.

2. It is difficult to get a sense of a list of data by looking only at the

numbers. However, if the numbers are organized into some kind of graph, it becomes easier to see trends and relationships.

3. Many possible answers.
    Example 1: If the vertical axis on a line or bar graph is cropped, it may be inferred that the changes are greater than they really are.

    Example 2: In an exploded circle graph, the isolated piece of the graph appears larger than it really is.

Section 10.3

1. (a) 0,0,0
    (b) 0, -0.5, no mode
    (c) 0, -0.05, no mode
    (d) $5 + \sqrt{2}$, $5 + \sqrt{2}$, no mode

2. (a) $\sqrt{2}/2$, $2\sqrt{2}$, $3\sqrt{2}$
    (b) π, π, $4 + \pi$
    (c) $\sqrt{3}/3 + \pi$, $(\sqrt{2} + \sqrt{3})/2 +$ π, $\sqrt{3} + \pi$

3. 2.87

4. 26 students

5. No. $27 \times 70 = 21 \times 90$. Thus, 21 scores above ninety would yield a total that would exceed 27×70.

6. (a) {1, 3, 8, 9, 9}; answers may vary.
    (b) {1, 1, 5, 9, 9}; answers may vary.

7. (a) Lowest score = 50, lower quartile = 59, median = 73, upper quartile = 82, highest score = 97.
    (b) 20, 40, 60

8. (a)
    (b) Class 2 performed better since

3	00 00 05 05 08 09 11 14 18 24
	24 26 28 29 42 55 55 61 63 64
	73 73
4	17
5	11

most statistics except the lowest score are higher than their counterparts from Class 1.

9. (a) The lower quartile: 21
    (b) The upper quartile: 42
    (c) The lower quartile: 25

10. (a)

stem	Leaves (× 100)
5	5
6	5 5 9
7	0 2 2 4 5 7 7 8 8
8	0 0 1 2 3 3 4 4 5 6 6 6 6 7 9
9	1 2 3 4 5 6 7 9
10	0 4 7 8 9
11	4 5 6
12	6 6 8
13	1 8
14	6
15	0

(b) There are no gaps. A cluster occurs in the eighties.
(c) There are no outliers.
(d) East:
Lowest value = 7000
Lower quartile = 8400
Median = 9550
Upper quartile = 11500
Highest value = 15000

West:
Lowest value = 5500
Lower quartile = 7300
Median = 8100
Upper quartile = 8850
Highest value = 14600

East has no outliers.
West has two outliers: 11400 (WY) and 14600 (NM).

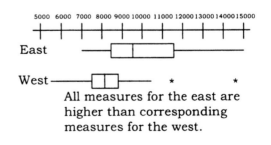

All measures for the east are higher than corresponding measures for the west.

11. (a)

    (b) Young's total of 511 is a mild outlier.

12. (a) 0,0   (b) 59.3, 7.7
    (c) 11.7, 3.4   (d) 11.1, 3.3

13. (a) 8; $\sqrt{8}$ (b) 8; $\sqrt{8}$ (c) 8; $\sqrt{8}$
    (d) 16; 4. Adding/subtracting a constant amount does not change the variance or standard deviation.

14. 18, 18.5, 19, 2.6, 1.612

15. .03, .38, -.66, -.84, -.31, .21, -1.01, -1.19, 1.26, 2.13

16. (a) Fiftieth Percentile
    (b)

z-SCORE	PERCENTILE
-2	2
-1	15 or 16
1	84 or 85
2	98

17. A: test score >95
    B: 85 < test score ≤ 95
    C: 65 < test score ≤ 85
    D: 55 < test score ≤ 65
    F: test score ≤ 55

18. (a) 57th percentile   (b) 43%

19. 77%-78%

20. 65, 55, 75

21. Approximately 111.5

22. 11 girls

23. 360/24 = 87.9 (to nearest tenth)

24. All the numbers are equal.

25. (a) For example, {1,2,3,4,5} and {1,1,3,5,5}
    (b) For example, {1,2,3,4,5} and {6,7,8,9,10}

26. 63 (rounded to 2 places)

27. (a) No
    (b) Yes (if all scores are equal, then all z-scores are zero).

28. (a) 32.5   (b) 30; no.

29. (a) $s = 1.41$, $s_{n-1} = 1.58$ (to 2 places)

    (b) Yes, $s_{n-1} = \dfrac{\sqrt{n}}{n-1} \cdot s$
    whenever $s_{n-1} \neq 0 \neq s$

Analyzing Student Thinking

30. Amber, although the number 3.9 has a 3 in it, it is really much closer to 4 than 3, so that is more positive than neutral. More importantly, a median of 5 indicates that at least half of the class gave lavender a 5. A few negative votes have a more powerful effect on the mean than on the median, but these figures indicate the class is quite happy with the new color.

31. Spike, don't forget that the median is the middle number, when the data are written in order. So, the median is actually 7.5.

32. No. The median of a set with four numbers is the average of the middle two numbers.

33. No. A set with the mean = median = mode would have the average = middle number = most frequent number. {0, 4, 4, 8} is just such a set, with 4 = mean = median = mode.

34. By looking at a Bell curve, we can see that 47.5% of the data points have the z-scores between 0 and 2 but at most 2.5% of the data

points have z-scores between 2 and 10.

35. Actually, Mckay, it's possible for a whisker to be shorter than the box, if the data in the middle half (represented by the box) are spread out and the data in the upper (or lower) quarter (represented by the whisker) are close together.

36. Whitney, consider the sets {0, 0, 0, 0, 10} and {0, 2, 5, 6, 10}. Both have a range of 10, but the spread in the data in each one is different, resulting in standard deviations that are not equal.

Problems Related to the NCTM Standards and Curriculum Focal Points

1. To construct a stem and leaf plot, each data value must be broken into the stem part and the leaf part. The point where the values are broken is between two place values like the tens and ones or the ones and tenths. Thus understanding is essential to constructing a stem and leaf plot. Other answers are possible.

2. The measures of central tendency – mean, median, and mode – as well as the measures of dispersion – variance and standard deviation – are all used to analyze and summarize data. The topic of z-scores combine central tendency and dispersion to indicate how a single value fits with the rest of the values. Finally, the normal distribution can indicate how a set of data all fit together. Answers may vary.

3. All three of the mean, median, and mode typically used to indicate the "middle" of a set of data. The mean is most impacted by an outlier that is particularly large or small. The median is above half of the values and below the other half and not impacted by outliers.

Since the mode is the value with the highest frequency, it will usually be in the middle but could be the lowest or highest value if it occurs most often. Answers may vary.

Chapter 11

Section 11.1

1. (a) Gift B or E
   (b) Gift A or C
   (c) No one

2. (a) {HH, HT, TH, TT]
   (b) {H1, H2, H3, H4, H5, H6, T1, T2, T3, T4, T5, T6}
   (c) {RG, RW, BG, BW}

3. (a) {R,G,B,Y,W}
   (b) {RR,RG,RB,RY,RW,GR,GG,GB, GY,GW,...,WR,WG,WB,WY,W} (25 pairs)
   (c) {RG,RB,RY,RW,GR,GB,GY,GW, BR,BG,BY,BW,YR,YG,YB,YW, WR,WG,WB,WY}

4. (a) {H1, H2, H3, H4, H5, H6, T1, T2, T3, T4, T5, T6}
   (b) {H1, H2, H3, H4, H5, H6}
   (c) {H3, T3}
   (d) {H2, T2, H4, T4, H6, T6}
   (e) {H5, H6}
   (f) {T1, T2, T3, T4, T5, T6, H5}

5. (a) C   (b) P   (c) I

6.
P	(H, P)	(T, P)
G	(H, G)	(T, G)
Y	(H, Y)	(T, Y)
	H	T

7. (a) 75/1000 = 0.075
   (b) 150/1000 = 0.15
   (c) 275/1000 = 0.275
   (d) 375/1000 = 0.375

8. (a) 1/2   (b) 11/12
   (c) 5/12   (d) 13/18
   (e) 5/18
   (f) In general, the answers for 500 rolls should be closer to the theoretical probability, but answers may vary.

9. (a) 0.5   (b) 0.25
   (c) 0.875   (d) 0.375
   (e) In general, the answers for 500 rolls should be closer to the theoretical probability, but answers may vary.

10. (a) 7/12   (b) 1   (c) 1/2

11. (a) 1/2   (b) 3/13
    (c) 10/13   (d) 3/26

12. (a) 37/75   (b) 64 times

13. (a) 7/22   (b) 3/22
    (c) 5/22   (d) 3/22
    (e) 15/22   (f) 9/22

14. (a) 5/9   (b) 27/38
    (c) 9/19   (d) 18/19

15. (a) 1/3   (b) 1/3
    (c) 1/3   (d) 1
    (e) 1/2, 1/8, 3/8, 1; yes.

16. (a) 1/6   (b) 5/6
    (c) 1/2   (d) 1/2
    (e) 2/3   (f) 1/3

17. (a) 7/13   (b) 3/4
    (c) 7/13   (d) 25/52

18. (a) 1/2   (b) 1/3   (c) 1/6
    (d) 1   (e) 7/12

19. (a) Either two or three heads appear; 1/2
    (b) Number of heads is not 2; 5/8
    (c) The second coin lands tails; 1/2
    (d) Two heads appear, one of which is on second coin; 1/4

20. (a) The probability of getting a spade or a face card.
    (b) The probability of getting a jack, queen, or king of spades.
    (c) The probability of not getting a face card.

21. (a) Each state not equally likely, since populations not equal.
    (b) Intersection of two events is not empty set, so property 4 does not apply. Probability cannot be greater than 1.
    (c) Winning and losing are complementary events, but 1/2 + 1/3 ≠ 1.

22. (a) 1/3   (b) 2   (c) 4

23. (a) 6; 1/2   (b) 30;7/30
    (c) 20;1/20

24. $\dfrac{100^2 - \pi(40)^2}{100^2} \approx 0.497$

25. $91/216 \approx 0.42$

Analyzing Student Thinking

26. Although the probability of getting 50 heads out of 100 tosses is the most likely, the probability of getting 48 or 49 or 51 or 52 or other numbers close to 50 is slightly less, but very close to the probability of getting 50. Since these outcomes have similar probabilities, a different outcome could occur on each of a small number of trials.

27. Jimmer is incorrect, in general. However, if the spinner is divided from center into 3 pie shaped pieces of equal area, then he is correct.

28. Kyle is incorrect. There are 6 × 6 = 36 possible outcomes for rolling two dice. There are 11 outcomes which result in either a 1 on the blue die or a 3 on the red die: {(1, 1), (1, 2), (1, 3), (1, 4), (1, 5), (1, 6), (2, 3), (3, 3), (4, 3), (5, 3), (6, 3)} Thus, the probability of this event is 11/36.

29. No, Jaisha, since there are 6 outcomes for each of the two dice, there are 6 × 6 = 36 outcomes when two dice are tossed.

30. James, let's list the outcomes in the sample space: S = {HH, HT, TH, TT}. There are four outcomes: two heads, two tails, and two outcomes with a head and a tail. Thus, the probability of getting two heads is 1/4.

31. Jennifer and Karen are both mistakenly reasoning that the first 5 tosses affect the probability of the 6th toss. However, each toss of the coin has a 50% probability of landing on heads.

32. Jessa, any event that is sure to occur has a probability of 1. For instance, consider the event, "The coin will land heads or tails."

Problems Related to the NCTM Standards and Curriculum Focal Points

1. An experiment with outcomes that are not equally likely is dropping a thumbtack to see if it will land point up or point down. An experiment with equally likely outcomes is tossing a coin. Answers may vary.

2. Probability is the fraction of the number of elements in an event divided by the number of elements in the sample space. Since an event is always a subset of the sample space, it is impossible to for the fraction to have a numerator that is larger than the denominator. Thus, the probability will always be less than or equal to one.

3. Two events are mutually exclusive if they have no elements in common. If two events are mutually exclusive then the probability of the union of these two events can be computed by simply adding the probabilities of the individual events.

Section 11.2

1.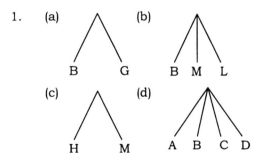

2. (a)

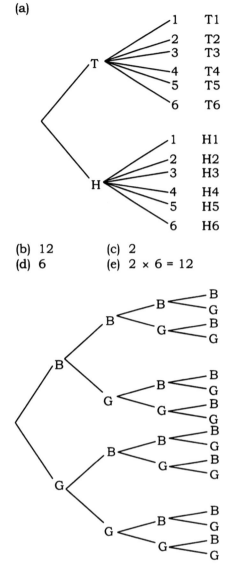

(b) 12   (c) 2
(d) 6   (e) 2 × 6 = 12

3.

4.

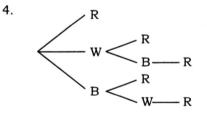

5.

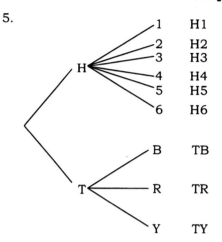

6.   20 ways

7.   36

8.   (a) R - 1/4, W - 1/4, B - 1/2
      (b) R - 1/5, W - 1/5, B - 3/5
      (c) R - 1/3, W - 1/6, B - 1/2

9.   (a) Y = 2/5, R = 3/5 appropriate
          for each branch
      (b) 4/25, 6/25
      (c) 4/25 + 6/25 + 6/25 = 16/25
      (d) 1 - 9/25 = 16/25

10.   (a)   (b)

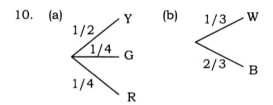

      (c)

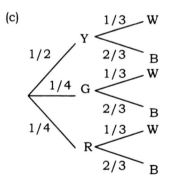

11. (a), (b) and (c)

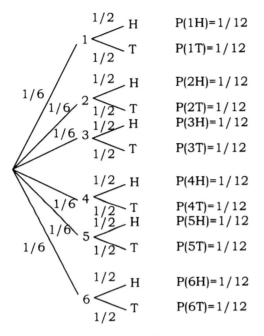

(d) P(even and head)
= P(2H) +P(4H) + P(6H)
= 1/12 + 1/12 + 1/12 = 1/4

12. (a) and (b)

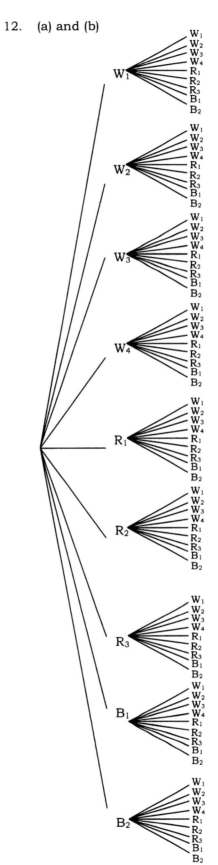

(c) Label each of the 9 branches in the first stage of the outcome tree with 1/9 and each of the 81 branches in the second stage with 1/9. The probability of each of the 81 outcomes is $1/9 \times 1/9 = 1/81$

(d) P(red and white) = P(R_1W_1) + P(R_1W_2) + P(R_1W_3)+ P(R_1W_4) + P(R_2W_1) + P(R_2W_2) + P(R_2W_3)+ P(R_2W_4) + P(R_3W_1) + P(R_3W_2) + P(R_3W_3)+ P(R_3W_4) + = 12/81

13. (a)

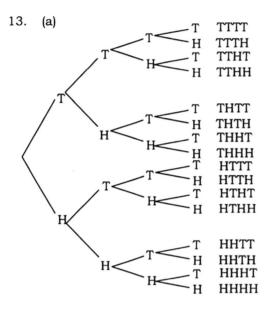

(b) 1, 4, 6, 4, 1
(c) same as 1, 4, ... row

14. (a) 10 × 10 × 10 × 10
= 10,000
(b) 10
(c) 10/10,000 = 1/1000
(d) 7/10,000

15. (a) 2 × 26 × 26 × 26 = 35,152
(b) 1/35,152 ≈ 0.00003

16. (a) 8 × 3 × 2 × 5 = 240
(b) 120
(c) 1/2
(d) 16/240 = 1/15

17. (a) 1, 5, 10, 10, 5, 1
(b) 5
(c) 10
(d) 5/16, 1/2

18. (a)

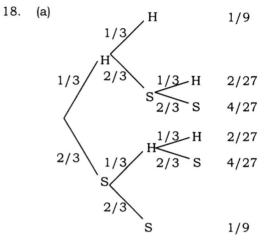

(b) 1/9, 4/9   (c) 4/9
(d) 2/27   (e) 20/27

19. (a)

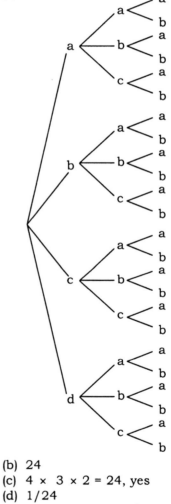

(b) 24
(c) 4 × 3 × 2 = 24, yes
(d) 1/24

20. (a) $(0.343)^3 \approx 0.04$
    (b) $(0.657)^3 \approx 0.28$
    (c) $1 - 0.28 = 0.72$
    (d) $3(0.343)(0.657)^2 \approx 0.45$

21. (a)

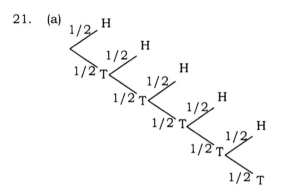

    (b) 1/2, 1/4, 1/8, 1/16
    (c) 1/32

22. (a)

    (b)   0.7

23. A = 3%, B = 16%, C = 31%,
    D = 31%, E = 16%, F = 3%

24. If the prisoner places one white ball in one box and the remaining balls (9 white and 10 black) in the other box, his chance of going free would be $(1 + 9/19)/2 = 0.737$ or 73.7%.

25. Switch! For curtains *A*, *B*, and *C*, suppose that the prize is behind *A*. Here are the possibilities:

    Choose *A* first. Then *B* or *C* is shown. Stay wins, switch loses.

    Choose *B* first. Then *C* is shown. Stay loses, switch wins.

    Choose *C* first. Then *B* is shown. Stay loses, switch wins.

26. (a) 1/3   (b) 4/11

27. Let *a*, *b*, *a* + *b*, *a* + 2*b* be four consecutive Fibonacci numbers. Then $(a + b)^2 - b^2 = a^2 + 2ab$, and $a(a + 2b) = a^2 + 2ab$. Thus, they are always equal.

Analyzing Student Thinking

28. Maxwell, *or* means 'plus' only when the two sets in question are disjoint. In this example, you counted one particular card, namely the king of hearts, twice. To adjust for that, P(king *or* heart) = P(king) + P(heart) - P(king of hearts). This equals 16/52, not 17/52. The 16 represents all of the hearts plus the kings of spades, clubs, and diamonds. In general, we have to subtract the items that are in the intersection of the two sets in question because we don't want them to be counted twice, so P(A *or* B) = P(A) + P(B) - P(A *and* B).

29. Parker, note that *for each* of the 52 possibilities on the first draw, there are 52 possibilities on the second draw. That means that there are 52 × 52 ways to draw two cards with replacement.

30. Megan, these two outcomes do not have the same probability. For drawing two aces in a row, the probability is 4/52 × 3/51 since, after drawing the first ace, there are only three aces left in the deck. However, the probability of drawing an ace then a 2 is 4/52 × 4/51 since, after drawing the ace first, there are still four 2s left in the deck.

31. Matthew, Pascal's Triangle can be used to compute only probability problems involving two equally likely outcomes. Since a die has six equally likely outcomes, Pascal's Triangle does not apply.

32. Nancy, since there is only 1 king of hearts in a deck of cards, the probability of drawing it is 1/52.

33. Riley has chosen the correct row of Pascal's Triangle, but the entries that correspond to the number of ways to get 3 or 4 heads are 10 and 5:

1	5	10	10	5	1
(0H)	(1H)	(2H)	(3H)	(4H)	(5H)

P(3 or 4) = (10 + 5)/2^5 = 17/32

34. No. By the Fundamental Counting Property, there are 2 × 2 × 2 × 2 = 16 possible outfits.

Problems Related to the NCTM Standards and Curriculum Focal Points

1. If a sample space were written out for this experiment, there would be three possible equally likely outcomes, R, R, and W. The definition of theoretical probability assumes that all of the outcomes are equally likely in order to write P(Red) =2/3. Suppose, however that the two red marbles were very small and difficult to find, then a sample space of equally likely outcomes could not be written and the theoretical probability could not be determined. Answers may vary.

2. If a two stage tree diagram with 3 outcomes in the first stage and 4 outcomes in the second stage were constructed, there would be a total of 12 branches. The number of possible outcomes could also be determined by using the Fundamental Counting Principle and multiplying 3 by 4.

3. Since each birth is independent and the probability of getting a boy on any given birth is $\frac{1}{2}$, the probability having 4 boys in a family of 4 children could be found

by using the multiplicative property of probability. We can compute $\frac{1}{2} \cdot \frac{1}{2} \cdot \frac{1}{2} \cdot \frac{1}{2} = \frac{1}{16}$.

Section 11.3

1. (a) $\frac{20!}{15!} = 20 \cdot 19 \cdot 18 \cdot 17 \cdot 16$
   $= 1,860,480$
   (b) $(n + 1)(n)(n - 1)$
   (c) $\frac{57!}{55!} = 57 \cdot 56 = 3192$

2. (a) $m = 23, n = 4$
   (b) $m = 11, n = 2$

3. (a) $\frac{10!}{7!3!} = \frac{10 \cdot 9 \cdot 8}{3 \cdot 2 \cdot 1} = 120$
   (b)
   $$\frac{23 \cdot 22 \cdot 21 \cdot 20 \cdot 19 \cdot 18 \cdot 17 \cdot 16 \cdot 15 \cdot 14}{10 \cdot 9 \cdot 8 \cdot 7 \cdot 6 \cdot 5 \cdot 4 \cdot 3 \cdot 2 \cdot 1}$$
   $= 1,114,066$
   (c) $\frac{50 \cdot 49 \cdot 48 \cdot 47 \cdot 46}{5 \cdot 4 \cdot 3 \cdot 2 \cdot 1}$
   $= 2,118,760$

4. (a) $m = 16, n = 4$
   (b) $m = 33, n = 28$

5. (a) $_6P_2$ (b) $_{12}P_2$
   (c) $_{12}P_2$ (d) $_{12}P_2$

6. (a) 90   (b) 45   (c) 45
   (d) 30   (e) 27

7. (a) 26^4
   (b) $26 \cdot 25 \cdot 24 \cdot 23 = 358,800$
   (c) 26^3

8. 8!

9. (a) $_{10}C_7 = 120$ (b) $_8C_5 = 56$

10. $_{11}C_7 = 330$

11. (a) 1, 20, 190, 1140
    (b) 1, 21, 210, 1330
    (c) 210 = 20 + 190
        1330 = 190 + 1140

12. (a) $15/64$
    (b) $20/64 = 5/16$
    (c) $1/64$

13. $\dfrac{17!}{20!} = \dfrac{1}{6840}$

14. $\dfrac{_{16}C_3 \times _{13}C_5}{_{19}C_6 \times _{13}C_5} = \dfrac{20}{969}$

15. $\dfrac{7}{_{10}C_4} = \dfrac{1}{30}$

16. (a) $n = 9$ (b) $n = 12$

17. $\dfrac{12}{_{14}C_3 \times _{11}C_5} = \dfrac{1}{14014}$

18. $\dfrac{_4C_2 \times _4C_2}{_{52}C_5} = \dfrac{3}{216580}$

19. (a) $3 \cdot 13! = 18,681,062,4000$
    (b) $3(_{13}C_3 + _{13}C_2 + _{13}C_1 + _{13}C_0) = 1134$

20. $5,428,503,678,976$
    $\approx 5.4285 \times 10^{12}$

21. (a) $5!$
    (b) $6! - 2 \times 5! = 4 \times 5! - 480$

22. $_{30}P_6 = 427,518,000$

23. $11! = 39,916,800$

24. 3 - Yes, 4 - Yes, 5 - No

25. (a) $(_4C_2 + _3C_2 + _2C_2)/_{10}C_2$
    $= (6 + 3 + 1)/45 = 2/9$
    (b) $(_4C_1 \times _6C_1)/_{10}C_2 = 24/45$
    $= 8/15$
    (c) $(_4C_1 \times _6C_1 + _4C_2 \times _6C_0)/_{10}C_2$
    $= (24 + 6)/45 = 2/3$
    (d) $(_4C_0 \times _6C_2/_{10}C_2 = 15/45$
    $= 1/3$

26. (a) $2 \times 6! = 1440$
    (b) $7! - 2 \times 6! = 3600$
    (c) $6 \times 5! = 720$

27. $12! = 479,001,600$
    $5! \times 4! \times 3! \times 6 = 103,680$

28. (a) $_8C_0 \times _6C_4 + _8C_1 \times _6C_3 +$
    $_8C_2 \times _6C_2 + _8C_3 \times _6C_1 +$
    $_8C_4 \times _6C_0 = 1265$
    (b) $_8C_2 \times _8C_2 = 784$
    (c) $_8C_4 = 70$
    (d) $_6C_4 = 15$

Analyzing Student Thinking

29. Margaret is incorrect.
    $\dfrac{8!}{16!} =$
    $\dfrac{8!}{16 \cdot 15 \cdot 14 \cdot 13 \cdot 12 \cdot 11 \cdot 10 \cdot 9 \cdot 8!} =$
    $\dfrac{1}{16 \cdot 15 \cdot 14 \cdot 13 \cdot 12 \cdot 11 \cdot 10 \cdot 9} =$
    $\dfrac{1}{518,918,400}$

30. If permutations were used, then the order of selection would be taken into account. Lowell is correct because the order in which the committee members are selected does NOT matter, so combinations are the correct way to count the committees.

31. Since the order of selection matters in this situation, permutations are the correct way to solve this problem.

32. Brielle, Pascal's Triangle can be used to solve only probability problems involving two equally likely outcomes. Since there are 52 possible outcomes for drawing a card from a deck, Pascal's Triangle does not apply.

33. Lily's statement is correct only for the even-numbered rows. The odd-numbered rows of Pascal's Triangle have an even number of entries, and thus no middle number. Thus, Lily should have said, "the middle number of the nth row, where n is an even number, must be $_nC_{n/2}$."

34. Julio is incorrect. Since there are 6 different items that may be added to the sandwich or not (2 choices), there are $2^6 = 64$ possibilities. And for each of these 64, there are two choices of bread and only one choice of meat so there are only $64 \times 2 \times 1 = 128$ sandwich combinations.

35. Jeff, to compute this probability, we'd need to divide the number of outcomes with 5 "yea" and 4 "nay" votes by the total number of ways the 9 justices could vote. Since there are two possible votes for each justice, we could use the 9th row of Pascal's Triangle to get $126/2^9 = 63/256$. Note, however, that by using Pascal's Triangle, we have made the assumption that a vote of "yea" is equally likely to a "nay" vote. Since justices don't vote randomly, this is probably not a good assumption to make. You can see that computing the probability of a 5-4 majority is more complicated than you first thought.

Problems Related to the NCTM Standards and Curriculum Focal Points

1. Sometimes the sample space of an experiment is too large to write out so the number of elements in the sample space or in an event can be determined by using permutations or combinations.

2. If there are a lot of outcomes for any stage of an experiment, then drawing a tree diagram can be overwhelming. Thus, combinations or permutations can be used to find the number of branches on a tree diagram or the number of elements in an event.

Section 11.4

1. Answers will vary.

2. Answers may vary but should be around 7 packages.

3. (a) Answers will vary.
   (b) The theoretical number is 21.74 or 22 pennies.

4. Step 1: Yes   Step 2: 2
   Step 3: 44
   (a) .88 (theoretical solution .63)

5. (a) Place pieces of paper corresponding to the chocolate candies in a bag. Draw out 2 pieces of paper and record the results.
   (b) Answer should be near $\frac{150}{812} \approx 0.185$, but will vary.
   (c) Place 5 ones, 7 twos, 8 threes, 5 fours, and 4 fives in the bin and draw 2. After 30 trials, the probability should be near 0.185.

6. Read the digits on the table and record numbers 1-6 as rolls. Ignore 0, 7, 8, 9. Starting on the top row, the first twenty rolls would be 1, 3, 1, 1, 2, 1, 2, 5, 2, 2, 3, 6, 5, 5, 2, 1, 6, 5, 2, 4.

7. 0.8

8. 4/5 (In long run such a sample will average just under one defective microscope.)

9. (a) $40,000   (b) $25
   (c) Scholarship A

10. Make $2,200

11. They are the same since they both reduce to 3:2.

12. (a) (i)   6:30 or 1:5
        (ii) 33:3 or 11:1
        (iii) 18:18 or 1:1
    (b) (i) 5:1   (ii) 1:11   (iii) 1:1

13. (a) 3:10   (b) 3:1
    (c) 1:51   (d) 10:3

14. (a) 3:5   (b) 7:1
     (c) 7:1   (d) 3:5

15. (a) 1:7, 7:1   (b) 2:3, 3:2

16. (a) 1/9   (b) 3/8   (c) 5/11

17. For example, the sum is...
     (a) not 8, 9, or 10
     (b) 6, 7, or 8
     (c) not 2.

18. (a) 10/21   (b) 1/3
     (c) 11/21   (d) 3/7
     (e) 3/10   (f) 5/11
     (g) 1/2   (h) 3/11
     (i) 3/7

19. (a) 1/4   (b) 1/5
     (c) 1/6   (d) 1/3

20. (a) 1/2, 3/4   (b) 1/2, 1/4

21. (a) 1/3   (b) 2/4 = 1/2
     (c) 3/5   (d) 1/2
     (e) 1   (f) 1/3

22. (a) 13/16   (b) 13/21
     (c) 15/16   (d) 5/14
     (e) 1   (f) 1/2

23. (a) and (b) Answers will vary.
     (c) 176/1024

24. Use a deck of 52 cards. Draw
     until 2 aces appear. Count and
     record the number of draws
     needed. Repeat n times, for your
     choice of n, say n = 100. Then
     compute the average number of
     draws needed. Theoretical
     expected value is 21.2.

25. Use slips of paper, numbered from
     1 to 20. Call your number 1, for
     example. Draw 12 slips from a
     hat; this is the first jury. Replace
     all 12 slips and draw 12 slips
     again. This is the second jury.
     Repeat this n times, say n = 100.
     Count the number of times out of
     n that your number came up on
     one (or both) of the juries. It
     should be around 80% of the time.
     Theoretical probability = .84.

26. Switches should win about 2/3 of
     the time.

27. Answers will vary.

28. Click on the numbers 1, 2, 3, 4, 5,
     6 to put in the box. Press Start.
     When each of the numbers 1-5
     have been drawn, press Pause and
     record the number of draws.
     Repeat 100 times.

29. True. Let the row sum be m.
     Then the sum of all numbers must
     be the sum of three rows, or $3m$, a
     multiple of 3.

30. (a) Set the "Longest run in heads"
         to 4 and the "Probability of
         heads" to 0.5. Start tossing
         until you get 4 heads in a row
         and record how many tosses it
         took. Repeat this 20 times and
         average the number of tosses it
         took to get 4 heads in a row.
     (b) A reasonable answer would be
         around 25 to 30 tosses.

Analyzing Student Thinking

31. Sanchez is incorrect. Assuming
     his past batting record applies to
     future at bats, the odds that
     Swinging Sam will not get a hit on
     his next at bat are   P(no hit):P(hit)
     = 4/7:3/7 = 4:3.

32. No. The expected value may not
     necessarily be greater than $20. If
     the outcome "greater than $20"
     has a value of $25 and the
     outcome "less than $20" has a
     value of $1, then the expected
     value, which is E = 25(3/4) +
     1(1/4) = $19, would not be greater
     than $20.

33. Alfred, we must consider that
     some sums are more likely than
     others. Also, there are 36
     possibilities when tossing two
     dice, not 11. If we list the
     outcomes with a prime sum, we
     can see there are 15 of them:
     (1, 1), (1, 2), (2, 1), (1, 4), (4, 1),

(2, 3), (3, 2), (1, 6), (6, 1), (2, 5), (5, 2), (3, 4), (4, 3), (5, 6), (6, 5). Thus, the odds of tossing a prime sum are P(prime sum):P(not prime sum) = 15/36:21/36 = 15:21 = 5:7.

34. Josh is correct. Assuming that the five hits were counted as part of the .333, the odds of a hit on Julio's next at bat would be P(hit):P(no hit). That is, 0.333:0.667 or 1:2.

35. Jackson's answer is correct, but his reasoning is not. Since it is given that the card is red, we don't need to consider the two black suits. So, $P(\text{heart} \mid \text{red}) =$

$$\frac{P(\text{heart and red})}{P(\text{red})} =$$

$$\frac{13/52}{26/52} = \frac{1}{2}$$

36. Luiza's statement is not always true. Consider the case when A and B are independent events:

$$P(A \mid B) = \frac{P(A \cap B)}{P(B)} = \frac{0}{P(B)} = 0.$$

Similarly, $P(B \mid A) = 0$ and $0 + 0$ is not equal to 1.

Problems Related to the NCTM Standards and Curriculum Focal Points

1. When drawing cards from a standard 52-card deck, the theoretical probability says the probability of drawing a spade is 1/4. If a simulation of drawing a single card is done 60 times, the following proportion could be used to determine how many times a spade is expected. $1/4 = x/60$. Answers may vary.

2. Theoretical probability is the ratio of the number of elements in an event compared to the number of elements in the sample space. The odds of an event, on the other hand, is the ratio of the number of elements in the event compared to the number of elements in the complement of the event.

3. For some experiments, the theoretical probability is difficult to determine. In those cases a simulation can be done to determine the experimental probability of an event. If the experimental probability were, for example, 3/8, and the same experiment were done 40 times, the proportion $3/8 = x/40$ could be used to make a conjecture about the number of times an event would occur in the 40 experiments.

Chapter 12

Section 12.1

1.   (a) Level 1
       (b) Level 0
       (c) Level 0

2.   (a) None
       (b) 7
       (c) 2
       (d) Level 1

3.   (a) {1, 2, 7} and {3, 4, 5, 6, 8, 9}. Shapes 1, 2, and 7 all have 4 congruent sides and the rest of the shapes do not. Answers may vary.
       (b) {4, 6, 8, 9} and {1, 2, 3, 5, 7}. Shapes 1, 2, 3, 5, and 7 all have at least two parallel sides and the rest of the shapes do not. Answers may vary.
       (c) Level 1
       (d) Level 1

4.   9 rectangles

5.   (a) 13   (b) 15   (c) 15

6.

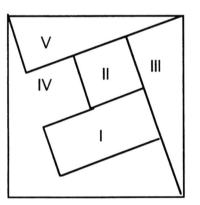

7.   (a) a, b, e, j
       (b) b, e, g, i, j
       (c) b, c, d, g, h, i, j
       (d) c, g, j

8.   (a) *ABRI, IRGH, IBMG*
       (b) *RDFG*
       (c) *IDEG*

       (d) *ABI, IBR, BMR, IRG, IGH, GRM, DEF*
       (e) *ICG*
       (f) *JOPQ*

9.   Yes. When the paper is folded so the ends of one line match, the ends of the other line also match.

10.   No. When the paper is folded along one line the ends of the other line match.

11.   (a)   (i) $\overline{AC}$ and $\overline{BD}$
           (ii) $\overline{AD}$ and $\overline{BC}$, $\overline{AD}$ and $\overline{BC}$
          (iii) $\overline{AD}$ and $\overline{DC}$, $\overline{DC}$ and $\overline{CB}$, $\overline{BA}$ and $\overline{AD}$
          (iv) E, $\overline{AC}$
       (b)   (i) $\overline{JL}$ and $\overline{IK}$
           (ii) $\overline{IJ}$ and $\overline{LK}$, $\overline{IL}$ and $\overline{JK}$
          (iii) $\overline{IL}$ and $\overline{LK}$, $\overline{LK}$ and $\overline{KJ}$, $\overline{KJ}$ and $\overline{JI}$
          (iv) M, $\overline{IK}$

12.   (a) (I)
       (b) (III)

13.   Yes.

14.   Lengths x and y are the same in each case.

15.   (a) 3   (b) 4

16.   All of them.

17.   (a) 7: $3 \times 2^2 + 4 \times 1^2 = 16$
          8:   $1 \times 3^2 + 3 \times 2^2 + 4 \times 1^2 = 25$
          9:   $9 \times 1^2 = 9$
              $1 \times 4^2 + 4 \times 2^2 + 4 \times 1^2 = 36$
         10: $2 \times 2^2 + 8 \times 1^2 = 16$
             $1 \times 4^2 + 9 \times 1^2 = 25$
         11: $1 \times 3^2 + 2 \times 2^2 + 8 \times 1^2 = 25$
             $2 \times 3^2 + 3 \times 2^2 + 6 \times 1^2 = 36$
         12: $1 \times 5^2 + 11 \times 1^2 = 36$
             $3 \times 3^2 + 9 \times 1^2 = 36$

13: $1 \times 2^2 + 12 \times 1^2 = 16$
$4 \times 2^2 + 9 \times 1^2 = 25$

14: $1 \times 3^2 + 1 \times 2^2 + 12 \times 1^2$
$= 25$
$2 \times 3^2 + 2 \times 2^2 + 10 \times 1^2$
$= 36$

15: $7 \times 2^2 + 8 \times 1^2 = 36$
$1 \times 4^2 + 2 \times 2^2 +$
$12 \times 1^2 = 36$

16: $16 \times 1^2 = 16$
$3 \times 2^2 + 13 \times 1^2 = 25$

(b) See (a)
(c) 9 and 16

18. Rotate 1/2 turn around the center, E. Then $\overline{AE}$ of the tracing coincides with $\overline{CE}$, and $\overline{BE}$ of the tracing coincides with $\overline{DE}$.

19. Rotate 1/2 turn around the center. Then opposite sides will coincide.

20. (a)

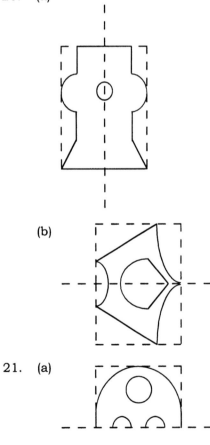

(b)

21. (a)

(b)

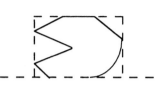

Figures here show the fold line at the bottom. They could also be drawn with the fold line at the top.

22.

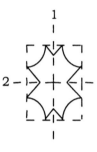

23.

Analyzing Student Thinking

24. These children's comments seem to reflect van Hiele Level 0, the visual level. Bernie does not recognize that straight sides are a property of triangles, and Chandra is visualizing a stereotypical triangle with slanted sides (which she calls "angles") and a horizontal base (which she calls "straight").

25. Yes; rhombi have perpendicular diagonals that bisect each other and squares fit into all three categories. Yes; non-isosceles trapezoids do not fit into any of these categories. See the following Venn diagram.

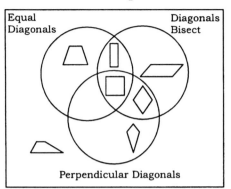

26. Level 0, because the orientation of the triangle on the page influenced Daniel's ability to recognize this as an isosceles triangle. Ask the student to investigate this triangle, as well as several other isosceles triangles with different orientations, constructed on a geoboard (or square dot paper). Because the geoboard can be turned and manipulated, this will help the student see that the orientation of a shape does not matter.

27. Tell Janet to cut out a paper rectangle and then ask how she can fold the rectangle to show that the opposite sides are the same length.

28. Carla seems to be at the initial level of Analysis, Level 1. Although she identifies the shape based on its general appearance (Level 0), this student's comments indicate that she notices the angles of the parallelogram are not the same as the angles of the rectangles she's seen. To help this student, emphasize that rectangles all have square corners.

29. Beth is incorrect. Building a quadrilateral around any two perpendicular line segments, as Beth describes, may not result in a rhombus, as the following example illustrates:

In order for Beth's method to work, she'd need to use the fact that a rhombus has diagonals that bisect each other.

30. Ask Becky to cut out the following parallelogram and fold it at point M so that $\overline{MA}$ lines up with $\overline{MC}$. Since these two line segments coincide, this shows that $\overline{BD}$ bisects $\overline{AC}$. Then ask Becky what she would need to do to show that $\overline{AC}$ bisects $\overline{BD}$.

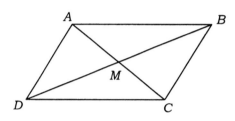

Problems Related to the NCTM Standards and Curriculum Focal Points

1. Identifying shapes is a level 0 activity unless students use properties to make the identification.

2. Describing shapes could be at a level 0 or level 1 depending on the level of detail of the descriptions. If they use properties in their descriptions, they are at a level 1.

3. The analysis in this focal point would indicate that students at grade 3 should have now moved to a level 1.

Section 12.2

1.

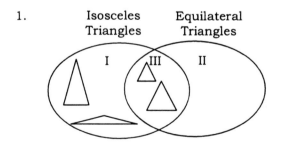

2.   Trapezoids   Rectangles

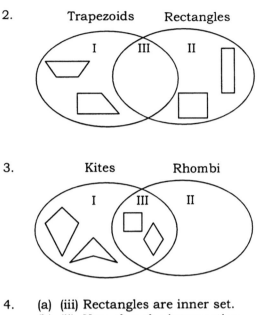

3.   Kites   Rhombi

4.   (a) (iii) Rectangles are inner set.
      (b) (ii) Note that the intersection
          is squares.
      (c) (iii) Squares inside rectangles.
      (d) (i)

5.   (a) *ABI, RBI, RBM, RMG, RGI,*
          HIG, FDE
      (b) *OQJ*
      (c) *ICGH*   (d) *ACI*
      (e) *GMDF*   (f) *GMDE*
      (Answers may vary.)

6.   Rhombi and kites both have
      perpendicular diagonals, and both
      have reflection symmetry. Rhombi
      have rotation symmetry, but kites
      do not. (Answers may vary.)

7.   (a) Reflections over both
          diagonals, half turn rotation
          around the center of the
          square.
      (b) 1/2 turn around the center of
          the square.

8.   (a) A,H,I,M,O,T,U,V,W,X,Y
      (b) B,C,D,E,H,I,K,O,X

9.   (a) Rotation, 180° about center of
          circle.
      (b) Reflection, vertical line
          through center; rotation, 120°
          or 240° degrees about center
          of circle.
      (c) Reflection, vertical line.

(d)   Reflection, 12 lines through
      center; rotation, 30° and
      multiples.

10.   (a)   (b)

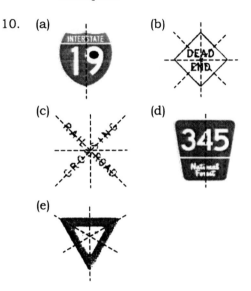

      (c)   (d)

      (e)

11.   (a) Fold on the dashed line.

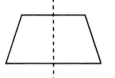

      (b) No, because the base angles of
          a non-isosceles trapezoid are
          not congruent.

12.   Rotate 1/2 turn around the
      center.

13.   A – Parallelogram
      B – Trapezoid
      C – Rhombus
      D – Square
      E – Rectangle
      F – Kite
      G – Quadrilateral

14.   (a)

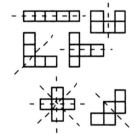

(b)

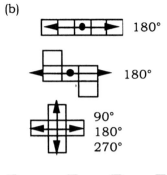

180°

180°

90°
180°
270°

15.

(a) For example:

(b) For example:

(c) One of many solutions:

Analyzing Student Thinking

16. Gerald is incorrect. An isosceles triangle is defined to be a triangle with at least two sides the same length. Thus, an equilateral triangle is a special type of isosceles triangle.

17. Yes, in general, Keith. However, if the kite is a rhombus, it will have two lines of symmetry.

18. No, Steve, because the definition of an isosceles trapezoid requires that the quadrilateral have exactly one pair of parallel sides; a rectangle has two pairs of parallel sides.

19. That's right, Elyse, since a square has 4 congruent sides, it fits the definition of a rhombus.

20. Bobby, some rectangles have a length that is different from the width, but the definition of rectangle does not require this. Whitney is right; a square fits the definition of rectangle since it has four right angles. Note however that we don't need to mention the parallel opposite sides since this is a *property* of rectangles, and not a requirement of the definition.

21. No. The following figure has reflection symmetry, but not rotation symmetry.

22. No.

When we fold the parallelogram on the line, the bottom half of the parallelogram does not coincide with the top half, so this is not a line of symmetry.

Problems Related to the NCTM Standards and Curriculum Focal Points

1. Rotational symmetry, reflection symmetry, perpendicular lines, parallel lines, convex and so on.

2. Opposite sides being parallel could be used to determine if the quadrilateral were a parallelogram or a trapezoid. If the adjacent sides are perpendicular then the quadrilateral may be a square or a rectangle. Answers may vary.

3. Paper folding works well for determining reflection symmetry. Paper tracing works well for determining rotation symmetry. Both of these tasks are

appropriate for elementary students.

Section 12.3

1. (a) {*L, M, N, R*}, {*Q, P, R*}, {*M, O, Q*}

    (b) {$\overrightarrow{LO}, \overrightarrow{MO}, \overrightarrow{NO}$}

    {$\overrightarrow{MN}, \overrightarrow{ON}, \overrightarrow{PN}$}

    {$\overrightarrow{OP}, \overrightarrow{QP}, \overrightarrow{NP}$}

2. $\overline{AB}, \overline{AC}, \overline{AD}, \overline{AE}, \overline{AB}, \overline{AF}, \overline{BC}, \overline{BD},$
    $\overline{BE}, \overline{BF}, \overline{CD}, \overline{CE}, \overline{CF}, \overline{DE}, \overline{DF}, \overline{EF}$

3. (a) ∠*LOM*, ∠*MON*, ∠*NOP*, ∠*NOQ*,
        ∠*POQ*

    (b) ∠*LOP*, ∠*LOQ*, ∠*MOP*, ∠*MOQ*

    (c) ∠*LON*

    (d) ∠*LOM* and ∠*MON*
        ∠*MON* and ∠*NOP*
        There are many others.

4. (a) 60°   (b) 30°   (c) 120°

5. (a) m(∠*C*) = 38°, m($\overline{AC}$) = 7 cm

    (b) m(∠*C*) = 55°,

        m($\overline{AC}$) = 6.4 cm
        Note: Answers will vary due to
        measurement error.

6. $\overline{AB}$ and $\overline{CB}$, $\overline{AD}$ and $\overline{CD}$, $\overline{AE}$
    and $\overline{CE}$.
    ∠*ADE* and ∠*CDE*,
    ∠*AED* and ∠*CED*
    ∠*DAE* and ∠*DCE*,
    ∠*EDA* and ∠*EDC*,
    ∠*BAE* and ∠*BCE*,
    ∠*BEA* and ∠*BEC*,
    ∠*AEB* and ∠*CEB*,
    ∠*ABE* and ∠*CBE*,
    ∠*DAB* and ∠*DCB*.

7. (a) ∠*LTO* and ∠*XVO*
        ∠*MUN* and ∠*XWV*
        ∠*NUX* and ∠*VWQ*
        There are many others.

    (b) ∠*STX* and ∠*XVO*
        ∠*NTX* and ∠*XVW*
        ∠*NUX* and ∠*XWR*
        ∠*TUX* and ∠*XWV*

8. (a) Yes; 36 + 78 + 66 = 180.

    (b) No; 124 + 56 + 20 ≠ 180.

    (c) No; 90 + 74 + 18 ≠ 180.

9. (a) 28   (b) 5   (c) 8

    (d) 15 = 28 - (5 + 8)

10. (a) $\overline{AP}$ is the same length as $\overline{CP}$,
        so P is the midpoint of $\overline{AC}$.

    (b) *P* is the midpoint of both
        diagonals.

    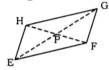

    (c) *P* is not the midpoint of either
        diagonal.

11. For example:

    (a)

    (b)

    (c)

    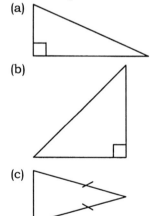

12. For example:

    (a)

(b)

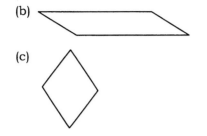

(c)

13. m($\angle AOB$) = 83°, m($\angle BOC$) = 7°

14. m($\angle X$) = 123°

15. m($\angle 1$) = 47°, m($\angle 2$) = 47°, m($\angle 3$) = 106°, m($\angle 4$) = 133°

16. (a) $l \parallel m$, given; m($\angle 3$) = m($\angle 4$), Alternate Interior Angles Property; m($\angle 3$) = m($\angle 1$), vertical angles have same measure; m($\angle 1$) = m($\angle 4$).
    (b) m($\angle 3$) = m($\angle 6$), given; m($\angle 4$) = m($\angle 6$), vertical angles have the same measure; m($\angle 3$) = m($\angle 4$); $l \parallel m$, Alternate Interior Angles Property.

17. (a) Equals 180°.
    (b) m($\angle 1$) + m($\angle 3$) = 180°, given; m($\angle 1$) + m($\angle 2$) = 180°, form straight angle; m($\angle 1$) + m($\angle 3$) = m($\angle 1$) + m($\angle 2$); m($\angle 3$) = m($\angle 2$), subtraction; $l \parallel m$, Alternate Interior Angles Property

18. The sum of the measures of any two consecutive angles of a parallelogram is 180°. Any two opposite angles of a parallelogram are congruent.

19. m($\angle a$) = 62°, m($\angle b$) = 45°, m($\angle c$) = 79°, m($\angle d$) = 56°, and m($\angle e$) = 39°.

20. (a) $a + b + c = 180°$ since the three angles form a straight angle.
    (b) A rectangle with a base half as long as $\overline{AC}$.
    (c) Yes, the results are the same.

21. 4 points → 6 lines
    5 points → 10 lines
    6 points → 15 lines
    n points → $\dfrac{n(n-1)}{2}$ lines

22. (a) No, there will always be at least one house not connected to one of the utilities.
    (b) Yes, one solution is shown next.

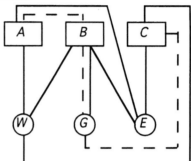

The problem stated above is related to a branch of mathematics called graph theory.

23. (a) Yes; by the Corresponding Angles Theorem and the Alternate Interior Angles Theorem, a parallelogram with one right angle must have four right angles—this is a rectangle.
    (b) No; for example, this quadrilateral has perpendicular diagonals, but is not a kite.

    (c) Yes, by the Corresponding Angles Theorem and Alternate Interior Angles Theorem, a parallelogram with a pair of adjacent sides congruent must have four congruent sides—this is a rhombus.

Analyzing Student Thinking

24. Yes, Jonas, this is the case when the kite is also a rhombus.

25. Alora is correct. Her brother likely made the mistake of reading the measure of the exterior angle.

26. Yes, Kent. First, by the Vertical Angle Theorem, the lower two angles labeled 2 are congruent. By the Alternate Interior Angles Theorem, the middle angles labeled 2 are congruent. Since the angle labeled 1 and the top angle labeled 2 form a straight angle, the sum of their measures is 180°. Thus, the measures of the original angles 1 and 2 add up to 180°.

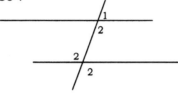

27. In this context, the word "vertical" is an adjective derived from the word *vertex*. Vertical angles are a pair of angles formed by a pair of intersecting lines such that the only point the two angles have in common is their vertex, which is the point of intersection of the lines. The lines themselves don't have to be vertical.

28. Parallel lines may be defined differently. In one case, they are defined as TWO lines in a plane that do not intersect. However, there is a good reason to allow a line to be parallel to itself. Thus, this is allowed in one definition. Some books do define a trapezoid to be a quadrilateral with at least one pair of parallel lines. However, others choose to limit the definition to exactly one pair of parallel lines.

29. No, there are only four rays since $\overrightarrow{RS}$ and $\overrightarrow{RT}$ are the same ray, and $\overrightarrow{TR}$ and $\overrightarrow{TS}$ are the same ray.

30. A triangle cannot be both scalene and isosceles since a triangle cannot have 3 sides of different length *and* at least two sides the same length. Also, a triangle cannot be both right and obtuse since a triangle with a 90-degree angle cannot have another angle that is greater than 90 degrees. In general, only combinations that that do not conflict are possible.

Problems Related to the NCTM Standards and Curriculum Focal Points

1. If the angles of a quadrilateral are measured, it can be determined if they are right angles or if consecutive ones are supplementary. In the first case it may indicate a rectangle and in the second case, it indicates parallel sides. Sides can be measured to see if all sides are congruent (rhombus) or opposite sides are congruent (parallelogram). Answers may vary.

2. The bottom (straight) edge is placed along one side of an angle with the center point of the protractor placed on the vertex of the angle. The second side of the angle can be seen under the curved part of the protractor. The number over the second side is the measure of the angle.

3. Concurrent lines: Where two walls meet each other and meet the floor, three lines are created. Those three lines are concurrent in the corner of the floor. Collinear points: The top corner of the three hinges on a door are collinear because the edge of the door is a straight line. Parallel lines: The top and bottom of a door are parallel lines. Many other answers are possible.

Section 12.4

1. (a) *S, C*   (b) none
    (c) none   (c) *S*

2. (a) 720°   (b) 900°

3. ∠*AGH* and ∠*FGL* are exterior
    angles. ∠*LGH* and ∠*GHI* are
    vertex angles. ∠*GMH* and ∠*GML*
    are central angles. (Answers may
    vary.)

4. (a) 72°, 144°, 216°, 288°
    (b) 60°, 120°, 180°, 240°, 300°
    (c) 51.4°, 102.9°, 154.3°, 205,7°,
        257.1°, 308.6°
    (d) 45°, 90°, 135°, 180°, 225°,
        270°, 315°
    (e) $\dfrac{x \cdot 180°}{n}$, for $x = 1, ..., n-1$

5. (a) 122°
    (b) 68°, 112°
    (c) 115°, 115°, 120°, 120°

6. (a) 154.3°, 25.7°, 25.7°
    (b) 160°, 20°, 20°
    (c) 170°, 10°, 10°
    (d) 171.4°, 8.6°, 8.6°

7. 18 sides

8. (a) 12   (b) 15
    (c) 60   (d) 180

9. (a) 3   (b) 30
    (c) 24   (d) 72

10. (a) 20   (b) 10
    (c) 120

11. (a) 40°   (b) 24°
    (c) $(180 - x)$°

12. (a) 144°   (b) 60°
    (c) $(180 - a)$°

13. (a)

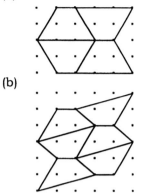

    (b)

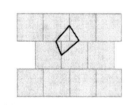

14. E and D are midpoints of $\overline{AB}$ and
    $\overleftrightarrow{AC}$, respectively. Lines $\overleftrightarrow{ED}$ and
    $\overleftrightarrow{BC}$ do not meet in the tessellation
    (extended), so are parallel. Since
    ED = BF = FC, we have BC = 2ED.

15. $a_1/a_2 = b_1/b_2$. In this case a_1/a_2
    = 1/2.

16. (a)

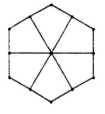

    (b) No

17. (a) Kites

(b) Triangles

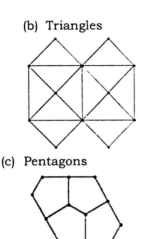

(c) Pentagons

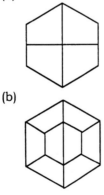

18. (a) (4, 8, 8)   (b) (4, 6, 12)
    (c) (3, 3, 3, 3, 6) (d) (3, 3, 4, 3, 4)
    (e) (3, 4, 6, 4)
    (f) (3, 3, 3, 3, 4, 4)
    (g) (3, 12, 12)   (h) (3, 6, 3, 6)

19. (a) (4, 4, 4, 4), (3, 3, 4, 12),
        (3, 3, 6, 6), (3, 4, 4, 6),
        (3, 4, 3, 12), (3, 6, 3, 6),
        (3, 4, 6, 4)
    (b) (3, 3, 3, 3, 6), (3, 3, 3, 4, 4),
        (3, 3, 4, 3, 4)
    (c) (3, 3, 3, 3, 3, 3)
    (d) no ways

20. Yes

21. No

22. (a) Pentagon: 1/5, 2/5, 3/5,
        4/5and 1 full turn around the
        center. Hexagon: 1/6, 1/3,
        1/2, 2/3, 5/6, and 1 full turn
        around the center.
    (b) *n.*

23. (a)

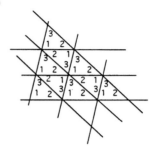

    (b)

24. (a)

    (b) Sum of measures of vertex
        angles of a triangle is 180
        degrees. Vertical angles have
        same measure.

25. $a = 45°$, $b = 45°$, $c = 65°$, $d = 80°$,
    $e = 30°$, $f = 70°$, $g = 20°$, $h = 55°$

26. Divide by 180, subtraction of
    fractions, addition property,
    division by 2 and distributivity.

27. (a) (3,7,42), (3,8,24), (3,9,18),
        (3,10,15), (3,12,12)
    (b) (4,5,20), (4,6,12), (4,8,8)
    (c) (5,5,10)
    (d) (6,6,6)
    (e) 10

28. (a) 5   (b) 10   (c) 5
    (d) (5,5,5), which does not
        surround point E
    (e) By putting triangle or
        Pentagon in the center, you get
        the same results except for
        (3,12,12).

29. (a) (4,4,4,4), (3,3,4,12), (3,3,6,6),
        (3,4,4,6)
    (b) (4,4,4,4)
    (c) (3,3,4,12), (3,4,3,12), (3,3,6,6),
        (3,4,4,6)
    (d) (3,6,3,6), (3,4,6,4)

30. (a) (3,3,3,3,6) and (3,3,3,4,4)
    (b) (3,3,3,3,6), (3,3,3,4,4),
        (3,3,4,3,4)
    (c) (3,3,3,3,3,3), regular
    (d) No, angle measure would have
        to be less than 60° (or have
        fewer sides than 2 then.)

31. (a) (i)   (ii)

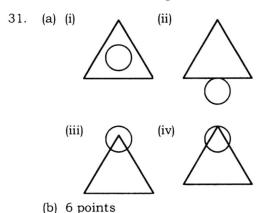

(b) 6 points

Analyzing Student Thinking

32. No. The sum of the measures of the four vertex angles of any quadrilateral is 360°. Thus, to tessellate a convex quadrilateral, surround each point by one copy of each vertex angle, matching the sides with the same length, as follows:

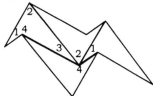

33. Tyrone, if you used regular pentagons (rather than a rough sketch) for your tessellation, you would be able to see there are gaps between the pentagons. This is because, since the angles of a regular pentagon measure 108°, when three pentagons are put together around a common vertex, these angles add up to 324°, not 360°.

34. This student is thinking about applying a formula that is appropriate for a *regular* pentagon where all five vertex angles are congruent. If the four angles are not all 108°, he needs to subtract the sum of the measures of the four angles from 540° to find the measure of the missing angle.

35. Yes. A regular octagon has 8 lines of symmetry. The first group used the 4 lines of symmetry that pass through opposite vertices to form 8 congruent triangles, while the second group used the 4 lines of symmetry that pass through the midpoints of the opposite sides to form 8 congruent kites.

36. Clifton, you certainly can make a polygon with so many sides that it looks like a circle. In fact, the more sides you give the polygon, the more it resembles a circle. However, a circle is not a polygon since a polygon is made up of line segments and a circle is not.

37. Jackie is correct. For each vertex of a polygon, there are two exterior angles (one for each of the sides that meet at that vertex), as the following figure illustrates. The sum of the measures of all of these exterior angles is 720°.

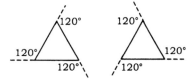

38. Ask Marty and Heather to explain more about what they're thinking. What does he mean by "plane figure?" And which angles is he referring to: vertex angles? Which angles is Heather referring to: central angles? Ask these students to check their claims with a few such figures/angles.

39. First, give Jared 6 toothpicks and ask him if he can arrange them into a hexagon with different sized angles (he'll be able to form a convex hexagon like the one shown below).

It is also possible to make a hexagon that has equal angles and not equal sides; for example:

Problems Related to the NCTM Standards and Curriculum Focal Points

1. The key to constructing a tessellation is fitting polygons around a single point so that no overlaps or gaps occur. The sum of the measures of the vertex angles of the different polygons must add to 360° for this to work.

2. You could use a protractor to find the sum of the interior angles of a polygon but the most accurate way is to cut the polygon into triangles as shown in Figure 12.4 and then adding of the angles of the triangles.

3. Tiles on a floor, bricks on a wall and plywood on a roof all form tessellations. Answers may vary.

Section 12.5

1. (a) $\{\overline{BG},\overline{CF}\},\{\overline{CF},\overline{DE}\},\{\overline{BG},\overline{DE}\}$
    (b) $\{\overline{DC},\overline{GF}\},\{\overline{AD},\overline{GF}\},\{\overline{EF},\overline{BG}\},$
        $\{\overline{AB},\overline{CF}\}$
        Other answers are possible.
    (c) Planes $DCFE$ and $BCFG$ with edge $\overline{CF}$. Other answers are possible.
    (d) Planes ADE and $CFDE$ with edge $\overline{DE}$.

2. (a) $1/2$, $\sqrt{3}/2$
    (b) $\sqrt{3}/2$
    (c) $AE = DE = \sqrt{3/2}$, $AD = 1$

3. (a) Yes. 6 total faces – 2 triangles, 2 quadrilaterals, and 2 pentagons.

(b) No. Faces are not polygons.
(c) No. Not a single enclosed space.

4. (a) Triangular prism
    (b) Rectangular prism
    (c) Hexagonal prism

5. Prisms: (a) and (c); pyramid: (b)

6. (a) right triangular prism
    (b) regular tetrahedron
    (c) right rectangular prism
    (d)

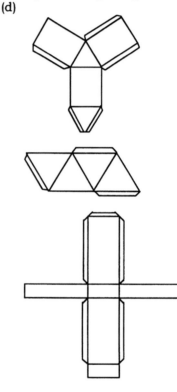

7.

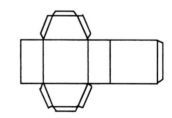

8.

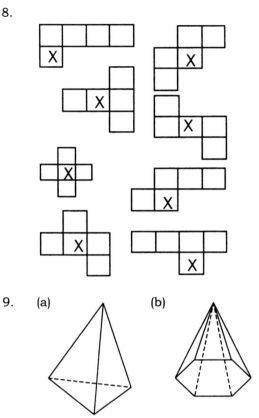

9.   (a)   (b)

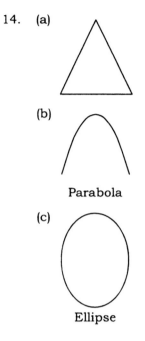

10.   (a) Triangle: 4, 4, 8, 6;
          quadrilateral: 5, 5, 10, 8;
          pentagon: 6, 6, 12, 10;
          hexagon: 7, 7, 14, 12;
          n-gon: $n+1$, $n+1$, $2n+2$, $2n$
      (b) Yes

11.   (a) (i) 10, 12, 22, 20;
          (ii) 9, 9, 18, 16
      (b) Yes

12.   Truncated icosahedron: 6-6-5
      Truncated dodecahedron: 10-10-3
      Cube octahedron: 4-4-3
      Small rhombicubahedrdon: 4-4-4-
      3
      On each polyhedron all vertex
      arrangements are the same, so
      they are all semiregular.

13.   (a)   (b)

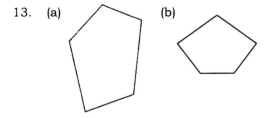

14.   (a)

(b)

Parabola

(c)

Ellipse

15.

16.

17.   (a) Either upper left or lower right.
      (b) Either, depending on
          perspective.

18.   34

19.   View (b). The tops in (a) and (c)
      should have a rectangle.

20. (a)

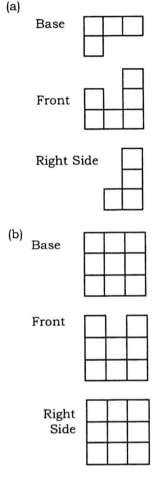

Base

Front

Right Side

(b) Base

Front

Right Side

21. Largest number = 19

2	3	2
2	2	2
2	2	2

Smallest number = 13

1	3	1
2	1	1
1	1	2

(Other base designs are possible.)

22. (a)
Sides	1	2	3	0
Cubes	0	0	8	0

(b)
Sides	1	2	3	0
Cubes	6	12	8	1

(c)
Sides	1	2	3	0
Cubes	24	24	8	8

(d)
Sides	1	2
Cubes	$6(n-2)^3$	$12(n-2)$

Sides	3	0
Cubes	8	$(n-2)^3$

23. They all are possible, for example (h)

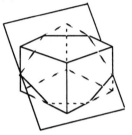

24. Yes for all parts.

25. (a) 6   (b) 4
    (c) 6   (d) infinite number

26. (a) 3 of order 2 (through midpoints of nonintersecting edges); 4 of order 3 (through vertex and center of opposite face)
    (b) 5 of order 2 (through midpoint of edge and center of opposite face); 1 of order 5 (through centers of bases)

27. (a) 1   (b) Infinite   (c) Infinite

28. 6

Analyzing Student Thinking

29. Rene, you're right about planes in the 3-dimensional space and about lines in 2-dimensional space. However, when we talk about lines in 3-dimensional space, we must consider that the two lines may be in different planes, in which case they may be neither intersecting, nor parallel; for example, a line on the ceiling where a wall meets the ceiling and

a line on the floor that is perpendicular to the wall.

30. Mario, it can get a little confusing when we use the same term for two different objects. To clarify, you could call the "sides" of a polygon, "edges," and the "sides" of a polyhedron, "faces."

31. Cheryl, the word "right" used with a prism or pyramid refers to the axis being perpendicular to (forming a right angle with) the base, as opposed to an oblique polyhedron which leans. "Right triangular pyramid" would usually be taken to mean a pyramid that has a triangular base, but not necessarily a right triangular base. This makes one wonder if, to specify a right pyramid with a right triangular base, one would need to say a "right, right triangular pyramid."

32. No. There is a need for two different definitions because a circle is a 2-dimensional figure and a sphere is 3-dimensional. A circle is the set of points *in a plane* that are the same distance from its center, whereas a sphere is a set of points *in space* that are the same distance from its center.

33. Alicia, a non-isosceles trapezoid is an example of a polygon with no lines of symmetry. An oblique prism with such a trapezoid as its base would have no plane of symmetry.

34. Koji, there must be at least 3 regular polygons meeting at each vertex of a regular polyhedron. If we put 3 hexagons together, each with a 120° angle, the total would be 360°. The polyhedron would flatten out, making it impossible to form a solid.

35. Jesse, to see this one, it might help to imagine two walls; you can see these intersect in a line at the corner of the room. Now, imagine a third wall that comes out from the corner of the room, as the following drawing shows. These three walls intersect in a line.

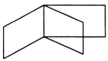

Problems Related to the NCTM Standards and Curriculum Focal Points

1. All of the faces of a polyhedron are polygons. They enclose space without any holes. They satisfy Euler's formula. Answers may vary.

2. It is called a dihedral angle. It is measured by drawing a line in each plane (face) of the angle that is perpendicular to the edge. Both lines also need to intersect the edge at the same point. These two lines and their point of intersection form a regular angle, which can then be measured.

3. Polyhedra or not, regular or not, semiregular or not, oblique or right. Answers may vary.

Chapter 13 - Measurement

Section 13.1

1. (a) $1\frac{2}{3}$, $1\frac{1}{4}$, $\frac{1}{4}$
    (b) 12, 12,
    (c) Whether the pencil is mechanical or wood or old. Whether the fingers are fat or skinny.

2. (a) Waist, hips, length from neck to waist or to hemline, bust or chest, length of arm.
    (b) Length and width of foot, height of arch.
    (c) Height, weight, heartbeat, blood pressure.
    (d) Height, strength, height of jump, number of sit-ups in 1 minute.

3. (a) 220   (b) 320
    (c) 640   (d) 4492.125
    (e) 512,000   (f) 1
    (g) 126   (h) 48

4.

TABLESPOON	LIQUID OUNCE	CUP	PINT	QUART	GALLON
256	128	16	8	4	1
1024	512	64	32	16	4
384	192	24	12	6	1.5
64	32	4	2	1	.25

5.

SQUARE INCHES	SQUARE FEET	SQUARE YARDS
2592	18	2
6480	45	5
79056	549	61

6. (a) 205 m   (b) 72 m
    (c) 512 km

7. (a) 10 L   (b) 200 mL
    (c) 200 L

8. (a) 25 g   (b) 7 g
    (c) 1715 kg

9. (a) -5° C   (b) 39° C

10. (a) 10 cents   (b) 1 cent
    (c) $10   (d) $1000

11. "Mega" means one million times, so winnings are millions of dollars.

12. (a) 12 m   (b) 0.03569 km
    (c) 26,000,000 cm
    (d) 0.786 m
    (e) 38.4 cm   (f) 1200 cm
    (g) 1,345,000 cm (h) 0.019 km
    (i) 46,780 km (j) 8.9 hm

13. (a) 10,000
    (b) four places to right
    (c) two places to the right
    (d) two places to the left.
    (e) are and hectare

14. (a) 2,000,000 cm³
    (b) 5,000,000,000 mm³
    (c) 16,000 cm³
    (d) 0.62 dm³
    (e) 0.056 m³
    (f) 1200 cm³

15. (a) 4750 mg
    (b) 0.057 hg
    (c) 32,000 mg

16. (a) 3.5 dL   (b) 0.56 L
    (c) 0.520 kL

17. (a) kg   (b) dm³, kg
    (c) mL, g

18. (a) 58°C   (b) 194°F
    (c) -22°F   (d) -88°C
    (e) -0.4°F

19. (a) 400 g/cm
    (b) 65 g/cm³
    (c) 0.972 ton/yd³
    (d) 98.2 mi/hr

20. (a) 48 farthings
    (b) 2 farthings

21. (a) 402.34 m   (b) 0.62 mi

22. (a) 750 mi/hr
    (b) 6,570,000 mi/yr

23. 1 jack = 1/8 james, 1/480 jennifers, 1/5760 jessicas;

1 james = 192 jills, 1/60 jennifers, 1/720 jessicas; 1 jennifer = 11,520 jills, 480 jacks, 1/12 jessicas; 1 jessica = 138,240 jills, 5760 jacks, 720 james

24. 261,100 watts

25. Approximately 85 ha

26. 89 kph (88.5 km/hr)
Note: most signs are reading 88 kph, which has us drive a little slower.

27. (a) 50 days   (b) 2.7 ft/hr

28. (a) 6,278,400,000 joules
(b) $88.39

29. -40° C = -40° F

30. (a) About 18 km/sec
(b) 5.4 × 10^9 km

31. 3.268 light years

32. This is impossible since the car has used up all the time required for the round trip by the time it reaches the first city.

33. (a) 1 hr/roll
(b) 18 rolls/hr or .055 hr/roll
(c) 2600 rolls

34. Surface area about 10243 m^2; Volume about 68292 m^3

Analyzing Student Thinking

35. Kimiko, standard units help in situations when we want to communicate our measurements to other people. Also, standard units are better when we need precise measurements, while nonstandard units are fine when the accuracy and precision are not important.

36. Jhoti, a square yard is a square that measures one yard (or 3 feet) on each side:

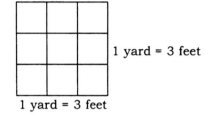

1 yard = 3 feet

1 yard = 3 feet

Counting the number of square feet we see that 1 square yard = 9 square feet.

37. Monique is incorrect. She needs to multiply 43,560 by 14 to find the total area of the plot, 609,840 sq. feet. Then, she should take the square root to find the length of the side of the square plot, 780.92 ft.

38. Scotty is incorrect. The volume of topsoil ordered is 1 yd^3 = 27 ft^3 = $27 \times 12 \times 12 \times 12$ in^3 = 46,656 in^3. But Scotty would require $15 \times 24 \times 1/6$ = 60 ft^3 = 60×12^3 in^3 = 103,680 in^3 of topsoil to cover his garden evenly to a depth of 2 inches.

39. Amy is incorrect. Imagine a square that measures 1 meter on each side (a m²). Then, each side measures 100 cm and there are 100 × 100 = 10,000 cm² in a m². In other words, 1 cm² = 1/10,000 = .0001 m². Similarly, it takes 100 × 100 × 100 = 1,000,000 cm³ to fill a cube that measures 1 m by 1 m by 1 m (a cubic meter), so 1 cm³ = 1/1,000,000 = .000001 m³.

40. Jeremy is incorrect 41°F = 5°C and 82°F = 28°C. Would that mean that in Celsius it was $5\frac{1}{2}$ times as hot as in the morning? Whether in Celsius or Fahrenheit, zero is not an absolute measure. Therefore, this type of comparison, by a factor, does not apply here.

41. Kobe, there are many reasons. First, the metric system has all the features of an ideal system of units: portability, convertability, and interrelatedness, whereas the US system lacks convertability and interrrelatedness. In short, the metric system is a better system. Also, nearly every other country in the world uses the metric system. If the US were to make the switch, many international activities, including trade and communication, would be made easier.

Problems Related to the NCTM Standards and Curriculum Focal Points

1. The height of a book; the length of a foot; the number of marbles in a bag; the height of a stack of blocks. Answers will vary.

2. It is easier to convert within a given type of measurement like meters to centimeters. It is easier to convert between different types of units like liters to cubic centimeters. Almost all other countries in the world already use the metric system. Answer will vary.

3. Foot- a persons foot; yard- one step; gallon-a gallon of milk; pound-a pound of butter; liter- a liter of soda or about a quart of milk; milligram- an ibuprofen pill usually contains 200 milligrams of medicine.

Section 13.2

1. (a) $9/2 - \sqrt{3}$ (b) $3\sqrt{3}$
   (c) 7.96 (d) 6.03

2. (a) $q - p$
   (b) $\dfrac{q - p}{2}$
   (c) $p + \dfrac{q - p}{2} = \dfrac{p + q}{2}$
   (d) Yes

(e) $\dfrac{-2.5 + 13.9}{2} = 5.7$

3. (a) -10.9   (b) -2.4

4. (a) $q - p$ (b) $\dfrac{2p + q}{3}$
   (c) $\dfrac{p + 2q}{3}$
   (d) $m = 2.9$, $n = 9.4$

5. (a) -10.2   (b) 11.1

6. (a) $P = 99.4$ units
   (b) $a = 7.6$ units
   (c) $b = 12$ units

7. 195.6 units

8. 90 units

9. (a) $r = 13.4/\pi$ units,
       $d = 26.8/\pi$ units
   (b) $d = 2\sqrt{15}$ units,
       $c = 2\pi\sqrt{15}$ units
   (c) $r = 9\pi$ units, $C = 18\pi^2$ units

10. (a) $A = 501.96$ sq. units
    (b) $a = 7.6$ units
    (c) $b = 12$ units

11. (a) $A = 25$ sq. units
        $P = 8 + 14\sqrt{2}$ units
    (b) $A = 20$ sq. units
        $P = 8 + 12\sqrt{2}$ units
    (c) $A = 22\dfrac{1}{2}$ sq. units
        $P = 14 + 14\sqrt{2}$ units
    (d) Figure (a) by $2\dfrac{1}{2}$

12. (a) 7 units   (b) $6\dfrac{1}{2}$ units
    (c) 8 units

13. 92 Pieces

14. (a) 8.2 km^2 (b) 60 m^2

15. 1292.94 sq. units

16.   418.86 sq. units

17.   (a) $\sqrt{13}$, 4, A_1 = 12, A_2 = 8;
          5, 2, A_1 = 6, A_2 = 8
      (b) The statement is false since
           parallelograms with the same
           length sides had different
           areas.

18.   (a) $(1/2)(2 + 6) = 4$ (b) 4
      (c) They are equal.

19.   (a) 2   (b) 18   (c) 1:9

20.   (a) r = 15.2 units,
          d = 30.4 units
      (b) $d = 2\sqrt{15}$ units,
          $A = 15\pi$ sq. units
      (c) $r = 9\pi$ units,
          $A = 81\pi^3$ sq. units

21.   (a) $6\sqrt{7}$ sq. units
      (b) 16 sq. units

22.   (a) Hypotenuse of 2 by 1 right
           triangle
      (b) 4 × 1   (c) 3 × 3
      (d) 5 × 2

23.   (a) $\sqrt{34}$ units   (b) 7 units

24.   (a) Yes   (b) Yes   (c) No

25.   (a) Acute

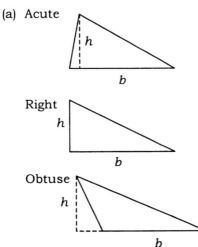

          b and h are the same on all
          triangles to give equal areas.
      (b) The perimeters are all
           different.

(c) There is no clear relationship.

26.   No. If a parallelogram is very long
      and narrow, the perimeter will be
      large but the area will be small.

27.   (a) Slant distance (13 ft) can be
           more easily measured than
           $6\sqrt{5}$ ft.
      (b) 3120 sq. ft.
      (c) 260 sheets
      (d) 120 sheets laid out in 15 rows
           by 8 rows. 10 sheets cut each
           into 2' by 3' pieces to be laid
           out end to end on top of
           others. 130 sheets for each
           half of the roof.

28.   Approximately 25 meters

29.   (a) $\sqrt{89} \approx 9.4$m   (b) $\sqrt{73} \approx 8.5$m
      (c) $\sqrt{34} \approx 5.8$m   (d) $\sqrt{98} \approx 9.9$m

30.   (a) 16, 30, 34
      (b) 105, 208, 233
      (c) 715, 1428, 1597
      (d) 1, 1, 2, 3, 5, 8, 13, 21, 34, 55,
           89, 144, 233, 377, 610, 987,
           1597   Yes

31.   (a) $\sqrt{3}$ units
      (b) $\sqrt{3}$ square units
      (c) $6\sqrt{3}$ square units

32.   250 square inches

33.   A 4 × 4 and a 6 × 3 rectangle.

34.   About 128 ft.

35.   40 posts

36.   (a) Obtuse   (b) No
      (c) Acute   (d) Acute
      (e) Right   (f) No

37.   (a) $\overline{RS} \parallel \overline{TU}$ since $\angle S$ and $\angle T$
           (interior angles on same side)
           are supplementary.
      (b) $(1/2)(a + b)(a + b)$
      (c) m ($\angle RVS$) + m($\angle RVU$) +
           m($\angle UVT$) = 180°, but
           m ($\angle RVS$) + 90° + m($\angle UVT$)

$= 180°$, so m($\angle RVU$) = $90°$.

(d) $(1/2)ab + (1/2)c^2 + (1/2)ab$

(e) $(1/2)(a + b)(a + b)$

    $= (1/2)ab + (1/2)c^2 + (1/2)ab$;

    $a^2 + 2ab + b^2 = 2ab + c^2$

    $a^2 + b^2 = c^2$.

38. (a) 63.7%   (b) 78.5%

    (c) Circular plug fits better into the square hole.

39. $x = 15$ units

40. Consider the possible ways of flattening out the room. The shortest distance between two points is given by a straight line. The shortest distance is 1133 cm or 11.33 m calculated as follows:

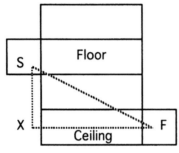

$SX = 200$ cm + 400 cm + 200 cm = 800 cm

$XF = 1$ cm + 800 cm + 1 cm = 802 cm

$SF = \sqrt{(800)^2 + (802)^2} = 1132.8$

41. (a)

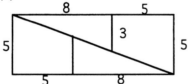

Area of square = 64 sq. units;
Area of rectangle = 65 sq. units; yes.

(b) 169, 168, yes; 441, 442

42. $4 - \pi$ sq. units

43. Area of equilateral triangle with side 1 = $\sqrt{3}/4$ sq. units. Area of 1/6 of circle is $\pi/6$ sq. units. Area of half-petal (shaded) is

$\pi/6 - \sqrt{3}/4$ sq. units. Total area of the hexafoil is

$12(\pi/6 - \sqrt{3}/4) = 2\pi - 3\sqrt{3}$ sq. units.

44. The shaded areas are equal. The total area of the three smaller circles is 36π. The area of the largest circle is 36π. The unshaded areas of overlap are both subtracted from 36π, leaving the same amount remaining.

45. (a) About 7,954,550 mi

    (b) About 318 times

46. (a) No, the ratios area C: area B: area A = 5:3:1, while the point ratios are 4:2:1.

    (b) Make the points 30, 18, 6.

47. (a) $9\sqrt{3}$ square units

    (b) $A = \dfrac{s^2\sqrt{3}}{4}$

48. When P, Q, and R are collinear.

Analyzing Student Thinking

49. Jordan, that formula works if you have a *regular* n-gon. However, to find the perimeter of a non-regular n-gon, you'd need to find the sum of the various lengths of the sides.

50. Elise, the orientation of the base does not matter. Each of the 3 sides of a triangle has a height associated with it, and you may use any of these to determine its area.

51. Ethan, the Pythagorean theorem states, "the sum of the squares of

the lengths of the legs of a right triangle is equal to the square of the length of the hypotenuse." Thus, when the hypotenuse has length a and the legs have lengths b and c, we have $b^2 + c^2 = a^2$. Often students memorize the Pythagorean theorem as $a^2 + b^2 = c^2$, but that assumes that the hypotenuse has length c and the legs have lengths a and b.

52. Alayna is correct. The circumference of a circle, $C = 2\pi r$, is a 1-dimensional measurement and has the variable r to the first power. The area of a circle, $A = \pi r^2$, is a 2-dimensional measurement, and has the variable r to the second power. This idea works with all figures, including the fact that formulas for volume would reflect 3-dimesionality.

53. Dana is correct in the first case, but not the second. The area of a square of side length s is $A = s^2$. Doubling the length of the side would give an area of $A = (2s)^2 = 4s^2$, 4 times the original area. However, when the side length is tripled, the new area would be $A = (3s)^2 = 9s^2$, 9 times the original area, not 6 times as Dana claimed.

54. Yes. When Carol got the answer 156 cm sq, she was done - that is the area. However, she took it one step further and squared 156. It seems she interpreted 156 cm² to mean $(156 \text{ cm})^2$, when in fact 156 cm² is simply an abbreviation for 156 square centimeters. That is, the unit of area is a square 1 cm by 1 cm.

55. Diana, you could choose any side for the base, as long as you use the altitude that corresponds to that base. If you want to use 10 as the length of the base, you'd need to know the length of the

segment through point C and perpendicular to $\overline{AB}$, namely $\overline{CE}$.

56. No; for example, the following rectangles show that a rectangle with a larger perimeter may not have a larger area.

2.5

P = 9 units   P = 12 units
A = 5 sq. units   A = 5 sq. units

Problems Related to the NCTM Standards and Curriculum Focal Points

1. Area is the physical quantity expressing the size of a part of a surface and can be measured with squares, or triangles or any shape that tessellates. Length is the long dimension of any object and is one-dimensional as opposed to two-dimensional like area.

2. First the equations of the areas of different triangles are developed so that a parallelogram can be split into two triangles. The equation for the areas of these two triangles is known and can be added to find the equation for the area of a parallelogram.

3. A regular polygon is inscribed in a circle and the perimeter of the polygon is determined. By inscribing polygons with more and more sides and looking at the corresponding perimeters, the equation for the circumference emerges.

Section 13.3

1. (a) 1248.1 in^2 (b) 186 m^2
   (c) 792 cm^2 (d) 173 cm^2

2. (a) SA $= 60 + 30 \times 20 = 660$ sq. units

(b) 254 sq. units

3. $864 + 432\sqrt{3}\,\text{cm}^2$ or
     approximately $1612\ \text{cm}^2$

4.   (a) $792\ \text{cm}^2$ (b) $173\ \text{cm}^2$

5.   (a) $766\ \text{cm}^2$ (b) $866\ \text{cm}^2$

6.   (a) 122 sq. units
     (b) 450 sq. units

7.   S = 564 sq. units

8.   (a) 1206 sq. units
     (b) 4825 sq. units

9. $1923\ \text{in}^2$

10. (a) $36\,\pi\ \text{cm}^2$
     (b) $610.09\,\pi\ \text{cm}^2$
     (c) 8.288 cm

11. $196\,\pi$ sq. units

12. Cube

13. 12 × 8 × 6 units

14. 8 units

15. (a) 72 square units
     (b) 272 square units
     (c) 1640 square units

16. (a) 4:25   (b) 4:25
     (c) 4 times original surface area

17. $347,538.7\ \text{ft}^2$

18. Approximately $230\ \text{m}^2$

19. (a) 384 sq. units
     (b) 192 sq. units

20. Each stripe covers 1/3 of the
     lateral surface area, so the red
     stripe covers about $2094\ \text{cm}^2$.

Analyzing Student Thinking

21. Carter is incorrect. He'd need to
     correct his statement in three
     ways: "If the bases of a *right* prism
     are *regular* hexagons, then the
     lateral surface area of the prism is
     six times the area of any of the
     lateral faces."

22. Amberly, notice that, if we use the
     distributive property to rewrite
     this expression for *S*, we get:
     $S = 2\pi r(r + h) = 2\pi r^2 + 2\pi rh$. The r^2
     and *rh* terms suggest this is a 2-
     dimensional measurement.

23. Tara, with the given perimeter of
     the base, you can find the length
     of one side of the base by dividing
     by the number of sides in the
     base. Then, use that, together
     with the known height to the apex,
     to apply the Pythagorean theorem
     and determine the slant height.

24. Kennedy is incorrect. Both of
     these measurements involve π
     since the lateral surface area of a
     right circular cylinder is the
     circumference of the base times
     the height of the cylinder, while
     the sum of the areas of the bases
     is the area of two circles. In fact,
     these two will be equal precisely
     when the height of the cylinder is
     equal to its radius so that
     $2\pi rh = 2\pi r^2$.

25. Mason, the surface area of the
     sphere quadruples when you
     double the radius since
     $S = 4\pi(2r)^2 = 4\pi \cdot 4r^2 = 16\pi r^2$ is
     four times the surface area of the
     original sphere, $S = 4\pi r^2$.

26. Have Jalen roll up a rectangular
     piece of paper. It should look like
     a cylinder without its bases. Then
     when he unrolls it, he can see
     what the lateral surface looks like,
     namely a rectangle.

27. If Mark wants to use the same size circle for both cones, he can. In the following circle, the larger sector will make the fatter, shorter cone and the smaller sector will make the skinny, taller cone. The radius of the circle becomes the slant height for each cone.

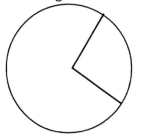

Problems Related to the NCTM Standards and Curriculum Focal Points

1. When finding surface areas, one can simply break the surface into its various parts like rectangles, triangles, circles, etc., find the areas of the parts and then add them up. This is a more powerful way to find surface areas than memorizing many different equations.

2. The surface area of a cone has two parts: the base and the lateral surface. The area of the base can be found by using the equation of a circle. The area of the lateral surface can be laid out flat to see that it is just the sector of a circle. The portion of the circumference that the sector takes up can be used along with the equation of the area of a circle to find the lateral surface area.

3. Similar to the answer to question 1, breaking the surface area into pieces and finding the areas of those pieces is a good general strategy for finding surface area.

Section 13.4

1. (a) 2508 in^3 (b) 148 m^3

2. $320\sqrt{3}$ in^3

3. 2160 m^3

4. (a) 540 π cm^3 (b) 12.5 π cm^3

5. (a) About 1562 cm^3
   (b) About 1951 cm^3

6. (a) 40 cu. units
   (b) 70 cu. units

7. (a) 10 cu. units
   (b) 20 cu. units   (c) part (b)

8. (a) 18 π cu. units
   (b) 96 π cu. units

9. (a) triples
   (b) nine times larger

10. (a) 51 cu. units
    (b) 157 cu. units

11. About 27.11 cm³.

12. (a) Volume = 10 cu. units
       Surface Area = 36 sq. units
    (b) Volume = 11 cu. units
       Surface Area = 38 sq. units
    (c) Volume = 21 cu. units
       Surface Area = 64 sq. units

13. (a) 296 cm^3 (b) 296 g

14. (a) All have volume 125,000 cm³.
    (b) A 15,000 cm²,
       B 17,500 cm²,
       C 19,500 cm²
    (c) No
    (d) Box A

15. (a) 120,000 cm³   (b) 31,000 cm²

16. (a) 3,072,000 cubic yards
    (b) 96,000 square yards

17. 4 trips

18. $h = 30/\pi \approx 9.55$ cm

19. $48.48

20. 6569 in^3

21. (a) 48%   (b) 32.5%

22. $151\frac{2}{3}$ pounds

23. (a) New volume is 8 times
       the original.
    (b) New surface area is 4 the
       times original.

24. (a) 4:25   (b) 8:125
    (c) 8 times original volume

25. (a) $8\sqrt{2} \approx 11.31$ inches on a side
    (b) 63.66%

26. 192 cm^3

27. Approximately 0.5 cm

28. $208/216 \approx 0.963$

29. 20.25 hours.

30. 160 ft

31. The one with the shorter side as
    height.

Analyzing Student Thinking

32. Yes. The surface area of a cube is
    equal to its volume precisely when
    $6s^2 = s^3$, which implies $s = 6$.

33. Yes. Since Nedra knew the area of
    the square base, she could
    determine the side length of the
    base. Then, using half this
    number and the slant height, she
    could apply the Pythagorean
    theorem to determine the altitude,
    which is all she needed for
    computing the volume.

34. Ask Carston to compare the
    volumes of two spheres, one with
    radius 1 unit and the other with
    radius 3 units. He should see
    that, in fact, the volume increases
    by a factor of 3^3.

35. Pedro is incorrect. Compare the
    volume of a cone, $V = \frac{1}{3}(\pi r^2)h$, to
    another that has had the radius
    doubled and the height tripled:
    $V = \frac{1}{3}\pi(2r)^2 \cdot (3h) = 4\pi r^2 h$. The
    new volume is 12 times larger
    than the original.

36. Suggest to Hester Ann that she
    could gain a better understanding
    of the problem by guessing and
    testing perfect cube numbers to
    see if any equal 56, the number of
    blocks. She'll find that fifty-six
    blocks cannot be made into a
    perfect cube. The nearest larger
    cube is 4^3 or 64. If the toy box is
    made so that 3" by 3" by 3" blocks
    can fit in it, then the 56 blocks
    will fit with room for 8 more later.
    The size of the box would be 12"
    on a side.

37. No. 1/3 of the surface area
    cannot be the volume since
    surface area is a 2-dimensional
    measurement and volume is 3-
    dimensional.

38. Yes, for instance: if the radius is
    10 cm and the height is $5/\pi$, the
    volume of the cylinder is 500 cm³.

**Problems Related to the NCTM
Standards and Curriculum Focal Points**

1. Since the surface area and volume of
   a shape are not necessarily related, it
   is not possible to know for sure
   without more information. The
   cylinder could be short and fat, tall
   and skinny, or have a comparable
   height and diameter.

2. The relationship between the volume
   of a cone and a cylinder that have the
   same radius and height is that the
   cylinder is 3 times as big.

3. Since the volume a cylinder and a
   prism are both found using the area
   of the base multiplied by the height,

one strategy is to break a shape into
some form of cylinder or prism.
Answers may vary.

Chapter 14

Section 14.1

1. $\triangle BAC \cong \triangle FEG$, $\triangle BCA \cong \triangle FGE$, $\triangle CAB \cong \triangle GEF$, $\triangle CBA \cong \triangle GFE$

2. (a) *EFD*   (b) *ZYX*

3. $\angle B \cong \angle H$, $\overline{BC} \cong \overline{HI}$ or $\angle A \cong \angle G$, $\overline{AC} \cong \overline{GI}$

4. (a) $\overline{GH} \cong \overline{ML}$ and $\overline{GI} \cong \overline{MN}$
    (b) $\angle H \cong \angle L$ and $\overline{HG} \cong \overline{LM}$ and $\overline{HI} \cong \overline{LN}$
    (c) $\angle I \cong \angle N$ and $\overline{IG} \cong \overline{NM}$ and $\overline{IH} \cong \overline{NL}$

5. $\angle A \cong \angle G$, $\angle B \cong \angle H$

6. (a) $\angle P \cong \angle S$, $\angle Q \cong \angle T$ $\overline{QR} \cong \overline{TU}$, and m($\angle R$) = m($\angle U$) = 80°, so $\angle R \cong \angle U$.
    (b) Yes.
    (c) m($\angle R$) = 80° = m($\angle U$), so we can use $\angle R$, $\overline{RQ}$, $\angle Q$ and $\angle U$, $\overline{UT}$, and $\angle T$.

7. $\overline{BC} \cong \overline{HI}$, $\overline{CA} \cong \overline{IG}$

8. $\triangle ABC \cong \triangle FDE$ by SSS or SAS ($\angle C$ and $\angle F$ are right angles).

9. (a) SSS   (b) SAS   (c) ASA

10. Yes; m($\angle Y$)= 30°, m($\angle O$) = 80°, so $\triangle AMY \cong \triangle JON$ by ASA.

11. (a) $\overline{AB} \cong \overline{DE}$ (leg), $\angle B \cong \angle E$, $\overline{AC} \cong \overline{DF}$ (hypotenuse)
    (b) No
    (c) $BC = EF = \sqrt{8}$, so $\overline{BC} \cong \overline{EF}$
    (d) Yes; SAS.

12. (a) $\angle A \cong \angle X$, $\angle B \cong \angle Y$, $\angle C \cong \angle Z$

    (b) No.
    (c) No; $\triangle ABC$ and $\triangle XYZ$ would satisfy conditions for AAA, but are not congruent. This is a counter-example to the AAA property.

13.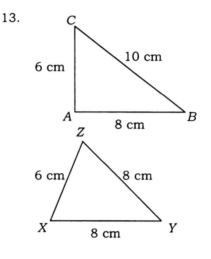

    m($\angle A$) = 90° > m($\angle X$)

14. Since the hexagon is regular, the length of hypotenuses ($\overline{YZ}$) are all equal. The legs are given to be congruent. Therefore all the right triangles are congruent. From the original congruent vertex angles, angles congruent to $\angle Y$ and $\angle Z$ are removed, leaving angles of the same size.

15. (a) For example, have 3 pairs of congruent angles
    (b) For example, have 3 pairs of congruent angles and 1 pair of congruent non-corresponding sides
    (c) See the Mathematical Morsel at the end of Section 14.1

16. $\triangle ABC \cong \triangle WXY$ (by SAS congruence property); $\angle 1 \cong \angle 5$, $\angle 3 \cong \angle 7$, and $\overline{AC} \cong \overline{WY}$ (corresponding parts of congruent triangles); m($\angle A$) - m($\angle 3$) = m($\angle W$) - m($\angle 7$) so $\angle 4 \cong \angle 8$ and m($\angle C$) - m($\angle 1$) = m($\angle Y$) – m($\angle 5$) so $\angle 2 \cong \angle 6$; $\triangle ADC \cong \triangle WZY$ (by ASA congruence property);

$\overline{AD} \cong \overline{WZ}$, $\angle D \cong \angle Z$,

$\overline{DC} \cong \overline{ZY}$ (corresponding parts of congruent triangles); so quad *ABCD* $\cong$ quad *WXYZ*.

17. $\overline{AB} \cong \overline{XY}$ (given), $\angle B \cong \angle Y$ (both right angles), $\overline{BC} \cong \overline{YZ}$ (Both have length $b = \sqrt{c^2 - a^2}$ by the Pythagorean Theorem) so $\triangle ABC \cong \triangle XYZ$ by the SAS congruence property

18. (a) Both a square and rhombus which is not a square could be drawn.
    (b) Both a rectangle and a parallelogram, which is not a rectangle could be drawn.
    (c) No, parts (a) and (b) have provided counterexamples.

Analyzing Student thinking

19. Yes. By the SSS Congruence Property, Danielle can prove that the two isosceles triangles formed by the diagonal of the rhombus are congruent. Hence, corresponding angles are congruent, so that, by the Alternate Interior Angles theorem, she can conclude that the opposite sides of the rhombus are parallel. In other words, a rhombus is a parallelogram.

20. Ask the student to indicate on his drawing which angles and side he's using when he applied the ASA Congruence Property. If he claims that the two pairs of non-right angles of the triangles are congruent, ask what property of rectangles he's using to justify that fact.

21. That's correct, Emily, since a rectangle is a parallelogram, the two pairs of alternate interior angles formed by the diagonal are congruent.

22. No, this is an example of SSA which is not sufficient to prove congruence, except in the case of a right triangle.

23. No. The congruence relationship $\triangle ABC \cong \triangle CAB$ means that $C \leftrightarrow A$, $A \leftrightarrow B$, and $B \leftrightarrow C$. Under these correspondences, the triangles are not congruent, since $\overline{AB}$ and $\overline{CA}$ don't necessarily have the same length. *But* we could say $\triangle ABC \cong \triangle BAC$ by SAS.

24. No. Notice that in one triangle the marked side is opposite the angle with two arcs and in the other triangle the marked side is opposite the angle with one arc. These are not corresponding sides. They could be congruent if the marked angles with one arc were congruent to the angles with two arcs. However, we cannot make that assumption.

25. Jose, the teacher's example had $\angle BAC \cong \angle DAC$ and $\angle BCA \cong \angle DCA$, so the two pairs of corresponding angles in the congruent triangles formed the angles $\angle A$ and $\angle C$, the bisected angles. However, for the parallelogram in your example, this is not the case; for instance $\angle EFH \cong \angle GHF$, but this pair of angles does not fit together to form either of the angles $\angle F$ or $\angle H$.

Problems related to the NCTM Standards and Curriculum Focal Points

1. The triangle can be drawn with a protractor and a straightedge. It can be seen by this construction that there is only one shape of triangle that can be built with these given dimensions which leads toward the ASA property of triangle congruence.

2. Examples 14.1 and 14.2 are both examples of reasoning and proof.

Any problem that asks for a justification or why would require reasoning and proof to answer.

3. Inductive arguments are based on patterns seen through many examples but may not "prove" that something is true for all cases. Deductive arguments are based on a logical sequence of statements that build on each other and can show a statement is true for all cases.

Section 14.2

1. (a) $\triangle LMN \sim \triangle OPQ$, by SAS similarity.
    (b) $\triangle RST \sim \triangle VWU$, by AA similarity.
    (c) Not similar. On one triangle, the 40° angle is between the proportional sides and on the other it is not.
    (d) $\triangle EFG \sim \triangle HJI$, by SSS similarity.

2. (a) $XY = \dfrac{27}{8}$ cm, $VW = \dfrac{128}{9}$ cm
    (b) $AB = 9$ in., $AC = 12$ in., $DC = 4$ in.

3. (a) $BC = \dfrac{65}{4}$ in., $AC = \dfrac{56}{9}$ in.
    (b) $RQ = 6$ in., $PT = 16$ in.

4. (a) False. Sides may be of different lengths.
    (b) False. Consider triangles whose angle measures are 80°, 80°, 20°, and 70°, 70°, 40°.
    (c) False. See part (a).
    (d) True. AA

5. $3/4 = 5/AD$, so $AD = 20/3$.

6. (a) $\triangle ABC \sim \triangle EDC$ by AA similarity because the vertical angles at C are congruent and both are right triangles.
    (b) 45°

7. 27 feet

8.

9.

10. $a = 13\ 1/3$ $b = 10$
    $c = 17\ 7/9$ $d = 42\ 7/9$

11. (a) No. If so, the two triangles would be similar. However, the sides are not proportional.
    (b) Yes. The triangles are similar by the SAS similarity property. Hence, by the corresponding angles property, the lines are parallel.

12. (a) bases 1:2, heights 1:2, areas 1:4
    (b) bases 3:4, heights 3:4, areas 9:16
    (c) lengths 1:3, widths 1:3, areas 1:9
    (d) The ratio of the areas is equal to the square of the ratios of the linear dimensions.

13. Yes. We can use either the AA or SAS similarity properties of triangles.

14. (a) Apply the alternate interior angles theorem and AA similarity property.
    (b) $a = 14$, $b = 60$

15.

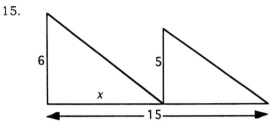

$6/x = 5/(15-x)$, thus Tom's shadow is 90/11 ft and Carol's is 75/11 ft.

16.   25.86 ft

17.   6.53 feet

18.   Assuming ACBD is a rectangle, we have $DC^2 = 50^2 + 70^2$, so $DC = 86$. But, $AB = DC$, so $AB \approx 86$ ft.

19. $AB = BC$ and $XY = YZ$ so $AB/BC = XY/YZ$ (equal 1) or $AB/XY = BC/YZ$ (interchanging means of the proportion). Since $\angle B \cong \angle Y$ and $AB/XY = BC/YZ$, $\triangle ABC \sim \triangle XYZ$ by the SAS similarity property. (Could also prove using AA similarity property.)

20.   (a)

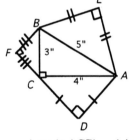

Area($\triangle ACD$) = 4 in^2
Area($\triangle BFC$) = 2.25 in^2
Area($\triangle AEB$) = 6.25 in^2
Therefore, Area($\triangle ACD$) + Area($\triangle BFC$) = Area($\triangle AEB$).

(b)

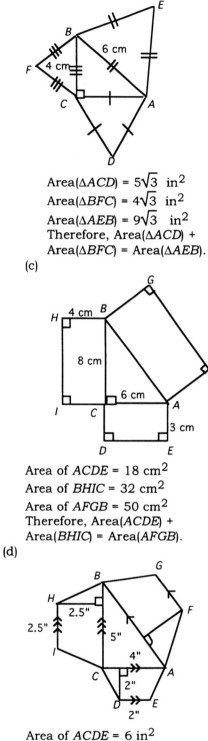

Area($\triangle ACD$) = $5\sqrt{3}$ in^2
Area($\triangle BFC$) = $4\sqrt{3}$ in^2
Area($\triangle AEB$) = $9\sqrt{3}$ in^2
Therefore, Area($\triangle ACD$) + Area($\triangle BFC$) = Area($\triangle AEB$).

(c)

Area of $ACDE$ = 18 cm^2
Area of $BHIC$ = 32 cm^2
Area of $AFGB$ = 50 cm^2
Therefore, Area($ACDE$) + Area($BHIC$) = Area($AFGB$).

(d)

Area of $ACDE$ = 6 in^2
Area of $BHIC$ = 9.375 in^2
Area of $AFGB$ = 15.375 in^2
Therefore, Area($ACDE$) + Area($BHIC$) = Area($AFGB$).

21. $AB = 5/3$, $AE = 7/4$, $DE = 21/4$

22.   Lines $\overrightarrow{A'B'}$, $\overrightarrow{B'C'}$, $\overrightarrow{A'C'}$ form transversals. These can be used with pairs of parallel sides and corresponding angles to show that $\angle A \cong \angle A'$, $\angle B \cong \angle B'$, and $\angle C \cong \angle C'$. Thus the triangles are similar by AAA similarity.

23.   (a) 4.5   (b) 6.75

     (c) 10.125   (d) $3^n \left(\dfrac{1}{2^{n-1}} \right)$

24.   (a) 3/4   (b) 9/16

     (c) 27/64   (d) $\left(\dfrac{3}{4} \right)^{n-1}$

Analyzing Student Thinking

25.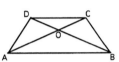

When the two diagonals of an isosceles trapezoid are drawn, there are actually 8 triangles formed. However, Selina is probably looking at the 4 non-overlapping triangles. $\triangle DOC \sim \triangle BOA$ by AA, and $\triangle AOD \cong \triangle BOC$ by AAS (after proving $\triangle DAC \cong \triangle CBD$).

26.   Yes, all 30°-60° triangles are right triangles since the sum of the measures of a triangle is 180°. Thus, Jade's claim is true by the AA Similarity Property.

27.   Israel is correct. A 45° right triangle is a 45°-45°-90° triangle, and so is similar, by the AA Similarity Property, to all other such triangles.

28.   Karli is correct. Each of the two smaller right triangles formed when $\overline{BD}$ is drawn share one angle with the original triangle $\triangle ABC$. Hence, by the AA Similarity Property, $\triangle ABC \sim \triangle ADB$

and $\triangle ABC \sim \triangle BDC$. Thus, all three triangles are similar.

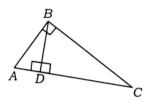

29.   Brennan, similar triangles have the same shape, while congruent triangles have the same shape and the same size. Thus, congruent triangles meet the conditions required to be similar.

30.   Edwardo, at noon the shadows may be too short (or nonexistent) for accurate measurement.

31.   No, Barbara, these rectangles are not similar since $\dfrac{4}{6} \neq \dfrac{5}{8}$. If we solve the proportion $\dfrac{4}{6} = \dfrac{5}{x}$, we see that the long side of the new photo would need to be $x = 7.5$ in order to have a similar rectangle, so that there would be ½ inch of blank space on the enlargement, as shown in the figure below:

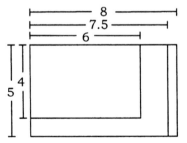

Problems related to the NCTM Standards and Curriculum Focal Points

1.   Problem: At the same time Alana (who is 5 feet tall) cast a 7.5 foot shadow, a tree nearby cast a 24 foot shadow. How tall is the tree?

     Answer: $\dfrac{5}{7.5} = \dfrac{x}{24}$; $x = 16$ feet.

2. Since similar triangles have proportional sides, if two of the lengths on one triangle are known and one of the corresponding lengths on a second triangle is known then a proportion can be created to find the other corresponding length on the second triangle.

3. A deductive argument was used for Exercise 6a of Set A. Since two angles of one triangle were congruent to two angles of the second triangle, it could be deduced that the triangles had to be similar by the AA similarity property. Answer may vary.

Section 14.3

1. Follow the steps of the *1. Copy a Line Segment* construction.

2. Follow the steps of the *2. Copy an Angle* construction.

3. Follow the steps of the *3. Construct a Perpendicular Bisector* construction.

4. Follow the steps of the *4. Bisect an Angle* construction.

5. Follow the steps of the *5. Construct a Perpendicular Line through a Point on a Line* construction.

6. Follow the steps of the *6. Construct a Perpendicular Line through a Point not on a Line* construction.

7. Follow the steps of the *7. Construct a Line Parallel to a give Line through a Point not on the Line* construction.

8. (a) Follow the steps of the *5. Construct a Perpendicular Line through a Point on a Line* construction.
   (b) Follow the steps of the *6. Construct a Perpendicular Line*

through a Point not on a Line construction.
   (c) Follow the steps of the *7. Construct a Line Parallel to a give Line through a Point not on the Line* construction.
   (d) Follow the steps of the *7. Construct a Line Parallel to a give Line through a Point not on the Line* construction.

9. (a) Follow the steps of the *5. Construct a Perpendicular Line through a Point on a Line* construction.
   (b) Follow the steps of the *7. Construct a Line Parallel to a give Line through a Point not on the Line* construction.
   (c) They are perpendicular to each other.

10. (a) Follow the steps of the *2. Copy an Angle* construction to copy the angle with measure $a°$ next to the angle with measure $b°$ as follows:

   (b) Follow the steps of the *2. Copy an Angle* construction to copy the angle with measure $a°$ next to another copy of the angle with measure $a°$ as follows:

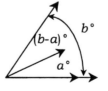

   (c) Follow the steps of the *2. Copy an Angle* construction to copy the angle with measure $a°$ in the interior of the angle with measure $b°$ as follows:

(d) Follow the steps in *4. Bisect an Angle* construction to bisect the angle in part (a) above.

11. Construct the midpoint of each side using the *3. Construct a Perpendicular Bisector* construction. Connect these midpoints with the corresponding vertices on the opposite side of the triangle.

12. For each vertex of the triangle and it's opposite side, follow the steps of the *6. Construct a Perpendicular Line through a Point not on a Line* construction.

13. (a) Use constructions 2 and 1 to copy angles and side.
    (b) Make copy of $\angle D$, copy length AB along both sides of the angle, and connect endpoints of two segments.

14. (b) By construction, $\overline{RS} \cong \overline{DE}$, $\overline{RT} \cong \overline{DF}$, and $\overline{ST} \cong \overline{EF}$. Thus, $\triangle RST \cong \triangle DEF$ by SSS congruence property.

15. $\triangle ADC \cong \triangle BDC$ by ASA so $\overline{AD} \cong \overline{BD}$.

16. (a) $RQ = 2a$, $\angle B \cong \angle Q$, $\angle C \cong \angle R$.
    (b) $\triangle ADC \sim \triangle PQR$ because all 3 corresponding pairs of angles are congruent and all 3 pairs of corresponding sides are proportional.
    (c) SAS similarity

17. They do in an equilateral triangle. In every isosceles triangle the perpendicular bisector of the base and the altitude to the base coincide.

18. This occurs when the triangle is isosceles and not equilateral.

19. (a) Construct right triangle with legs 3 and 1
    (b) Construct right triangle with legs 2 and 1 and hypotenuse

$\sqrt{5}$, then construct right triangle with legs $\sqrt{5}$ and 1 .
(c) Construct isosceles right triangle with legs $\sqrt{6}$ [see part (b)].
(d) Construct right triangle with hypotenuse 4 and leg 1. The other leg will be $\sqrt{15}$.

20. $\triangle ABC \sim \triangle AQP$ by AA similarity and $\triangle ACD \sim \triangle APR$ by AA similarity. Therefore, $ABCD \sim AQPR$, since corresponding angles are congruent and corresponding sides are proportional

21. $\overline{AC} \cong \overline{BC}$ (equidistant), $\overline{AD} \cong \overline{BD}$ (midpoint) , $\overline{CD} \cong \overline{CD}$ (common side), $\triangle ACD \cong \triangle BCD$ (SSS), $\angle ADC \cong \angle BDC$ (corresponding parts of congruent triangles), $\angle ADC$ and $\angle BDC$ are right angles (congruent and supplementary), $\overline{CD}$ is perpendicular bisector of $\overline{AB}$.

22. The line should be the perpendicular bisector of the segment $\overline{AB}$.

Analyzing Student Thinking

23. In an isosceles triangle, the altitude, median, and angle bisector from the *vertex* angle all lie on the same line. In Gwennette's case, she is looking at the altitude, median and angle bisector from one of the two *base* angles, and the theorem does not hold there (unless the triangle is equilateral).

24. Yes, Tammy, it does make a difference. Changing the radius of the compass will, as you note, give you a perpendicular, but it won't bisect the line segment.

25. Ty, doing so will result in a rhombus *BPRQ*, which is a special type of kite. Therefore, the

justification of this construction will be identical to the one following Figure 14.30. Hence, it is not necessary to choose point R so that $\overline{BP} \cong \overline{PR}$, but it works if you do so.

26. Yes, Bo, that is correct since $\overline{PA}$ and $\overline{QA}$ were constructed to each have length r as were $\overline{PA}$ and $\overline{PB}$.

27. Madison, the following construction would work: for example, swing an arc on one side of radius 1 and on the other side of radius 2. Draw the segment connecting the intersections, call it x. To copy the angle on another line segment, swing an arc of length 1 with center at one end point. Also swing an arc of length 2 from the same point. Put the point where the arc of length 1 intersects the line segment and swing an arc of length x until it hits the arc of length 2. By SSS the two congruent triangles will be formed.

28. Marlena is correct. When Latisha says, "the triangles won't match," she is probably referring to the orientation of the new triangle. Orientation may change, but the new triangle will be congruent no matter which side you start with, by SSS.

29. Glen, in the case of an obtuse triangle, only the altitude from the obtuse angle will be inside the triangle. The following figure shows how the altitude from an acute angle is outside the triangle.

Problems related to the NCTM Standards and Curriculum Focal Points

1. By doing the construction of the perpendicular bisector one may come to realize the property that all of the points on the perpendicular are equidistant from the endpoints of the segment. Answers may vary.

2. Each of the new construction in this section is accompanied with a justification of why the construction works. These justifications are deductive arguments.

Section 14.4

1. Construct perpendicular bisectors (Construction 3).

2.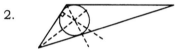

3.   (a) Inside
  (b) On the hypotenuse
  (c) Outside
  (d) Yes

4.   (a) Inside   (b) Yes

5. Construct a circle with the center on one endpoint of the given segment and the radius point on the other endpoint. Construct another circle reversing the roles of the endpoints. Where the two circles intersect is the third point of the triangle.
This is similar to the compass and straightedge construction except the circles are replaced with compass arcs.

6.   (a) Dodecagon
  (b) 24-gon, 48-gon.

7.   (a) Decagon
  (b) 20-gon
  (c) 40-gon, 80-gon

8. 3, 4, 5, 6, 8, 10, 12, 15, 16, 17, 20, 24, 30, 32, 34, 40, 48, 51, 60, 64, 68, 80, 85, 96 (24 polygons).

9. 3, 5, 6, 7, 9, 10, 12, 13, 14, 15

10. (a) Use the same procedure except mark off four congruent segments on $\overline{AC}$.
    (b) Use construction 3 to find midpoint M of $\overline{AB}$. Then repeat construction 3 to bisect $\overline{AM}$ and $\overline{MB}$.

11.

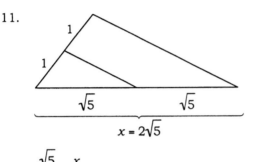

$x = 2\sqrt{5}$

$$\frac{\sqrt{5}}{1} = \frac{x}{2}$$

12. (a) Add together a right angle and 45°.
    (b) Subtract 60° from 135° angle.
    (c) Take central angle of regular pentagon.
    (d) Bisect 72° and add that 36° to 72° to get 108°.

13. (a) Construct triangle with sides 1 and 2.
    (c) $(\sqrt{5} - 1)/2$

14. Let P be equidistant from A and B. Then $AP = BP$. Let m be the line through the mid point M and P, then $AM = BM$ and $PM = PM$ so $\triangle APM \cong \triangle BPM$ by SSS. Thus $\angle AMP \cong \angle BMP$ so $m\angle AMP = 90°$ which means that m is the perpendicular bisector of $\overline{AB}$. Therefore P is on the perpendicular bisector of $\overline{AB}$.

15. (c) It is the midpoint of the hypotenuse.

16. Yes

17. (c) $M_1M_3 = M_2M_4$ and $M_1M_3 \perp M_2M_4$ (Aubel's theorem).

18. (a) About 26°   (b) $\dfrac{360°}{7}$
    (c) First double the angle to get on which measures $\dfrac{360°}{7}$. Then draw a circle so that $\dfrac{360°}{7}$ is a central angle whose sides intersect the circle at A and B. Set radius of compass to AB and mark off arcs around the circle. Connect points to get the regular heptagon.

19. Draw $\overline{AB} \perp \overline{XY}$ and $\overline{AC} \perp \overline{YZ}$.
    $AB \cong AC$, since A is equidistant from YX and YZ. $\overline{AY} \cong \overline{AY}$. Thus, $\triangle ABY \cong \triangle ACY$ by HL for right triangles. $\angle AYB \cong \angle AYC$, since they are corresponding parts of congruent triangles and therefore $\overrightarrow{YA}$ bisects $\angle XYZ$.

20. (a) QR
    (b) QS
    (c) Yes; $\angle RAQ \cong \angle SAQ$ (angle bisector), $\angle ARQ \cong \angle ASQ$ (both right angles), $\angle RQA \cong \angle SQA$ (third pair of angles of triangles are congruent if other 2 pairs are), $\overline{AQ} \cong \overline{AQ}$ so $\triangle ARQ \cong \triangle ASQ$ by the ASA congruence property.
    (d) $\overline{QR} \cong \overline{QS}$ because they are corresponding sides of congruent triangles.
    (e) Refer to procedure of construction 9. Since Q is on line 1, the bisector of $\angle CAB$, Q is equidistant from $\overline{AC}$ and $\overline{AB}$. Also Q is on line m, so Q is equidistant from $\overline{AC}$ and $\overline{BC}$. Hence, Q is equidistant from $\overline{AB}$, $\overline{BC}$, and $\overline{AC}$, the

sides of $\triangle ABC$. Thus, Q is the incenter of $\triangle ABC$.

Analyzing Student Thinking

21. Rosanne, two are sufficient, assuming they are correct. If you want to check, constructing the third is recommended.

22. Mallory is incorrect in general, but her statement is true for acute triangles. The circumcenter of an obtuse triangle is always outside the triangle and the circumcenter of a right triangle will be on its hypotenuse.

23. An equilateral triangle has three 60° angles. If 6 equilateral triangles are gathered around a common vertex, the sum of the angles would be 360°. Furthermore, since all of Craig's triangles are congruent, the "radial" sides will match in length, the angles of the hexagon formed will be 120° (60°+ 60°), and the sides of the hexagon will all be equal in length. So Craig's method will work.

24. Samantha is incorrect. The centroid will always be inside becaue the medians of a triangle will always meet inside the triangle.

25. Chase is correct. This is true because the perpendicular bisectors of the sides of an equilateral triangle coincide with the bisectors of its angles.

26. Spencer is incorrect. The orthocenter is inside the triangle if the triangle is acute, outside for an obtuse triangle, and equal to the vertex of the right angle for a right triangle.

27. Roberto is correct. The diagonal of a rectangle is the hypotenuse of a right triangle, with legs being adjacent sides of the rectangle.

Thus, if the sides of the rectangle are 1 unit by 2 units, the diagonal of rectangle has length $\sqrt{5}$ units, by the Pythagorean theorem.

Problems related to the NCTM Standards and Curriculum Focal Points

1. One possible answer is that a unique circle can be constructed in the inside of any triangle that touches each side exactly once. Another possible answer is that a unique circle can be constructed through the three vertices of any triangle and the center of that circle is equidistant from these vertices. Answers may vary.

2. Each of the new constructions in this section is accompanied by a justification, which is an explanation of why the construction works.

Section 14.5

1. (a) For example, $\overline{AB} \cong \overline{AD}$, $\overline{BC} \cong \overline{DC}$.
   (b) $\overline{AC} \cong \overline{AC}$ (congruent to itself)
   (c) SSS
   (d) Corresponding parts of congruent triangles are congruent.
   (e) By definition of angle bisector.

2. (a) $\angle 2 \cong \angle 4$, $\angle 1 \cong \angle 3$
   (b) Yes; base angles of isosceles triangle
   (c) Yes; $\angle 1 \cong \angle 2 \cong \angle 3 \cong \angle 4$ from parts (a) and (b).

3. $\angle P \cong \angle Q$ since they are opposite the congruent sides $\overline{QR}$ and $\overline{PR}$. Further, $\angle Q \cong \angle R$ since they are opposite the congruent sides $\overline{PR}$ and $\overline{PQ}$. Thus, $\angle P \cong \angle Q \cong \angle R$.

4. $m(\angle A) + m(\angle D) = 180°$ (interior angles on same side of transversal are supplementary), $m(\angle D) =$

m($\angle C$) (base angles congruent), so m($\angle A$) + m($\angle C$) = 180° (substitution). Thus, $\angle A$ and $\angle C$ are supplementary. Similarly, $\angle B$ and $\angle D$ are supplementary

5. $WXYZ$ is a rectangle. Since opposite sides of a parallelogram are congruent, $\overline{DE} \cong \overline{FG}$ and $\overline{EF} \cong \overline{DG}$. Since $\overline{DE} \cong \overline{EF}$ is given, $\overline{FG} \cong \overline{DE} \cong \overline{EF} \cong \overline{DG}$ and all 4 sides are congruent.

6.   Since $\angle W$ and $\angle Z$ are supplementary (90° + 90° = 180°), $\overline{WX} \mid\mid \overline{ZY}$ (since interior angles on same side of transversal are supplementary). Similarly, $\angle W$ and $\angle X$ are supplementary and $\overline{WZ} \mid\mid \overline{XY}$. Therefore, $WXYZ$ is a parallelogram since both pairs of opposite sides are parallel.

7.   Since HIJK is a rectangle, it has 4 right angles. We need to show that it has four congruent sides. Since HIJK is a parallelogram, opposite sides are congruent; thus $\overline{HI} \cong \overline{JK}$ and $\overline{HK} \cong \overline{IJ}$. Combined with the given information $\overline{JK} \cong \overline{HI} \cong \overline{IJ} \cong \overline{HK}$. Therefore, HIJK is a square.

8.   Construct $\overline{AB}$ with the length of the side. At A and B construct perpendiculars $\overline{AS}$ and $\overline{BT}$. With compass set the length of the diagonal mark an arc centered at A and intersecting $\overline{BT}$ (call intersection point C). Similarly, with the same compass setting, mark an arc centered at B intersecting $\overline{AS}$ (call intersection point D). ABCD is the desired rectangle.

9.   Construct $\overline{AB}$ with length d, then construct perpendicular bisector of $\overline{AB}$. Bisect the original segment of length d and mark off the other vertices C and D on the perpendicular diagonal using one half the length of d as the compass setting. Thus, ACBD is the desired square.

10. (a) A quadrilateral with diagonals that bisect each other is a parallelogram, and a parallelogram with perpendicular diagonals is a rhombus (shown in earlier problems).

     (b) Construct $\overline{AB}$ with length a, then construct perpendicular bisector of $\overline{AB}$ Bisect the original segment of length b and mark off other vertices C and D on perpendicular diagonal using one half the length of b as the compass setting.

11. $\angle D \cong \angle F$ and $\angle R \cong \angle T$ (base angles of isosceles triangle are congruent). Since $\angle D \cong \angle R$, it follows that $\angle D \cong \angle R$. Hence, $\triangle DEF \sim \triangle RST$ by AA similarity property.

12. $AD/CD = CD/DB$ (CD is geometric mean) and $\angle ADC \cong \angle CDB$ (both are right angles) so $\triangle ADC \cong \triangle CDB$ (SAS similarity property). $\angle A \cong \angle DCB$ since they are corresponding angles of similar triangles. However, m($\angle ACD$) + m($\angle A$) = 90° (acute angles of right triangles are complementary) so m($\angle ACD$) + m($\angle DCB$)= 90° and $\angle ACB$ is a right angle. Thus, $\triangle ABC$ is a right triangle.

13. (a) 36° (central angle of decagon), 72°, 72° (base angles of isosceles triangle)
     (b) 72°, 36°
     (c) 36°, isosceles (since base angles are congruent)
     (d) x, 1 - x,
     (e) $AC = AB = 1$, $BC = x$, m($\angle A$) = 36°, m($\angle B$) = m($\angle C$) = 72° $BD = BC = x$, $CD = 1 - x$, m($\angle B$) = 36° ,

m($\angle C$) = m($\angle D$) = 72°
Yes (by the AA similarity
property)

(f) *BD, CD, x,* 1 - *x*

(g) 1 - *x* = *x*² or $x = \dfrac{1 \pm \sqrt{5}}{2}$

(h) Yes, we can construct the
length $\sqrt{5}$ then subtract length
1, and bisect it.

14. If *AC = A'C'*, then △*ABC* ≅ △*A'B'C'*
by SAS. If not, let *AC = A'D'*.
Then, △*ABC* ≅ △*A'B'D'* by SAS.
Therefore, $\angle B$ ≅ $\angle A'B'D'$. But,
from the given information,
$\angle B$ ≅ $\angle B'$. Thus, $\angle B$ ≅ $\angle A'B'D'$,
which is a contradiction.

15. △*BAD* ~ △*B'A'C'* by SAS. Thus the
sides of △*BAD* are proportional
respectively to the sides of
△*B'A'C'* which, by the given, are
proportional respectively to the
sides of △*BAC*. Since △ *BAD* and
△*BAC* share the side $\overline{AB}$, the two
triangles must be congruent by
the SSS congruence property.
Therefore, $\angle$ *BAC* ≅ $\angle$*BAD* ≅
$\angle$B'A'C'. Thus, △*BAC* ~ △*B'A'C'* by
SAS similarity property.

Analyzing Student Thinking

16. Willard, while it may be obvious
that a certain rhombus is a
parallelogram, we cannot be sure
from one example, or even many
examples, that *every* rhombus is a
parallelogram. A proof will help us
see why this must be so.

17. No. The property that Victoria is
trying to prove could be stated as
follows: "In an isosceles triangle,
the angle bisector of the vertex
angle divides the opposite side into
two congruent segments." What
we have been "given" is an
isosceles triangle and the angle
bisector of the vertex angle. So
Victoria can infer that, since she
has an isosceles triangle, *PK = KC*.
She can infer that since *KI* is an
angle bisector, $\angle PKI$ ≅ $\angle CKI$. She

cannot assume that *PI = IC*,
because that is what she is trying
to prove. She cannot assume that
angles $\angle PIK$ and $\angle KIC$ are right
angles, because it has not been
"given." However, she can prove
that △*PIK* ≅ △*CIK* by SAS.
Therefore, *PI = IC*.

18. Charlotte, the congruence of
opposite sides of a parallelogram
is a direct consequence of the
definition of parallelogram. The
proof that diagonals bisect each
other relies on this result, so
cannot be used to prove it. Any
attempt to do so would lead to
circular reasoning. In general, a
certain property of parallelograms
must be proven before it is used in
the proof of other properties.

19. Yes. Using SAS, the midquad
forms two pairs of congruent
triangles, as shown in the
following figure. So the midquad
of an isosceles trapezoid is a kite.
It has also been proved that the
midquad of any quadrilateral is a
parallelogram. Thus, the opposite
sides of the kite are congruent,
making it a rhombus.

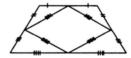

20. Braymen is correct. For a
parallelogram to be a rectangle,
congruent diagonals is sufficient—
a known right angle is not
necessary. There is enough given
information to prove you have a
rectangle. On the other hand,
using Wenston's idea, it can also
be shown that a parallelogram
with one right angle is a rectangle.
In this case, known congruent
diagonals is not needed for the
proof.

21. No. The following rectangle has a
midquad that is not a square.

A square is the only quadrilateral that has a square for its midquad.

22. If it is has been *proved* that a rhombus has two pairs of parallel sides, then it can be concluded that a rhombus is a parallelogram. If Caesar is only saying that the rhombus and the parallelogram share a property, then he might believe that a rhombus is a parallelogram *and* a parallelogram is a rhombus. This is not true. A teacher needs to consider the various Van Hiele levels which might represent Caesar's perspective.

Problems related to the NCTM Standards and Curriculum Focal Points

1. In order to prove properties of quadrilaterals it is common to first prove that a pair of triangles are congruent and then use the other congruent corresponding parts. Example 14.11 does this by proving $\triangle ABC \cong \triangle DCB$ and then using the corresponding parts of the congruent triangles $\overline{AC} \cong \overline{DB}$. These corresponding parts are also the diagonals of the rectangle. Answers may vary.

2. A conjecture is something that a person believes to be true but has yet to prove that it is true. A conjecture usually results from observing a pattern and using inductive reasoning to come up with an educated guess.

Chapter 15

Section 15.1

1. (a) $\sqrt{73}$ (b) 7

2. (a) $2\sqrt{5} + 4\sqrt{5} = 6\sqrt{5}$; yes
   (b) $\sqrt{212} + \sqrt{13.25} = \sqrt{331.25}$; yes

3. (a) (1, 7)   (b) (-9, 3)
   (c) (7, 5)   (d) (2, -5)

4. (a) $GH = 8$, $HI = \sqrt{32}$. Since $GH^2 = HI^2 + GI^2$, $\triangle GHI$ is a right triangle.
   (b) $LM = 2\sqrt{5}$, $MN = \sqrt{5}$, $LN = 5$. Since $LM^2 + MN^2 = LN^2$, $\triangle LMN$ is a right triangle.

5.

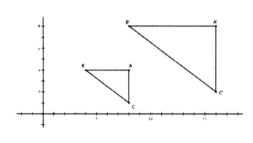

     (a) Double   (b) Same

6. (a) -5/7   (b) no slope

7. (a) Yes   (b) Yes

8. (a) Rises to the right
   (b) Vertical
   (c) Horizontal
   (d) Rises to the left

9. Not collinear

10. (a) No
    (b) Yes
    (c) No

11. (a) Top, bottom are horizontal,
    $\dfrac{2-(-2)}{4-1} = \dfrac{4}{3}$, $\dfrac{2-(-2)}{6-3} = \dfrac{4}{3}$,
    parallelogram

(b) $\dfrac{10-(-5)}{-5-10} = -1$, $\dfrac{5-(-10)}{-10-5} = -1$,
    parallel; $\dfrac{10-5}{-5-(-10)} = 1$,
    $\dfrac{-5-(-10)}{10-5} = 1$, parallelogram

12. (a) Slope of $\overline{AB} = 1/6$, slope of $\overline{PQ} = -6$; $-6(1/6) = -1$.
    (b) Slope of $\overline{AB} = 1$, slope of $\overline{PQ} = -1$; $1(-1) = -1$.

13. (a) and (b) are right triangles.

14. All.

15. (a) False for both.
    (b) True for both.
    (c) False for both.
    (d) True for (ii) only.

16. (a) 3   (b) 2

17. (a) Scalene obtuse
    (b) Scalene acute

18. Trapezoid with right angles at A and B.

19. (a) (7,-9), (-3,15), or (13, -1)
    (b) Area = 56 square units in each case.

20. (a)

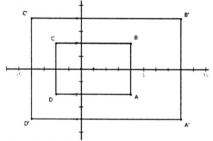

(b) $B'(12,6)$, $C'(-6,6)$, $D'(-6,-6)$
(c) perimeter of $A'B'C'D'$ = 3(perimeter of $ABCD$)
(d) area of $A'B'C'D'$ = 9(area of $ABCD$)
(e) $A'(2,-1)$, $B'(2,1)$, $C'(-1,1)$, $D'(-1,-1)$
Perimeter of $A'B'C'D'$ = (1/2)(perimeter of $ABCD$)

area of $A'B'C'D'$ =
(1/4)(area of $ABCD$)

21. (a) 792 ft
    (b) 28,512 ft (This is higher than any mountain in North America!
    (c) Percent grade is the absolute value of the slope times 100.

22. Slope of $l = \dfrac{b}{a}$, slope of $m = -\dfrac{y}{b}$.
    Hence $(b/a)(-y/b) = -1$, so $a = y$.
    Also, $OQ^2 + OP^2 = b^2 + y^2) + (a^2 + b^2) = 2a^2 + 2b^2$, and $QP^2 = (a + b)^2 + (b - y)^2 = (a^2 + 2ab + b^2) + (b^2 - 2yb + b^2) = 2a^2 + 2b^2$
    $= OQ^2 + OP^2$. Thus, $\triangle OPQ$ is a right triangle, so $l \perp m$.

23. (a) All but Rio and Sydney.
    (b) Nome
    (c) No. All points in the contiguous United States are east of the 180° meridian.
    (d) 52° S
    (e) 106° E
    (f) 34° N 29° W

24. (a) (a, y, z)
    (b) $\sqrt{(y - b)^2 + (z - c)^2}$
    (c) $QR = |x - a|$
    (d) $PQ = \sqrt{QR^2 + PR^2} =$
        $\sqrt{(x - a)^2 + (y - b)^2 + (z - c)^2}$

Analyzing Student Thinking

25. Brayden, a vertical line has no slope since the ratio of its rise to run is $y/0$, which is undefined, while a horizontal line has zero slope since the ratio of rise to run is $0/x$ (x not zero).

26. The slope of a line is constant. A line cannot have more than one slope. Since $15/3 = (-1)(15)/(-1)(3) = -15/-3$, you both found the same number for the slope.

27. Both students are correct. The first student's method works because the slopes of

perpendicular lines are negative reciprocals; if this is the case for the two shorter sides, she can conclude it's a right triangle. The second student's method works because the distance formula may be used to determine the lengths of the sides of the given triangle; if these satisfy the Pythagorean theorem, she can conclude it's a right triangle.

28. Two lines with slopes 4 and -4 will have the same "steepness," but the line with positive slope will rise from left to right, while the one with negative slope will fall from left to right.

29. Both students are correct. The first student's method works because three points P, Q, and R are collinear if the slopes of all the line segments they determine are the same. The second student's method works because, if the sum of the lengths of the two shortest line segments three points determine is equal to the length of the longest line segment, then the three points are collinear.

30. No. Janice did not follow the order of operations. The correct answer is $D = \sqrt{(9 - 3)^2 + (6 - 7)^2} = \sqrt{6^2 + (-1)^2} = \sqrt{36 + 1} = \sqrt{37}$.

31. The distance formula is
    $D = \sqrt{(x_2 - x_1)^2 + (y_2 - y_1)^2}$, so
    Janelle makes a good point about subtracting the y-values of the two points in the same order as the x-values. It turns out that Edmund will get the correct answer though because of the squaring. That is, $(7 - 6)^2 = (1)^2 = 1$ and $(6 - 7)^2 = (-1)^2 = 1$. Even though the order in which we subtract doesn't affect the answer in this instance, there are other times when we need to pay attention to order—computing

slope is an example of one such instance.

All such points must have *x*-coordinate -2.

Problems related to the NCTM Standards and Curriculum Focal Points

1. The lengths and slopes of the sides could be determined by using the coordinates. These values could them be used to decide if certain sides are congruent or parallel or if certain angles are right angles.

2. In general terms the slope is the steepness of a line. More specifically, it shows how much the *y* values increase for each increase in the *x* values. For example, if income were graphed as a function of hours worked, the slope would be the hourly wage and would show how much the income increases for each hour of work. Answers may vary.

3. Find the slopes and lengths of all four sides. If all sides were the same length and if adjacent sides were perpendicular, the quadrilateral would be a square.

Section 15.2

1. (a) $(-2)7.5 = -15$ and $6(-3) + 3$
        $= -15$
    (b) $4(4) + 2 = 18$ and $3(6) = 18$

2. There are three points given in each answer, however, there are infinitely many correct possibilities in each case.
    (a) $(4,0), (5,1), (6,2)$
    (c) $(3,0), (3,1), (3,-5)$

3. (a) $-3, 2$ (b) $5/2, -3$

4. (a) $y = 1/4$, slope $= 0$, y-intercept
        $= 1/4$
    (b) $y = (3/4)x - 3$, y-intercept $= -3$

5. (a) $y = -2x + 5$
    (b) $y = -(7/3)x - 2$
    (c) $y = -(-3)x - 1/4$

6. $(-2, 1), (-2, 0)$

7. (a)

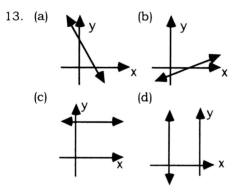

    (b) They are parallel.
    (c) They are the set of all lines in the plane parallel to the line $y = cx$. Each has slope c and y-intercept d, for a particular value of d.

8. (a) $y = -3x - 5$ (b) $x = -2$
    (c) $y = -x + 5$

9. (a) $(y - 1) = 4(x + 5)$
    (b) $(y - 6) = (-2/5)(x - 2)$

10. (a) $y = -x - 1$
    (b) $y = (-3/5)x - 19/5$

11. (a) $y = (1/2)x + 6$
    (b) $y = (-2/3)x - 22/3$

12. (a) (i) $y - 2 = -1/2(x + 5)$ or
                $y - 1 = -1/2(x + 3)$
          (ii) $y = -1/2x - 1/2$
    (b) (i) $y - 7 = 0$
          (ii) $y = 7$

13. (a)   (b)
    (c)   (d)

14. (a) (2, 2)   (b) (4, 8)
    (c) No solution
    (d) $\{(x, y)\mid 3y = 5x + 1\}$

15. (a) (3,2)   (b) (3,-4)
    (c) No solution   (d) (31/2, 3/2)

16. (a) (1,4)   (b) (1/2, 5/4)

17. (a) (5,0)   (b) (1,4)
    (c) (3,1)

18. (a) No solution
    (b) Unique solution
    (c) Infinitely many solutions

19. (a) $(-3 + 1)^2 + (7 - 2)^2 = 4 + 25 = 29$
    (b) $(\sqrt{15})^2 + (-3 + 5)^2 = 5 + 4 = 9$

20. (a) (2,-5), $r = 8$
    (b) (-3,4), $r = 2\sqrt{5}$

21. (a) $(x + 1)^2 + (y + 2)^2 = 5$
    (b) $(x - 2)^2 + (y + 4)^2 = 41$
    (c) $(x - 1)^2 + (y - 4)^2 = 8$

22. (a) 0   (b) No solutions

23. $y = -3x + 5$

24. $y = 1/2x,\ y = -1/2x + 3$

25. $y = (-2/5)x + 29/10$

26. (a) $5.60; $13.10
    (b) $y = 0.5x + 0.6$

27. (a) $y = 0.65x + 350$
    (b) $y = x$
    (c) 1,000 items

28. (a)

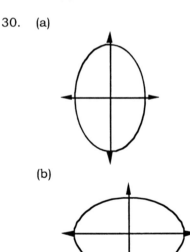

    (b) If $x = 0$, there is no solution for y, and vice versa.

(c) When $x > 0$ and near 0, y is very large. When $x < 0$ and near 0, y is very small.

29. (a)

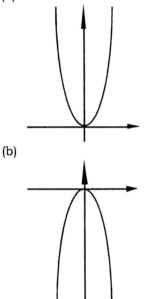

    (b)

The graph in (b) is the reflection image of the graph in (a), in the x-axis.

30. (a)

    (b)

The graph in (b) is a 90° rotation image of the graph in (a), around the origin.

31. $(x - 4/3)^2 + (y + 4/3)^2 = 425/9$

Analyzing Student Thinking

32. Stuart, to find another point, you need to use the fact that it is a horizontal line. Since the point (3, 4) is on the line, we know all the points on the line have a y-coordinate of 4. So, for example, (5, 4) is also on the line. Applying the slope formula with these two points gives a value of $m = 0$, and we see that the line's equation is $y = 4$. The slope of all horizontal lines is zero since the y-coordinates of all the points on a horizontal line are the same.

33. Bethany, sketch a graph of the vertical line through the point (3, 4). Notice that this line does not cross the y-axis, so there is no y-intercept. Its equation is $x = 3$.

34. Jimmie, you can choose either point since both are points on the line. That is, both pairs of x- and y-values are solutions to the equation $y = (-1/4)x + b$, so you will get the same value of b, no matter which point you substitute.

35. No. Many students think that when they know x, their problems are over. However, geometrically, we are looking for the intersection of two lines. If the lines intersect in one point, we must find both coordinates, x *and* y.

36. No. The center is in the interior of the circle, not one of the points *on* the circle itself.

37. Cole, because you know the coordinates of the center and the coordinates of a point on the circle, you can use the distance formula to determine the radius.

38. The numbers on the coordinate axes are not evenly spaced.

Problems related to the NCTM Standards and Curriculum Focal Points

1. Solving an equation means finding the values of the variable that when plugged in would make the equation true.

2. The y-intercept is the value of y where the graph of the line crosses the y axis. It is also the value of y when $x = 0$.

Section 15.3

1. (a) $(-1,5)$ (b) $(1,4)$

2. (a) $(-1, -3\sqrt{3})$
   (b) $(-4,6)$ and $(2,6)$

3. $(a + b, c)$

4. (a) $(a + b, c)$
   (b) $b^2 + c^2 = a^2$ since MP = MN = a

5. (a) $(-5,0), (5,0), (5,8), (-5,8)$
   (b) $(-5,-4), (5,-4), (5,4), (-5,4)$

6. $AB = 1 - (-4) = 5$,
   $BC = \sqrt{(4-1)^2 + (3+1)^2} = 5$,
   $CD = 4 - (-1) = 5$,
   $DA = \sqrt{(-1+4)^2 + (3+1)^2} = 5$. Since $AB = BC = CD = DA$, $ABCD$ is a rhombus.

7. $AB = BC = CD = AD = \sqrt{17}$ and $AB \perp BC$ since the slope of $AB = -1/4$ and the slope of $BC = 4$.

8. The midpoint of $\overline{EG}$ is $(-3/2, -5/2)$ and the midpoint of $\overline{FH}$ is $(-3/2, -5/2)$. Since the diagonals meet at the midpoint of both, the diagonals are bisected.

9. (a) $y = -2x + 15$
   (b) $y = x - 12$
   (c) $x = 9$
   (d) $(9, -3)$; yes it lies on $x = 9$.
   (e) $\sqrt{90}$ for all three distances

(f) circumcenter

10. The midpoint is $M(\frac{b}{2}, \frac{a}{2})$.

$$AM = \sqrt{\left(\frac{b}{2}\right)^2 + \left(\frac{a}{2}\right)^2} =$$

$$\frac{1}{2}\sqrt{b^2 + a^2}$$

$$MB = \sqrt{\left(\frac{b}{2}\right)^2 + \left(\frac{a}{2}\right)^2} =$$

$$\frac{1}{2}\sqrt{b^2 + a^2}$$

$$MC = \sqrt{\left(\frac{b}{2}\right)^2 + \left(\frac{a}{2}\right)^2} =$$

$$\frac{1}{2}\sqrt{b^2 + a^2}$$

Thus, $AM = MB = MC$.

11. (a) $3\sqrt{53}$; $2\sqrt{53}$; $2/3$
     (b) $3\sqrt{29}$; $2\sqrt{29}$; $2/3$
     (c) $6\sqrt{5}$; $4\sqrt{5}$; $2/3$
     (d) On any median, $2/3$ of the distance from the vertex point.

12. $b^2 + c^2 = a^2$;

Slope of $\overline{AC} = \dfrac{c}{b+a}$.

Slope of $\overline{BD} = \dfrac{c}{ba}$;

$$\left(\frac{c}{b+a}\right)\left(\frac{c}{b-a}\right) = \frac{c^2}{b^2a^2} =$$

$$\frac{a^2 b^2}{b^2 a^2} = -1. \text{ So } \overline{AC} \perp \overline{BD}.$$

13. (a) Slope of $\overline{QG}$= slope of $\overline{QM_2} = 2b/(2a - c)$ so that Q, G, and M_2 are collinear.
     (b) Slope of $\overline{RG}$= slope of $\overline{RM_1} = b/(a - 2c)$ so that R, G, and M_1 are collinear.

14. (a) $QG = \sqrt{\left(a - \dfrac{a+c}{3}\right)^2 + \left(b - \dfrac{b}{3}\right)^2} =$

$$\frac{\sqrt{(2a - c)^2 + (2b)^2}}{3}$$

$$GM_2 = \sqrt{\left(\frac{a+c}{3} - \frac{c}{2}\right)^2 + \left(\frac{b}{3}\right)^2} =$$

$$\frac{\sqrt{(2a - c)^2 + (2b)^2}}{6} = \frac{1}{2}QG$$

Hence $QG:GM_2 = 2:1$

(b) $RG = \sqrt{\left(c - \dfrac{a+c}{3}\right)^2 + \left(-\dfrac{b}{3}\right)^2} =$

$$\frac{\sqrt{(2c - a)^2 + b^2}}{3}$$

$$GM_1 = \sqrt{\left(\frac{a+c}{3} - \frac{a}{2}\right)^2 + \left(\frac{b}{3} - \frac{b}{2}\right)^2} =$$

$$\frac{\sqrt{(2c - a)^2 + b^2}}{6} = \frac{1}{2}RG$$

Hence $RG:GM_1 = 2:1$

15. (a) $(a/2, \sqrt{3}\,a/2)$
     (b) $x = a/2$, $x = a/2$, $x = a/2$, yes
     (c) Yes, $y = (\sqrt{3}/3)x$
     (d) Yes, $y = -(\sqrt{3}/3)x + (\sqrt{3}/3)a$
     (e) In an equilateral triangle, the median and altitude to a side is contained in the perpendicular bisector of that side.

16. (a) Let $A = (0, 0)$, $B = (m, n)$, $C = (p, q)$, $D = (r, s)$. Then $M = (p/2, q/2)$ and $N = ((m + r)/2, (n + s)/2)$. Also, $AB^2 = m^2 + n^2$, $BC^2 = (m - p)^2 + (n - q)^2$, $CD^2 = (p - r)^2 + (q - s)^2$, $DA^2 = r^2 + s^2$, etc.

(b) If $ABCD$ is a parallelogram, then $N = M$. Thus, the sum of the squares of the sides of a parallelogram equals the sum of the squares of the diagonals.

17. Solution: Top--13, 2, 10, 3; Middle--5, 6, 9, 8; Bottom--4, 11, 1, 12 such that one side face has 13, 5, 4, 6 around it.

18. 24 3-point questions and 7 4-point questions.

19. Gold--16 g.; Silver--13 g.; Copper--15 g.

20. 66 and 82

21. 20

22. Yes, a 5 × 12 mat or a 6 × 8 mat.

Analyzing Student Thinking

23. No, Holly. Since you are trying to prove something is true for *any* quadrilateral, you don't want to make any assumption that would result in a special type of quadrilateral. For instance, if you tried to use only four letters by assuming the fourth vertex has coordinates (0, *d*), rather than (*d, e*), you'd have a kite.

24. Holly, first use the midpoint formula to determine the coordinates of the midpoints of each side of the given quadrilateral. Each pair of midpoints of consecutive sides determines a side of the new quadrilateral. To prove this is a parallelogram, you can show its opposite sides have the same slope, using the slope formula with the coordinates you found in the first step.

25. Yes, Molly, your vertices will work just fine. The proof of this result that is given in your book may be only slightly easier than the one with your chosen vertices only because all the coordinates are positive.

26. Jolene's choice of coordinates is fine, but she doesn't need three

variables to name the vertices—two will suffice. Since the right angle is at the point (*a*, 0), *b* must be equal to *a*, as the following figure illustrates:

27. Herbert is incorrect. The line through the midpoint of the hypotenuse and (0, 0) bisects the hypotenuse, but will be perpendicular to the hypotenuse only in the case that *a* = *b*.

The perpendicular bisector, shown in the figure below, contains the point (*a*/2, *b*/2) and has slope equal to the opposite reciprocal of the slope of the hypotenuse, $m = -(-b/a) = a/b$

Its equation is given by

$$y = (a/b)x + \left(\frac{b^2 - a^2}{2b}\right).$$

28. It can be *proved* that the diagonals of a rhombus bisect each other and are perpendicular to each other. Thus, *if* Shelley has this information from previous work, her placement and labeling are correct.

Problems related to the NCTM Standards and Curriculum Focal Points

1. First, a general parallelogram with variable coordinates would be drawn on a set of axes. Using the coordinates of opposite vertices, the equations of the diagonals can be determined. These equations

are used to find the point of
intersection of the two diagonals.
Finally, the distances from the
intersection point to each of the
vertices will show that the
diagonals bisect each other.

2.   In problem #1, the distance
      formula was used to determine if
      the point of intersection of the two
      diagonals was the same distance
      from opposite vertices. Answers
      may vary.

3.   1) Diagonals of a parallelogram
      bisect each other. 2) Diagonals of
      a rhombus are perpendicular to
      each other (Set B #12). 3) The
      perpendicular bisector of the three
      sides of a triangle are concurrent
      (Set B #9). Answers may vary.

Chapter 16

Section 16.1

1. (a)

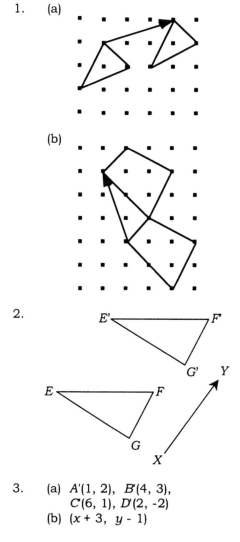

(b)

2.

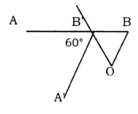

3. (a) $A'(1, 2)$, $B'(4, 3)$,
    $C'(6, 1)$, $D'(2, -2)$
    (b) $(x + 3, y - 1)$

4. Construct image of A, image of B,
    image of C and connect.

5. (a) 180°   (b) -20°

6. (a)

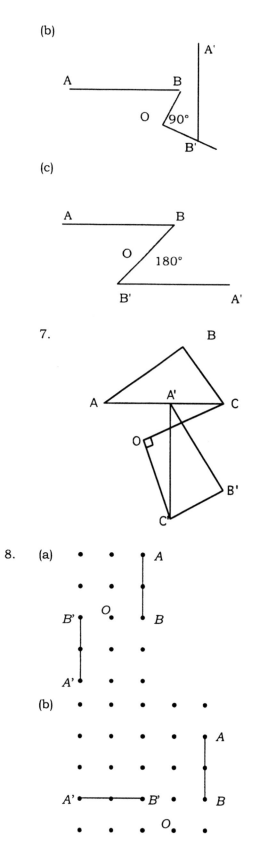

(b)

(c)

7.

8. (a)

    (b)

9.   (a)

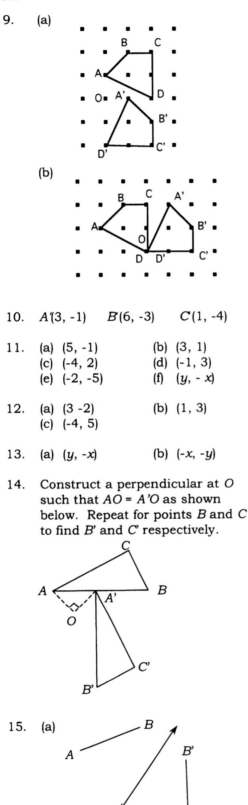

(b)

16.

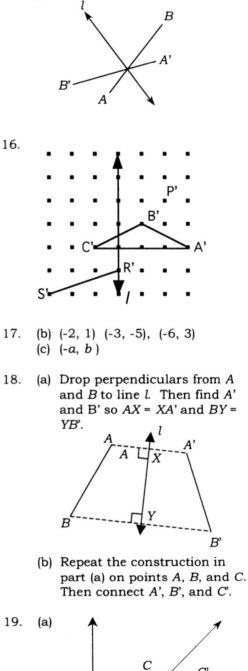

10. $A'(3, -1)$ $B'(6, -3)$ $C'(1, -4)$

11.   (a) (5, -1)   (b) (3, 1)
      (c) (-4, 2)   (d) (-1, 3)
      (e) (-2, -5)   (f) $(y, - x)$

12.   (a) (3 -2)   (b) (1, 3)
      (c) (-4, 5)

13.   (a) $(y, -x)$ (b) $(-x, -y)$

14.   Construct a perpendicular at O
      such that $AO = A'O$ as shown
      below. Repeat for points B and C
      to find B' and C' respectively.

15.   (a)

17.   (b) (-2, 1) (-3, -5), (-6, 3)
      (c) $(-a, b)$

18.   (a) Drop perpendiculars from A
           and B to line l. Then find A'
           and B' so $AX = XA'$ and $BY =$
           YB'.

      (b) Repeat the construction in
           part (a) on points A, B, and C.
           Then connect A', B', and C'.

19.   (a)

      (b) (3, 3), (3, 5), (8, 6)

(c) $(y + 2, x + 2)$

20. Construct lines, through A and B, parallel to $\overrightarrow{XY}$ and mark off the translation. Then construct perpendiculars to l through A' and B' to find reflection of the translated image.

21. (a) and (c). The original image $ABCDE$ is traversed clockwise as are the images for (a) and (c).

22. (a)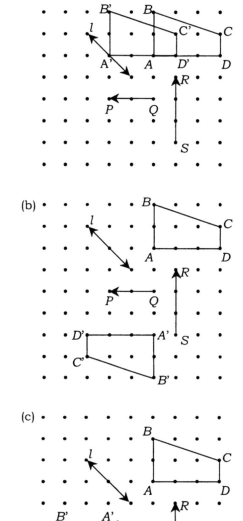

(d)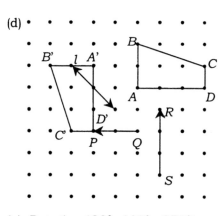

23. (a) Rotation (90°, 180°, 270°), Reflection (4 lines)
     (b) Rotation (90°, 180°, 270°),
     (c) Rotation 180°, Reflection (2 lines)
     (d) None

24. (a) 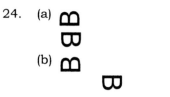 (b)

     (b)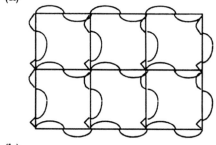

25. (a)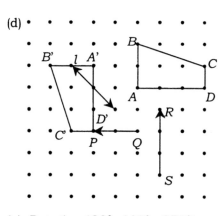

     (b)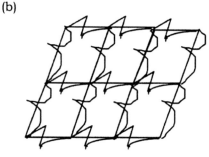

26. (a)

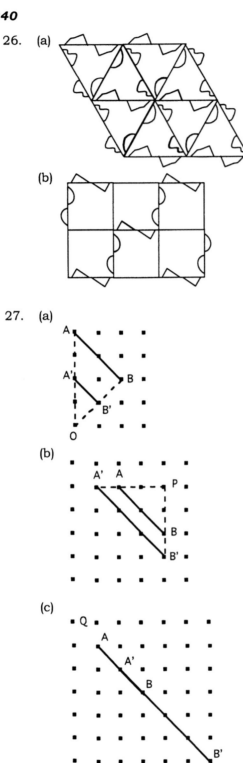

(b)

27. (a)

(b)

(c)

28. (a) $S_{P,1/2}$ Note: The scale has been changed so that the figure can fit this column.

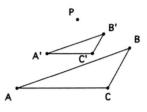

(b) $S_{P,3}$
Note: The scale has been changed so that the figure can fit this column.

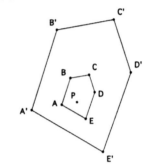

29. (a) T_{XY}

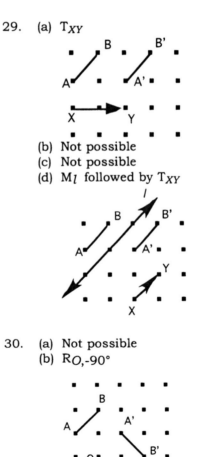

(b) Not possible
(c) Not possible
(d) M_l followed by T_{XY}

30. (a) Not possible
(b) $R_{O,-90°}$

(c) Not possible

(d) M*l* followed by T*XY*

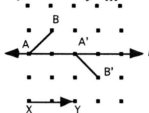

31. (a) None

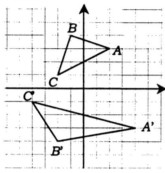

(b) Rotation

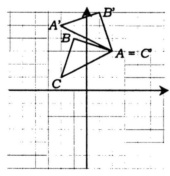

(c) Glide reflection

32. (a)

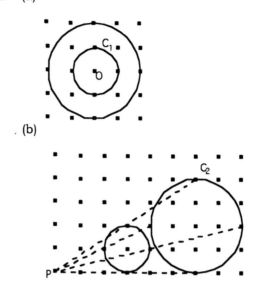

. (b)

33. No, the location of the line of reflection does not affect the size and shape of the image. It only effects the location of the image

Analyzing Student Thinking

34. Yes. Although one can think of this as one slide or two slides, mathematicians tend to minimize and call it one. In this case the slide is $4\sqrt{2}$ units on a line 45° below the horizontal.

35. No since a flip reverses orientation, but a turn does not. Take a circle for example. A turn in the center and a flip across a diameter would look the same. However, if you labeled three points on the circle with letters and saw what happened to them under a 180-degree turn and a flip, you'd see they'd have reverse orientations.

36. No. Two reflections preserve orientation, but one reverses it. Thus, they are different.

37. No. Two glide reflections preserve orientation while one reverses it. Thus, they are different.

38.   No. A motion that reverses orientation followed by a motion that reverses orientation ends up preserving orientation.

39.   Yes.

length $k \cdot OP$

length $m \cdot OP'$

$OP'' = m \cdot OP' = m \cdot (k \cdot OP) = km \cdot OP$
Thus, $S_{O, k}$ followed by $S_{O, m}$ is equal to $S_{O, km}$.

40.   No. $S_{O, -k}$ is not defined since k must be a positive real number. However, if $S_{O, k}$ is followed by $S_{O, 1/k}$, the result will be no transformation (or size transformation by a factor of 1), by #39 above.

41.   Yes. Any similitude can be expressed as a size transformation followed by an isometry, and also as an isometry followed by a size transformation. Thus, a combination of two similitudes can be expressed as two size transformations followed by two isometries. Since two size transformations is a size transformation and two isometries is an isometry, we have a size transformation followed by an isometry. In other words, it's a similitude.

Problems related to the NCTM Standards and Curriculum Focal Points

1.   Translations, rotations, reflections, and glide reflections all preserve size so the image is congruent to the original figure.

2.   By starting with polygons that tessellation, an irregular side created in one part of the polygon can be translated or rotated to another part of the polygon so that

the resulting image will still tessellate (see Figure 16.19).

3.   Slide, turns, and scaling (size transformations) all maintain the orientation of a figure. Flips change the orientation of the figure.

Section 16.2

1.   (a) $A = (-3, 1)$, $B = (1, 2.5)$
      (b) $A' = (1, 6)$, $B' = (5, 7.5)$
      (c) $AB = \sqrt{(31)^2 + (12.5)^2} = \sqrt{18.25}$. $A'B' = \sqrt{18.25}$, as well.

2.   (a) $\sqrt{(c - a)^2 + (d - b)^2}$
      (b) $A' = (a + p, \ b + q)$, $B = (c + p, \ d + q)$
      (c) $\sqrt{(c - a)^2 + (d - b)^2}$
      (d) Yes

3.   (a) $A'(-1, \ -2)$, $B'(3, \ 0)$, $C(0, \ 5)$
      (b) Yes, by SSS; $AB = A'B' = 2\sqrt{2} \ AC = A'C' = \sqrt{50}$, $BC = B'C' = \sqrt{34}$
      (c) Yes, since $\triangle ABC \cong \triangle A'B'C'$, the corresponding angles are congruent.

4. $A' = (2, -3)$, $B' = (3, 1)$;
      $AB = \sqrt{1^2 + 4^2} = 17$,
      $A'B' = \sqrt{(-1)^2 + (-4)^2} = 17$,
      so $AB = A'B'$.

5.   (a) $A = (4, 2)$ and $B = (-1, \ -3)$
      (b) $A' = (4, \ -2)$ and $B' = (-1, \ 3)$
      (c) $AB = \sqrt{(4 + 1)^2 + (2 + 3)^2} = 5\sqrt{2}$,

      $A'B' = \sqrt{(4 + 1)^2 + (-2 - 3)^2} = 5\sqrt{2}$

6.   (a) $(-a, b)$
      (b) $AB = \sqrt{(a - c)^2 + (b - d)^2}$; $A' = (-a, b)$, $B' = (-c, d)$ and

$A'B = \sqrt{(-a+c)^2 + (b-d)^2} =$

$\sqrt{(a-c)^2 + (b-d)^2}$

7. (a) $A'(2, -2)$, $B'(3, 1)$, $C'(-1, 4)$
   (b) Yes, by SSS; $AB = A'B' = \sqrt{10}$,
       $AC = A'C' = 3\sqrt{5}$,
       $BC = B'C' = 5$
   (c) Yes, since $\triangle ABC \cong \triangle A'B'C$,
       the corresponding angles are
       congruent.

8. (a) $(-2, 1)$, $(2, 3)$
   (b) $(-2 + p, -1)$, $(2 + p, -3)$
   (c) $AB = \sqrt{(-2-2)^2 + (1-3)^2} = 2\sqrt{5}$
       $A'B' =$
       $\sqrt{[(-2+p)-(2+p)]^2 + (-1+3)^2} =$
       $2\sqrt{5}$

9. (a) Reflection (b) Glide refection
   (c) Rotation

10. (a) Rotation   (b) Glide reflection

11. (a)

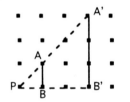

   (b) $PA' = 3\sqrt{2}$, $PA = \sqrt{2}$, so
       $PA' = 3PA$
   (c) $PB' = 3PB = 1$, so $PB' = 3PB$
   (d) $1, 3$; $A'B' = 3AB$ (same scale
       factor)

12. (a) P is at lower right corner of
       lattice, $k = 2$
    (b) $h = 1/2$
    (c) They are reciprocals

13. (a) $T_{C_1C_2}$ followed by $S_{C_1, 3/2}$ would
       map A_1 to A_2.
    (b) Yes; the transformation
        $T_{C_1C_2}$ followed by $S_{C_1, r_2/r_1}$ maps
        one circle (center C_1, radius
        r_1) to a second circle (center
        C_2, radius r_2)

14. (a) For example, $S_{B, 5/2}$ followed
        by $R_{C, -90°}$.
    (b) For example, $S_{B, 2/3}$ followed
        by a glide reflection.
    (c) For example, $S_{B, 2}$ followed by
        a glide reflection.

15. Since translations map lines to
    parallel lines, $p \mid\mid p'$ and $q \mid\mid q'$.
    Thus, since $p \mid\mid q$, we have that
    $p' \mid\mid q'$.

16. Since rotations preserve distances,
    $AB = A'B'$, $AC = A'C'$, and $BC =$
    $B'C'$. Since A, B, and C are
    collinear, $AB + BC = AC$.
    Therefore $A'B' + B'C' = AB + BC =$
    $AC = A'C'$ and A', B', and C' are
    collinear.

17. Since rotations preserve distance,
    $\overline{AB} \cong \overline{A'B'}$, $\overline{BC} \cong \overline{B'C'}$, and
    $\overline{CA} \cong \overline{C'A'}$. Thus, $\triangle ABC \cong \triangle A'B'C'$.
    Therefore, $\angle BAC \cong \angle B'A'C'$ since
    they are corresponding parts of
    congruent triangles.

18. Since reflections preserve
    distance, $\overline{BP} \cong \overline{B'P'}$. Also, since l
    is the perpendicular bisector of
    $\overline{BB'}$, $\overline{BQ} \cong \overline{B'Q}$. Further,
    $\overline{PQ} \cong \overline{PQ}$ so $\triangle BPQ \cong \triangle B'PQ$ by the
    SSS congruence property.
    Therefore, $\angle BPQ \cong \angle B'PQ$ since
    they are corresponding angles of
    congruent triangles.

19. (a) Both are perpendicular to
        $\overline{AC}$ and therefore parallel.
    (b) $M_l(A) = C$ since l is the
        perpendicular bisector of
        $\overline{AC}$. Then, $T_{CB}(C) = B$.

(c)

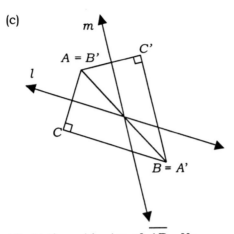

(d) At the midpoint of $\overline{AB}$. No.

20. $p \mid\mid q$ implies $\angle 1 \cong \angle 2$. Since an isometry preserves angle measure, $\angle 1 \cong \angle 3$ and $\angle 2 \cong \angle 4$. Thus, $\angle 3 \cong \angle 4$ and $p' \mid\mid q'$, by the corresponding angles property.

21. (a) One; the reflection line is the perpendicular bisector of $\overline{PQ}$.
    (b) Infinitely many; reflect P to S in any line through the midpoint of $\overline{PQ}$, then translate T_{SQ}.

22. Construct ray $\overrightarrow{PB}$ and line through A' parallel to $\overline{AB}$. They intersect at B'. In a like manner, draw ray $\overrightarrow{PC}$ and line through B' parallel to $\overline{BC}$. They intersect at C'. A similar procedure yields D'.

23. Construct line through P parallel to $\overline{PR}$, and also the line through Q' parallel to $\overline{QR}$. These two lines will intersect at the point R'.

24. 1. $X = X$ (by definition of reflection)
    2. Vertical angles, corresponding angles of $\triangle AXP$ and $\triangle A'X'P$, vertical angles
    3. $180°$, $m(\angle A'X'B') = m(\angle A'X'B) + m(\angle BX'Q) + m(\angle QX'B') = b + 2a = 180°$, yes
    4. Case (2) of reflection preserves distances: point X is on the reflection line.

5. $AB = AX + XB$ (collinear with X between A and B) = $A'X' + X'B'$ (part 4) = $A'B'$ (collinear with X' between A' and B').

25. Yes it is a rotation around the intersection of the two lines of reflection. The angle of rotation is twice the angle between the intersecting lines

Analyzing Student Thinking

26. Racquel is correct. Isometries preserve the shape and size of the original figure. So the area of a triangle is preserved under an isometry.

27. Yes, Monica. We proved in problem #20 that isometries preserve parallel lines.

28. Yes, Thomas, in a size transformation angle measure is preserved, so parallel lines (and perpendicular lines) within a figure will retain their relationship after transformation. The same is not true for similitudes since they are combinations of size transformations and isometries (for example, a rotation).

29. Yes, Kristi, by the definition of congruence. Also, if the two shapes have the same orientation, then the transformation is translation or a rotation. If they have opposite orientations, then the transformation is either a reflection or a glide reflection.

30. Eli, a similitiude consists of a size transformation followed by an isometry. The similitude will preserve orientation, but if the isometry is a reflection or glide reflection, orientation is reversed.

31. Petra, congruent triangles are similar. Thus, any property of similitudes is also a property of isometries.

32. This depends on whether you count a glide-reflection as an isometry or as a combination of two isometries. Including it, there would be four isometries: translation, reflection, rotation and glide-reflection.

Problems related to the NCTM Standards and Curriculum Focal Points

1. Since congruent figures are the same size and shape, one could pick up a figure and move it using slides, flips, and turns to exactly coincide with a second congruent figure.

2. Every size transformation requires a scale factor. Thus, if the scale factor were 3, then every side of the transformed figure will be 3 times as big as the corresponding side of the original figure. Also each point on the transformed figure would be 3 times further away from the center of the transformation as the corresponding point on the original figure.

3. The image of every size transformation or similitude is similar to the original figure. Also, for any two similar shapes there is a similitude that maps one shape onto the other.

Section 16.3

1. All of them.

2. $R_{G,120°}$, $R_{G,240°}$, $R_{G,360°}$, M_{AF}, M_{BD}, M_{CE}

3. M_{AI}, M_{BJ}, M_{CF}, M_{DG}, M_{EH}, $R_{O,72°}$, $R_{O,144°}$, $R_{O,216°}$ $R_{O,288°}$; $R_{O,360°}$

4. H_P; $R_{P,360°}$

5. (a) $H_C(H_B(H_A(H_C(H_B(H_A(P)))))) = P$

   (b) $H_C(H_B(H_A(H_C(H_B(H_A(Q)))))) = Q$

   (c) The combinations of six half turns, around the vertices of a triangle in succession, maps each point to itself.

6. Apply $T_{AA'}$ to $\triangle ABC$ first, for example. Let $B^* = T_{AA'}(B)$ and $C^* = T_{AA'}(C)$. Then the rotation with center A' and directed angle $\angle B^*A'B'$ (or $\angle C^*A'C'$) will map $\triangle A^*B^*C^*$ to $\triangle A'B'C'$.

7. $A^* = M_r(A)$, $B^* = M_r(B)$, $C^* = M_r(C)$. Then $M_r(\triangle ABC) = \triangle A^*B^*C^*$ and $S_{O,1/2}(\triangle A^*B^*C^*) = \triangle A'B'C'$

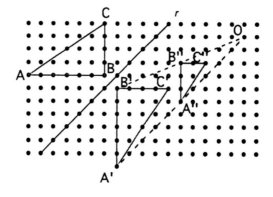

8. (a) $S_{A,2}(P) = B$, by definition. $S_{A,2}(R) = C$, by definition. $S_{A,2}(A) = A$, by definition. Hence, $S_{A,2}(\triangle APR) = \triangle ABC$. Other size transformations are possible.

   (b) $\overline{PR} \parallel \overline{BC}$ since the size transformation image of a line is parallel to the line. Hence, $\overline{PR} \parallel \overline{BQ}$. Similarly $\overline{RQ} \parallel \overline{PB}$ so $PBQR$ is a parallelogram.

9. $H_P(\overline{BC}) \parallel \overline{BC}$ and since

$H_P(A) = C$, we must have that $H_P(B)$ is on $\overline{AD}$. Similarly, $H_P(B)$ is on $\overline{CD}$ by considering $H_P(\overline{AB})$. Hence $H_P(B) = D$. Thus, P is the midpoint of $\overline{BD}$ also.

10. $M_l(A) = C$ and $M_l(C) = A$ by definition of M_l. Also, $M_l(B) = B$, so $M_l(\overline{AB}) = \overline{CB}$. Hence, $AB = BC$.

11. (a) $PA = PA' = PA''$. Also, PA' and r form an angle measuring $x°$, while PA'' and s form an angle measuring $y°$. Hence, $m(\angle APA) = 2x°$ and $m(\angle A'PA') = 2y°$. Thus, $A'' = R_{P,2(x+y)}(A)$. Since A was arbitrary, and orientation is preserved, M_r followed by M_s is $R_{P,2(x+y)}$.

   (b) Point P, the intersection of r and s, is the center of the rotation. The measure of the angle of the rotation is twice the measure of the angle between r and s.

12. (a)

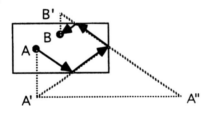

   (b) Argument is similar to the billiard problem in set A.

13. Let $P = \overline{AC} \cap \overline{BD}$ as was shown earlier, $\overline{AC} \perp \overline{BD}$ and $\overline{AC}$ and $\overline{BD}$ are perpendicular bisectors of each other. Hence, $M_{AC}(B) = D$ and $M_{BD}(A) = C$. Thus, M_{AC} followed by M_{BD} maps $ABCD$ to $CDAB$, i.e. M_{AC} followed by M_{BD}

is equivalent to the half turn H_P. (See also problem 5.) Thus, $\overline{AB} \parallel \overline{CD}$ since a half turn maps a line to a line parallel to it. Similarly, $\overline{AD} \parallel \overline{CB}$.

14. Use $R_{B,90°}$ to map $\triangle ABD$ to $\triangle FBC$. Use $R_{C,-90°}$ to map $\triangle ACE$ to $\triangle KCB$.

15. $\dfrac{\pi - \sqrt{3}}{2}$

Analyzing Student Thinking

16. Annie is correct because an isosceles triangle has two congruent sides, so the triangle together with its reflection will have four congruent sides. Therefore, it is a rhombus by definition.

17. Chris is correct. He can use an isometry to move any figure to a congruent figure. Isometries are comprised of translations and rotations (which can be expressed as two reflections), a reflection, or a glide reflection (which can be expressed as three reflections).

18. Rueben is correct. A half turn is a 180° rotation. A reflection over a horizontal line followed by reflection over a vertical line is the same as a 180° rotation about the point of intersection of the two lines.

19. Eva is incorrect. Fold the parallelogram along the proposed line and notice that the two halves that result do not coincide.

20. If this were a reflection, angle measure would be preserved. However, the angle at top left is obtuse, and the angle at lower left is acute, so obviously one is not the image of the other under a reflection.

21. Jamie's path, as drawn, is not possible since when the ball hits a wooden board at the edge of the green, it must bounce away at an angle that equals the angle at which it approached the board. Jamie will need a more complicated path, which can be found by using reflections.

Problems related to the NCTM Standards and Curriculum Focal Points

1. Problem 9 of Set *B* has students use transformations to prove that the diagonals of a parallelogram bisect each other. Problem 12 of Set *B* has students show that a rhombus is a parallelogram by using transformations. Answers may vary.

2. Problem 6 of Set *B* requires one to find a combination of isometries that will map one triangle onto another. Answers may vary.

Epilogue

1. $\angle ABD \cong \angle CDB$ (alternate interior angle property with $\overline{AB} \parallel \overline{DC}$, $\overline{BD} \cong \overline{DB}$, so $\triangle ABD \cong \triangle CDB$ (by SAS congruence property), $\angle ADB \cong \angle CBD$ (corresponding parts of congruent triangles) so $\overline{AD} \parallel \overline{BC}$ (alternate interior angle property) and $ABCD$ is therefore a parallelogram.

2. (a) $M = \left(\dfrac{a}{2}, \dfrac{b}{2}\right)$ and $N = \left(\dfrac{c+d}{2}, \dfrac{b}{2}\right)$

   Hence, $MN = \dfrac{c+d-a}{2}$,

   $AB = d$, and $DC = c - a$.
   $AB + DC = d + c - a$ or $2MN$.

   Thus, $MN = \dfrac{1}{2}(AB + DC)$.

   Slopes of AB and MN are 0, thus $\overline{MN} \parallel \overline{AB}$.

3. (a) The diagonals, $\overline{AC}$ and $\overline{BD}$, *bisect* each other at point P. Hence, by the definition, $H_P(A) = C$ and $H_P(B) = D$.

   (b) $H_P(C) = A$ and $H_P(D) = B$, as well, so H_P maps the parallelogram onto itself. Notice that $H_P(\overline{AB}) = \overline{CD}$, etc. for the other sides, since an isometry maps a line segment to a line segment. The parallelogram rotates onto itself under a 180° rotation, hence has rotation symmetry.

4. $\overline{BE} \cong \overline{DE}$ and $\overline{AE} \cong \overline{CE} \cong$ (diagonals bisect each other). $\angle BEC \cong \angle DEA$ (vertical angles are congruent), so $\triangle BEC \cong \triangle DEA$ (SAS congruence property). Thus, $\angle BCE \cong \angle DAE$ (corresponding parts of congruent triangles) so $\overline{BC} \parallel \overline{AD}$ (alternate interior angle property). Similarly, $\angle BAE \cong \angle DCE$ and $\triangle BEA \cong \triangle DEC$ (SAS congruence property) so $\angle BAE$

$\cong \angle DCE$ (corresponding parts of congruent triangles) and $\overline{AB} \parallel \overline{DC}$ (alternate interior angle property). Since both pairs of opposite sides are parallel, $ABCD$ is a parallelogram.

5. Since $ABCD$ is a rhombus, $AB = AD$.

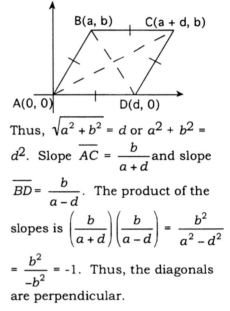

   Thus, $\sqrt{a^2 + b^2} = d$ or $a^2 + b^2 = d^2$. Slope $\overline{AC} = \dfrac{b}{a+d}$ and slope $\overline{BD} = \dfrac{b}{a-d}$. The product of the slopes is $\left(\dfrac{b}{a+d}\right)\left(\dfrac{b}{a-d}\right) = \dfrac{b^2}{a^2-d^2}$

   $= \dfrac{b^2}{-b^2} = -1$. Thus, the diagonals are perpendicular.

6. $\overline{LP} \cong \overline{NP}$ and $\overline{MP} \cong \overline{OP}$ (diagonals of parallelogram bisect each other) and $\angle LPM \cong \angle NPM \cong \angle NPO \cong \angle LPO$ (diagonals are perpendicular), so $\triangle LPM \cong \triangle NPM \cong \triangle NPO \cong \triangle LPO$ (SAS congruence property). Therefore, $\overline{LM} \cong \overline{NM} \cong \overline{NO} \cong \overline{LO}$ (corresponding parts of congruent triangles) and $LMNO$ is a rhombus by definition.

7. Since $ABCD$ is a trapezoid, we have the following coordinates.

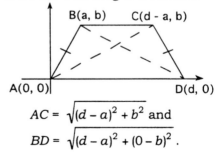

   $AC = \sqrt{(d-a)^2 + b^2}$ and
   $BD = \sqrt{(d-a)^2 + (0-b)^2}$.

Thus, $AC = BD$.

8. A parallelogram with perpendicular diagonals is a rhombus and thus has four congruent sides. Therefore, *HIJK* is a square.

Section T1 - Part B

1. (a) Roses are red and the sky is blue.
    (b) Roses are red and the sky is blue or turtles are green.
    (c) If the sky is blue, then roses are red and turtles are green.
    (d) Turtles are not green and turtles are green implies that roses are not red.

2.

p	q	$p{\to}q$	$\sim(p{\wedge}q)$	$p{\wedge}q$	$q{\to}p$
T	T	T	F	T	T
T	F	F	T	F	T
F	T	T	T	F	F
F	F	T	T	F	T

3. (a) T (b) F (c) T (d) T

4. $p \to q$ and $p \vee q$ have the same truth table.

5. (a) Hypotheses:
        All football players are introverts and Tony is a football player
        Conclusion:
        Tony is an introvert.
    (b) Hypotheses:
        Bob is taller than Jim and Jim is taller than Sue.
        Conclusion:
        Bob is taller than Sue.
    (c) Hypotheses:
        All penguins are elegant swimmers and no elegant swimmers fly.
        Conclusion:
        Penguins don't fly.

6. (c) and (e)

7. (a) Necessary
    (b) Sufficient
    (c) Sufficient

8. (a) T   (b) T
    (c) Unknown   (d) T
    (e) F   (f) Unknown
    (g) T   (h) T
    (i) Unknown   (j) F
    (k) T   (l) Unknown
    (m) Unknown (n) T (o) T

9. (a) $[(w \to t) \wedge t] \to w$ Invalid
    (b) $[(s \to l) \wedge \sim s] \to \sim l$ Invalid
    (c) $[(\sim s \to e) \wedge (w \to \sim e)] \to$ $(w \to s)$ Valid
    (d) $[(m \wedge s) (j \to m)] \to j$ Invalid

10. (d), (e), and (f)

Section T2 - Part B

1. (a) 6 and 6
    (b) 6 and 6
    (c) 2 and 2
    (d) 4 and 4
    (e) Multiplication distributes over addition and subtraction in clock arithmetic.

2. (a) 1 and 1   (b) 0 and 0
    (c) 0 and 0
    (d) The exponent rule $a^m b^m = (ab)^m$ holds in clock arithmetic.

3. 1, 4, 5, 2, 3, 6

4. (a) 4 (b) 1 (c) 4 (d) 4
    (e) 3 (f) 2 (g) 0 (h) 0

5. (a) -17, -12, -7, -2, 3, 8, 13, 18
    (b) -17, -10, -3, 4, 11, 18
    (c) 2, 4, 8
    (d) 2, 3, . . . , 20

6. $3 \times 4 = 0$

7. (a) 0, 2, 4, 6
    (b) 0, 2, 4, 5, 6, 8
    (c) 0, 2, 3, 4, 6, 8, 9, 10
        For the 36-clock, 0, 2, 3, 4, 6, 8, 9, 10, 12, 14, 15, 16, 18, 20, 21, 22, 24, 26, 27, 28, 30, 32, 33, 34.

8. (a) 7 (b) 4 (c) 11 (d) 9
    In clock n, $n - 1$ is its own inverse.

9. a is the square root of b if $a^2 = b$.
    (a) 2   (b) 1, 3, 5, 7
    (c) 3   (d) 7
    Numbers may have zero or many square roots depending on the clock number.

10. Let 1 be positive. Then, if the sum of two positives is positive, 1 + 1 = 2, 2 + 1 = 3, 3 + 1 = 4, and 4 + 1 = 0 are all positive . Thus all numbers in the 5-clock are positive.

11. Multiplication is closed because addition is closed and multiplication can be viewed as repeated addition.

12. If $a \equiv b \bmod m$, then $m \mid (a - b)$. But then $m \mid (a - b)c$, or $m \mid (ac - bc)$. Thus, $ac \equiv bc \bmod m$.

13. $2 \times 3 \equiv 4 \times 3 \bmod 6$, but 2 is not congruent to 4 mod 6.

14. $7^2 \equiv 1 \bmod 8$. So $(7^2)^{50} \equiv 1^{50} \bmod 8$, or $7^{100} \equiv 1 \bmod 8$. Therefore, $7^{101} \equiv 7 \bmod 8$, so the remainder when 7^{101} is divided by 8 is 7.

Introduction to Graph Theory (on the Web)

1. (a) A = F = 2, B = C = 3, D = E = 1
   (b) B = C = E = F = 3, A = D = 2
   (c) A = B = E = F = G = H = 3, D = C = 4

2. (i) (a) A: B, F; B: A, C, F; C: B,D,E.
       (b) A: B,F; B: A, E, F; C: D,E,F.
       (c) A: B,D,F; B: A,C,G; C: B,D,H
   (ii) The degree of a vertex is the same as the number of vertices it is adjacent to.

3.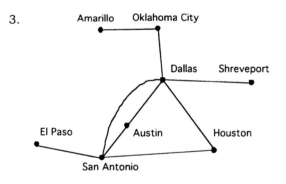

Amarillo Oklahoma City

Dallas Shreveport

El Paso Austin Houston

San Antonio

4. (a) Connected since there is a path from any vertex to any other vertex.
   (b) Not connected. For example, U does not have a path to X.
   (c) Connected since there is a path from any vertex to any other vertex.

5. (i) and (v) are equivalent; (ii) and (iii)are equivalent.

6. (a) (i) Yes, exactly two odd vertices
       (ii) Euler Path by Euler's Traversable Graph Theorem.
   (b) (i) No, four odd vertices.
       (ii) None
   (c) (i) Yes, all even vertices.
       (ii) Euler Circuit by Euler's Traversable Graph Theorem.
   (d) (I) Yes, exactly two odd vertices.
       (ii) Euler Path by Euler's Traversable Graph Theorem.

7. (a) Hamiltonian Path LMNOPQ
   (b) None, since the graph is not connected.
   (c) Hamiltonian Circuit ACDEBA

8. (a)

   (b)

9. Since R + V = E +2, we have V = E + 2 – R, or V = 13 + 2 – 8 = 7.

10. (a) Hexagonal prism
    (b) Hexagonal pyramid
    (c) Pentagonal pyramid

11. Add 2 edges. For example HJ and
     LM. An Euler Circuit is
     NJINLMLKJHIKNHMN

12   (a)

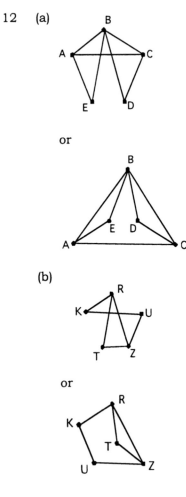

     or

     (b)

     or

13. (a)

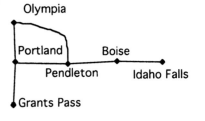

     (b)

(c)

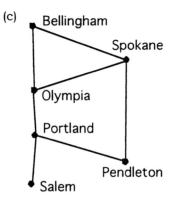

14. (a) 1a: 12 1b: 16; 1c: 26; 4a: 14;
          4b: 16; 4c: 16.
     (b) 1a: 6; 1b: 8; 1c: 13; 4a: 7; 4b:
          8; 4c: 8
     (c) The sum of the degrees of the
          vertices is twice the number of
          edges.

15.

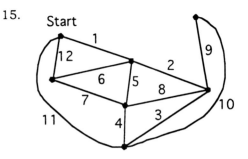

16. (a) 1a: 2; 1b: 2; 1c: 3.
     (b) 1a: BC, DE; 1b: AE, BC; 1c:
          AF, BF, EH.
     (c) 3; one edge for each pair of
          odd vertices.

17. Many solutions possible. Two are
     shown.

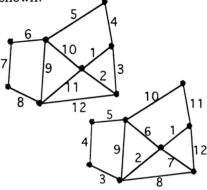

Logo Programs

L12.1. REPEAT 10[FD 20 RT 360/10]

L12.2. TO REG.POLY :N
    REPEAT :N[FD 20 RT 360/:N]
    END

L12.3. TO RIGHT.TRI :A :B
    BK :A
    RT 90
    FD :B
    HOME
    END

L13.1.   (a) TO RECTANGLE :A :B
    HT
    REPEAT 2[FD :A RT 90
       FD :B RT 90]
    REPEAT INTEGER
       (:A/10) [FD 10
       RT 90 FD :B BK :B
       LT 90]
    HOME
    RT 90
    REPEAT INTEGER
       (:B/10) [FD 10
       LT 90 FD :A BK :A
       RT 90]
    HOME
    END
   (b) 100
   (c) 28

L14.1. Let :ANGLE=180.

L14.2.   (a) TO SAS.TRI :SIDE 1 :ANGLE
    :SIDE 2
    BK :SIDE 1
    RT :ANGLE
    FD :SIDE 2
    HOME
    END
   (b) (i) :ANGLE=90
     (ii) :SIDE 1=:SIDE 2
     (iii) : ANGLE > 90 and :
     ANGLE=90
     (iv) :SIDE 1=:SIDE 2
     (v) : ANGLE=90 and :
     SIDE 1 ≠ :SIDE 2
     (vi) :SIDE 1=:SIDE 2 and
      :ANGLE=60

L14.3. TO MAGNIFY.TRI :SIDE 1
    :ANGLE :SIDE 2 :K
    SAS.TRI :SIDE 1 :ANGLE
    :SIDE 2
    BK :K*:SIDE 1
    RT :ANGLE
    FD :K*:SIDE 2
    HOME
    END

L15.1. TO TRI.COORDS :X1 :X2 :Y1 :Y2
    AXES
    SETXY :X1 :Y1
    SETXY :X2 :Y2
    HOME
    END

L15.2. TO TRI.COORDS.MDPTS :X1 :X2
    :Y1 :Y2
    TRI.COORDS :X1 :X2 :Y1 :Y2
    PU
    SETXY (:X1)/2 (:Y1)/2
    PD
    SETXY (:X2)/2 (:Y2)/2
    PU
    HOME
    PD
    END

L15.3. AXES
    SETXY 20 90
    SET X Y 100 30
    HOME
    SETXY 60 60
    PU
    SETXY 20 90
    PD
    SETXY 50 15
    PU
    SETXY 100 30
    PD
    SETXY 10 45
    PU
    HOME
    PD

L15.4. TO MEDIANS :X1 :Y1 :X2 :Y2
    SETXY :X1 :Y1
    SETXY :X2 :Y2
    HOME
    SETXY (:X1+:X2)/2
    (:Y1+:Y2)/2
    PU

```
    SETXY (:X1)/2 (:Y1)/2              HOME
    PD                                 TRANS :X1 :Y1 :X2 :Y2 :X3
    SETXY :X2 :Y2                          :Y3 :M
    PU                                 TRI.PLOT (-:X4) :Y4 (-:X5)
    SETXY :X1 :Y1          :Y5         (-:X6) :Y6
    PD                                 END
    SETXY (:X2)/2 (:Y2)/2
    HOME
    END
```

L16.1.
```
    TO X.REF :X1 :Y1 :X2 :Y2 :X3 :Y3
    SET X 100
    SET X (-100 )
    HOME
    TRI.PLOT :X1 :Y1 :X2 :Y2 :X3
        :Y3
    TRI.PLOT :X1 (-:Y1) :X2
        (-:Y2) :X3 (-:Y3)
    END
```

L16.2.
```
    TO TRANS :X1 :Y1 :X2 :Y2 :X3
        :Y3 :N : M
    TRI.PLOT :X1 :Y1 :X2 :Y2 :X3
        :Y3
    MAKE "X4 :X1+N
    MAKE "Y4 :Y1+M
    MAKE "X5 :X2+N
    MAKE "Y5 :Y2+M
    MAKE "X6 :X3+N
    MAKE "Y6 :Y3+M
    TRI.PLOT :X4 :Y4 :X5 :Y5 :X6
        :Y6
    END
```

L16.3.
```
    TO ROTATE.90 :X1 :Y1 :X2 :Y2
        :X3 :Y3
    TRI.PLOT :X1 :Y1 :X2 :Y2 :X3
        :Y3
    TRI.PLOT(-:Y1):X1(-:Y2):X2
    (-:Y3) :X3
    END
```

L16.4.
```
    (a)  TO GLIDE.REF.X :X1 :Y1 :X2
            :Y2 :X3 :Y3 :N
        TRANS :X1 :Y1 :X2 :Y2
            :X3 :Y3 :N
        X.REF :X4 :Y4 :X5 :Y5 :X6
            :Y6
        END
    (b) TO GLIDE.REF.Y :X1 :Y1 :X2
            :Y2 :X3:Y3 :M
        SETY 100
        SETY (-100)
```

Answers To Even Numbered Problems In The
PROBLEM SOLVING STUDY GUIDE

1.   Guess and Test

1-B.   13 and 78

1-2.   53 and 32

1-4

2.   Use a Variable

2-B.
$$n + 10$$
$$n \qquad n + 2$$
$$n + 8 \quad n + 4 \qquad n + 6$$

2-2.   Bruce was 52 years old in 1988.
He was born in 1936 = 44 × 44.
1988 - 1936 = 52.

2-4.   11 cows and 2 turkeys.
$4c + 2t = c + t + 35$
$3c + t = 35$

3.   Draw a Picture

3-B.   30 seconds
2.5 seconds per floor
middle floor is 17
12 × 2.5 = 30

3-2.   The fence will cost $2280.
120 posts and 120 sections

3-4.   Jason will be halfway to his office
at 6:56 A.M.

4.   Look for a Pattern

4-B   (a) H 29 30 31
(b) R 69 70 71
(c) M 49 50 51
(d) P 61 26 63
(e) V 85 86 87

4-2.   18 girls and 12 boys
18 × 18 + 12 × 12 = 468

4-4.   99,225
99,225 = 315 × 315 = 9 × 11,025

5.   Make a List

5-B   The total number of coins cannot
be 18.
10 coins : 10 quarters
13 coins : 5 dimes and 8 quarters
16 coins : 10 dimes and 6
quarters
19 coins : 15 dimes and 4
quarters
22 coins : 20 dimes and 2
quarters
25 coins: 25 dimes

5-2.   36 ways; 3 pennies: 1 way,
4 pennies: 3 ways,
. . . , 10 pennies : 36 ways

5-4.   Box Z: 9 marbles (X:18   Y:9)

6.   Solve a Simpler Problem

6-B   There are 864 dots on the 864
chips.

6-2.   Largest 4-digit cube is 21^3 = 9261.
9261 - 45 = 9216
Possible answers: 4 36 64
4 9 256   9 16 64

6-4.   (a) 9,801 = 99^2
(b) 27,000 = 30^3
(c) 178 = 89 × 2

7.   Draw a Diagram

7-B   Nine are red, not compact, and
have 4 doors.

7-2.   18 ways Ted, Amy, Bart
       126   162   216   261   612
       621   135   153   315   351
       513   531   234   243   324
       342   423   432

7-4.   120 youth T-shirts, 80 adult

8.   Use Direct Reasoning

8-B   Ask either computer this question: What will the other computer answer if I ask it to tell   me which box contains $100?"

8-2.   There are 89 ways to get to the top step.
1 step stairway : 1 way
2 step stairway : 2 ways
3 step stairway : 3 ways
4 step stairway : 5 ways
. . . 10 step stairway : 89 ways

8-4.   The thousands digit is 8.
hundreds : 6
tens : 2
ones : 4

9.   Use Indirect Reasoning

9-B   Suppose that there is a triangle on the back side of card A. Then the statement on card A is true. This means that the statement on card B is also true. But this conclusion contradicts the fact that one statement is true and the other is false. Hence, the triangle must be on the back side of card B.

9-2.   (a) 1   (b) 2   (c) 6

9-4.   My vacation was 18 days, 13 with rain and 5 with no rain.

10.   Use Properties of Numbers

10-B   7,840

10-2.   There are 3 × 28 = 84 different triangles.

10-4.   Possible solutions:
Games/ 1 peg
Games/ 3 pegs
Games/ 4 pegs
5   14   1
6   11   3
7   8   5
8   5   7
9   2   9

11.   Solve an Equivalent Problem

11-B   There are 28 possible two-girl committees.

11-2.   Eight dogs
Cans/dogs/days:
5/4/1   40/32/1   40/8/4

11-4.   Suppose the chip under cup Z is not red. This means that Linda would have been able to guess the color of the chip under cup Y. Hence, the chip under cup Z must be red.

12.   Work Backward

12-B   Karen stated with $36.

12-2.   There are 92 girls.

12-4.   7/8
1/2 × 5/6 = 5/12
2/3 - 5/12 = 1/4
2 × 1/4 = 1/2
3/8 + 1/2 = 7/8

13.   Use Cases

13-B   Cody cannot place his cards as described in the problem. When the total in any two piles is even, the total in the other three piles must be odd and vice versa.

13-2.   7 children: 3 boys and 4 girls.

13-4.   Go second and then always make exactly the same move as your opponent.

14.   Solve an Equation

14-B   Jeff's number is 8.
$100n + 100 = 900$
If you decrease the final result by 100 and then divide by 100, the answer will be the original number selected.

14-2.   16 red-odd chips, 75 blue-even chips

14-4.   40 members
$18x = 24(x - 10)$ yields $x = 40$

15.   Look for a Formula

15-B $(1/2)^{30}$
$1 - 1/2 = 1/2$
$1 - 1/2 - 1/4 = 1/4$
$1 - 1/2 - 1/4 - 1/8 = 1/8 \ldots$

15-2.   16,800
$(1/3)n + (1/5)n + (1/6)n + (1/4)n + 42 = n$ implies $n = 840$
$0.05\,e = 840$
$e = 16,800$

15-4.   The snail will be 4 cm from the top.
$23/24 \times 96 = 92$
$96 - 92 = 4$

16.   Do a Simulation

16-B   Answers will vary.

16-2.   Both cases have a probability of 3/8 that exactly two of the children will be girls.

16-4.   There were 240 chickens.
$x - 0.3x + 0.2x = 216$
$x = 240$

17.   Use a Model

17-B   A model will show that figure I cannot be separated as shown.

17-2.   The total value cannot be $3.
(a) 6 nickels + 4 dimes = $3.40
(b) 3 nickels + 7 dimes = $5.35

(d) 7 nickels + 6 dimes = $6.05

17-4.   One possible solution:
0 1 2 3 4 5   1 1 1 7 7 7

18.   Use Dimensional Analysis

18-B   About 10.24 kilometers per liter

18-2.   1,200,000,301
The nth term is $9n - 2$. Hence, two more than any number in the sequence must be divisible by 9.

18-4.   20 20 0 0
20 12 8 0 $\rightarrow$ 20 0 8 12 $\rightarrow$
18 0 8 14 $\rightarrow$ 18 8 0 14 $\rightarrow$
18 8 8 6 $\rightarrow$ 20 8 6 6

19.   Identify Subgoals

19-B   8400 ways = 6 × 20 × 70

19-2.   3 to 2
$7j + 3c = 81$
$j = (81 - 3c)/7$
Hence $c = 6$ and $j = 9$.
$j : c = 9 : 6 = 3 : 2$

19-4.   A tennis court, 36' by 78', has a perimeter of 228 feet.

20.   Use Coordinates

20-B   Isosceles triangle: Two sides are 5 units long.
Right triangle: Two sides have slopes 4/3 and -3/4.
$(4/3 \times -3/4 = -1)$
The area of the triangle is 12.5 square units $(1/2 \times 5 \times 5)$.

20-2.   11 A. M. on Friday.
LCM(15, 28, 40) = 840 minutes = 14 hours

20-4.   If x and y are the lengths, cut the longer rope at a distance $(x + y)/3$ from one end.

21.   Use Symmetry

21-B.

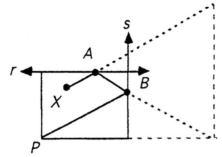

21-2.   20,000
6/150 = 4%, estimate 4% tagged
4% p = 800
p = 20,000

21-4.   2,950 π square feet

CPSIA information can be obtained at www.ICGtesting.com
Printed in the USA
BVOW052139220712

295813BV00001B/9/P